RB

Also by Allen Edwardes

JEWEL IN THE LOTUS
*A historical survey of the sexual culture
of the East*

THE CRADLE OF EROTICA (with R. E. L. Masters)
*A study of Afro-Asian sexual expression
and an analysis of erotic freedom in social
relationships*

Preface

El-layl w'el-khayl w'el-baydā ta'rifnī,
W'es-sayf w'edz-dzayf w'el-qirtās w'el-qelm:

I'm known to the night, the desert and steed,
The nomad and sword, the paper and reed. [*]

El-Mutenabbi

Although this "exposé" of Sir Richard Francis Burton appears in the guise of a romantic biography, none of it is fabricated. Every character actually played his or her part in the drama; and everything said, thought, written, or done by the *dramatis personae* is based on seven years of research. It is therefore a conscientious recreation of past reality.

The Burton bibliography is monumental, comprising nearly a hundred volumes of personal narrative and knowledge. This rich resource of subjective exposition has barely been tapped by his handful of biographers.

In this sophistical age of psychology, which Burton dis-

[*] All verse introducing the chapters throughout text are original couplets by Richard F. Burton.

missed as a pseudoscientific fad, many biographers seem to develop an unconscious fear of their subjects whenever they fail to comprehend them. Thus they create or perpetuate a legend, and of necessity endow their subjects with a nature which they perhaps never owned in actuality. Hence there is the difference between idealistic and realistic biography.

Burton is an overwhelming individual. We may know him, but we can never fully understand him. Nor is there any reason that we should. Since the "illusion of truth" is a purely personal matter, each has his own lesson to learn from the life of another. These lessons need not be preached or generalized. They are self-evident.

Burton advisedly cast a veil over his natural identity. It is laughable that biographers should run from pillar to post in a vain effort to unravel the riddle. It is equally amusing that Burton's three most recent biographers were somehow beguiled into (mis)representing him as an atheistic roué. This is the very impression "that blackguard Burton" wished to convey to his contemporaries. It is the grotesque image he was ironically reviving and living down according to the tide of events and his own vagrant temperament.

There is no evidence whatsoever to prove the rather prurient and puerile assumption that Burton was the avid whorehound a host of wishful thinkers imagine him to have been. To one who has assiduously studied the writings of Sir Richard Burton, the "wild man of Mecca" reveals himself as a Don Quixote tilting at windmills, as a man who squared the circle to evince his insatiable thirst for acceptance and affection.

The cliché of the adventurous rake who beds a dozen

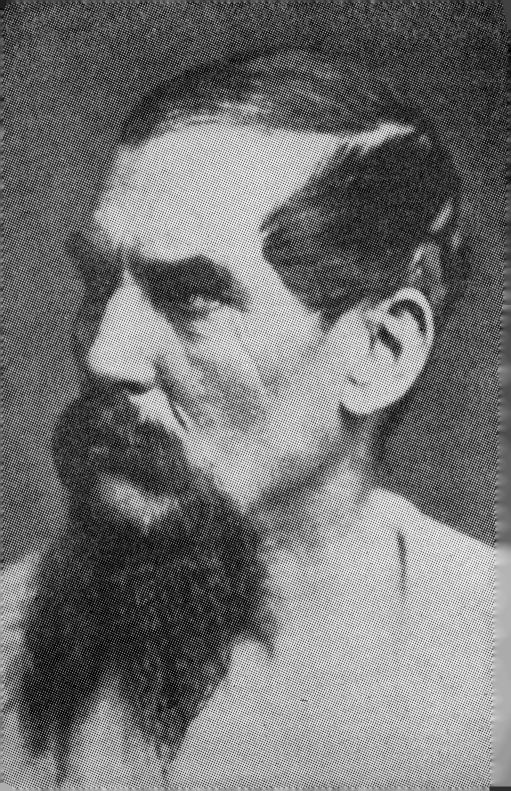

DEATH RIDES A CAMEL

A biography of

SIR RICHARD BURTON

by Allen Edwardes

The Julian Press, Inc., *Publishers*

1963  NEW YORK

Published by The Julian Press, Inc.
80 East 11th Street, New York 3
Library of Congress Catalog Card Number 63–13187
© Copyright 1963 by Allen Edwardes
Manufactured in the United States of America
by H. Wolff, New York
Designed by Marshall Lee

Second Printing , August 1963

Slowly we wind athwart the wild, and while young Day its anthem swells,
Sad falls upon my yearning ear the tinkling of the camel bells:

O'er fiery waste and frozen wold, o'er horrid hill and gloomy glen,
The home of grisly beast and ghoul, the haunts of wilder grislier men.

R.F.B.

Contents

damsels in distress and then rides off to slay the dragon may be a fitting formula for romance, but has little to do with reality. The fabulous mental and physical feats that Burton performed were the products of his unconscious sublimation of sexual energy through "orgasms of the brain." As he himself admitted, "I'm no hot amorist."

It may be said that Burton, despite his outwardly rabid originality, was a puritan at heart. That is often the case with conservative romanticists. They kick against the pricks. Burton lived a contradiction, contesting in his conscience against two personalities each of which hated the other—the sensualist versus the ascetic, the intellectual versus the daredevil, the conformist versus the nonconformist, the idealist versus the realist. Not being a man to compromise, and being no devotee of the "golden mean" (*aurea mediocritas*), Burton was rarely at peace with himself or with the Western world in general. Nor is there any reason that he should have been. It was this inner conflict that drove him to greatness.

Among many other never-told tales is the "strange" relationship of Burton with Speke. It was an ill-fated homosexual affair, as the subsequent tragedy seems to indicate. Burton's recently whitewashed "friendship" with the fair and effeminate Swinburne was far from platonic, but because it had no direct or indirect bearing on Burton's life it is not depicted in this book.

Perhaps the most extraordinary aspect of all is Burton's meeting and mating with a devout and doting Roman Catholic, Isabel Arundell, supporting his supposition that "nature (human) commands a union of contrasts." Their early association may appear invented, but it is true as far as recorded history is concerned.

Many disenchanted readers may refuse to believe the macabre account of Burton's tour of Dahomey, as well as other savage episodes in his incredible career. Let them be enlightened. Anthropologist Melville Herskovits, who visited Dahomey in the 1930's, substantiated all of Burton's startling observations. Documentary proof is also available for those who may wish to disbelieve anything else he did. It is these unparalleled exploits that make Burton such a formidable subject to the idealistic biographer.

Burton scholars will wonder at the erotic incident in Harar. Aside from numerous hints in the writings of "Ruffian Dick," his excessive interest in eunuchism as well as circumcision, plus evidence uncovered by French explorers, Dr. F. Grenfell Baker (Burton's private physician from 1887-90) exploded the old scandal that the "devil's disciple" had been caught in a harem and castrated. However, Burton disclosed to the doctor that his testicles had been so damaged by "an accident in East Africa" as to render him sterile. This is virtually unknown and perhaps an explanation of the fact that he and Isabel never had a child.

The purpose of this book is to reveal the *real* Sir Richard Burton through his own deeds, his own words, his own thoughts, and his own writings. It is the story of the man, not the figment of romantic fancy. Burton need not be taken *au sérieux* as an untamed libertine later turned (by his wife) into a tamed martyr. This is not a co-biography of Isabel Burton, nor does it perpetuate the popular notion that she determined her husband's destiny.

Now, as never before, the tragicomic life of Sir Richard Francis Burton is unveiled in the nude—without fig leaf, and without codpiece as well.

RB

1 : The home of the stranger

Friends of my youth, a last Adieu! *Perhaps someday we'll meet again.*
Yet never the selfsame men shall meet. The years shall make us other
men.

"You shall have plenty to choose from. Ah yes, many young men could be yours to love. But you will wait for years, because you are destined to *him* from the beginning." The gypsy queen's kohl-rimmed eyes glimmered with prophecy. There was a stillness in the camp. The hour of siesta was stirred only by twittering birds of the English countryside.

A yellow-haired girl sat trembling with excitement, listening as in a dream while the fierce-eyed matriarch foretold the future:

"You will cross the sea. You will be in the same town with your Destiny but know it not. Soon thereafter, when you come to know it, every obstacle will rise up against you. Such a combination of circumstances will require all your courage, energy, and intelligence to meet them."

The girl's bright blue eyes widened in anticipation. The gypsy glared at her divinatory markings in the dust. Her voice was deep and cutting:

"Your life will be like one swimming against the big waves. But God will be with you, so you will always win. You will fix your eye on your polar star. You will go for that without looking right or left. You will bear the name of our tribe and be right proud of it."

"You mean—" the girl murmured, "you mean I'll take the name of Burton—that a man named Burton is my Destiny?"

The gypsy nodded without lifting her eyes from the ground. "You will be as we are, but far greater than we. Your life will be all wandering, change, and adventure. One soul in two bodies in life or death, never long apart."

"Oh, what happiness!" the girl sighed. "It will be the answer to all my prayers."

The gypsy leered, her lip curled. "The name of our tribe shall cause you many a sorrowful, humiliating hour. But when the rest who sought him in the heyday of his youth and strength fade from his sight, you shall remain bright and pure to him as the morning star which hangs like a diamond drop over the sea."

The gypsy scrawled her prophecy in Romany, handing it to the wide-eyed girl. "Show this to the man you take for your husband." She then grinned for the first time—a ghoulish grin that frightened the girl—adding: "Remember, child. Be ever-constant and your destiny will triumph. The name I have given you will be yours; and the day will come when you will pray for it, long for it, and be proud of it."

The gypsy queen rose, her eyes afire. "God be with you, Daisy," she said, clasping the girl's hand. "Remember, Daisy Burton. Remember your Destiny."

That evening, before she went to bed, the yellow-haired "Daisy" penciled feverishly in her diary:

My ideal is about six feet in height; he is a Hercules of manly strength. He has black hair and large, black, wondrous eyes—those strange eyes you dare not take yours from —with long lashes. He is a soldier and a man. He is one of those strong men who lead, the mastermind who governs. My ideal is to be such a man's wife, comrade, friend—everything to him—to sacrifice all for him, to follow his fortunes to any part of the world. Such a man only will I wed.

I love this myth of my girlhood next to God, and I look to the star that Hagar Burton the gypsy said was the star of my destiny. . . .

Isabel nudged her sister. "That's the man!" she whispered excitedly.

"What man?" Blanche scowled, glancing up in the direction her sister was looking.

"The man I'm going to marry!"

"Who, *him?* Don't make me laugh!"

Isabel grabbed her sister's arm. "Blanche, quit staring like that!" Her fair cheeks turned crimson. "He might see us and think—"

"Think nothing!" Blanche smirked. "That's Dick Burton, the most hard-to-get bachelor in Europe. Look—he doesn't even know you exist."

Isabel stole a glance. "Oh, Blanche, he's looking at us! No—oh, God—he's looking at *me!*"

"At *you?* Why you're more conceited than he is! Dick's

not looking at you; he's looking at me. So why worry?"

Blanche turned her head and smiled as they walked by. Isabel lowered her eyes, too frightened to meet the gaze of Richard Francis Burton.

There he stood, decked out in an unbuttoned black jacket and tight white trousers, leaning against a poplar on the tree-lined ramparts of Boulogne in the warm spring of 1851.

Isabel had often watched him from afar, peering entranced as he swaggered down the shaded walk swinging a thick iron stick. Now, at this awe-inspiring moment, she passed within a few feet of him.

There he stood—god or devil, she could not imagine—tall, lean, and muscular. The man of her dreams. He flexed his sinewy wrists by flicking the iron stick from one broad shoulder to the other, puffing away at a long black cheroot and gazing out over the channel. His grin was almost fiendish, magnified in its demonic aspect by long drooping black mustachios. His dark flashing eyes and long lashes made him fiercely handsome.

Fascination suddenly overwhelmed her, and Isabel glanced up. For a second her deep-blue eyes met his, and all her senses were paralyzed. He looked at Isabel in a way that seemed to penetrate the depths of her most hidden desires. Secret thoughts and forbidden dreams were laid bare by those savage eyes, that sinister glare.

Isabel was stunned. She almost stopped and dropped her books. She stared but a second, then broke the spell and walked past. Sweating in a heat of infatuation, Isabel murmured to Blanche: "I don't care what you say. That man will marry me!"

:

On the following afternoon, while strolling along the ramparts, Burton noticed a group of girls heading his way. The tallest and eldest was Isabel. His eyes were instantly focused upon her beautiful body.

Isabel's radiant golden-brown hair, which yesterday blanketed her shoulders, today was swept up in an elegant and highly fashionable style that accentuated her classic features. Isabel's plump and shapely form tantalized this notorious wooer of well-built blondes. As far as Burton was concerned, she stacked up with the most curvaceous cuties in all Europe.

Seeing that he had attracted her attention, Burton pulled a piece of chalk out of his pocket and printed on the stone wall:

MAY I SPEAK TO YOU?

Leaving the chalk on top of the parapet, he sauntered over to the other side of the walk to await her answer.

Isabel, excited and intrigued, stepped over and read the message. The other girls stood grinning and giggling. Picking up the piece of chalk, she scrawled under his request:

NO. MOTHER WILL BE ANGRY.

Isabel left the chalk on the ledge, looked over at Burton with a guilty smile, then hurried off blushing with her tittering girl friends.

Burton shrugged and made a gesture of *"c'est la vie"* to a passing fisherman, who laughed and said with a characteristic flick of the arm: *"Les femmes—eh!* Better luck next time, *m'sieu."*

For the next several weeks Burton and Isabel eyed each other on the ramparts. She was lured by his untamed aspect, his dark piercing eyes, his enigmatic smile and burning expression.

Isabel Arundell, the eldest daughter of an old and influential family of erstwhile-wealthy English Catholics, had fallen hopelessly in love with a man she did not even know—the wild and notorious Lieutenant Burton of the Indian Army.

Burton, now thirty, devoured this twenty-year-old damsel with his penetrating gaze. He sized up her Grecian face and Arabian form—the dark-blue eyes and soft golden hair, the gracefully curved nose and delicate lips—her body straight and tall as a young birch, her full firm breasts arching her blouse like a pair of pomegranates, her buttocks as lovely as billows of sand. *Praise be to Allah!*

When Isabel's fashionable cousin Louisa gave a dancing party, she invited all the eligible young English bachelors in Boulogne. Among them was the beau of the ball, the envy of one and all, Dick Burton.

Isabel was thrilled to observe how the other gay blades steered clear of this formidable figure, fearing he might challenge them to a duel for some misplaced remark or ill-advised action. They respected him for his reputation as a hot-tempered fire-eater, the one man whom no other dared to defy.

As usual, all the flirtatious fillies flocked around Burton as though he were the only stallion in the room. This made modest Isabel painfully jealous and disgusted. She pitied the poor lieutenant that he had to endure such artful endearments. But Burton was in his glory and enjoyed himself immensely. He was now the life of the party, deliberately shocking and delighting the innocent young ladies and naturally arousing and enrapturing the more sophisticated ones.

When the band struck up, Burton broke away from his mob of admirers and strode to where Isabel sat alone with her mother and her younger sisters. When she saw him coming her tension mounted and her breathing was stilled. It was wonderful, yet frightening. His scarlet shell jacket nearly blinded her with its brilliance.

"By 'er leave, ma'am," he bowed to Mrs. Arundell, then gazed into Isabel's eyes, "may I claim the honor of the first dance?"

"You may, sir," said Mrs. Arundell, "if you'll please introduce yourself to me and my daughter."

Burton clicked his heels and saluted, never once taking his eyes from Isabel. "Left'nant Richard F. Burton, 18th B.N.I."

"Bengal—?"

Burton scowled slightly, turning his piercing gaze to Mrs. Arundell and fingering his mustachios. "No, Bombay Native Infantry."

"Indeed!" she blurted. "Very well, lieutenant—"

Burton grinned, his eyes ablaze, and took Isabel's uplifted hand. He led her to the middle of the floor, and it was as though she were walking in a fabulous dream. Everything around her became awesome and unreal. The band was playing *The Blue Danube* waltz. But to her, in those first fantastic seconds, it was nameless, powerful and pulsating music. She felt the dynamic strength of his arm around her waist as he swept her off her feet, whirling around and around the room. Isabel was breathless, unable to utter a sound. She could only look up at him, enchanted by his magnetic gaze.

Burton suddenly broke the silence. "Your name, miss?"

Isabel remained spellbound. It was as though she had not heard him. His commanding and abrupt manner frightened her.

"*Ha-ha!* Now don't tell me you've forgotten your name. Why you're shivering like a pup."

Isabel blushed, then words flowed from her. The same tension that had silenced her now made her chatty. "My name's Isabel—Isabel Arundell—but everybody calls me 'Zoo' for short."

"Well, Miss Zoo, what a lovely creature you are for such a suggestive name! Let me label you a perfect specimen of the *sexus femininus*. To wit, the body beautiful—the thing divine!"

Isabel averted her eyes, blushing furiously. "Oh look," she said, "we're practically the only ones dancing. I think everyone's watching us!"

"Well I'll be damned!" Burton laughed. "I was right after all! The only kitten worth looking at and waltzing with in this room is you. By god, you ought to be right proud of yourself, young lady—attracting so much attention."

He held her even tighter—whirling, whirling to the wondrous rhythm.

The other girls had been startled to see the rakish and devil-may-care Lieutenant Burton lead the demure Miss Arundell out on the dance floor. Leering looks and heated muttering followed this incredible pair.

When the music stopped, Burton bowed to kiss Isabel's hand. "An honor, Miss Arundell," he said.

"Thank you, lieutenant," she replied, sighing.

"Would you like some punch?"

"Oh I'd love it!" But her complexion suddenly paled and her lively smile weakened with anxiety. "No, I'd better not. I'm afraid Mother might object."

"Object to what? Don't be silly. Just look at the old girl. She's so busy beating her gums with Mrs. Gadabout and Gobetween she doesn't even know the music's stopped. Come. Hurry, before she misses you. What harm in a cup of punch and some quick conversation?"

"Well, all right—" She beamed broadly again. "What harm indeed!"

Burton led her to the punch bowl.

"Well now, Miss Isabel—or Zoo, *s'il vous plaît*—what brings you and your folks to Boulogne?" Burton handed her a cup of punch.

"*Merci beaucoup, mon cher lieutenant,*" she said, curtsying *à la jeune coquette*. "We're here for change, quiet, and economy—the main object being to put me and my sisters in the Sacré Coeur to learn French."

"*Hmmm.* You're coming along quite well with it, I must say!"

"Why thank you, kind sir!"

"Rather well for a woman indeed!"

"How do you mean?"

"I mean that women rarely make good linguists."

"Oh. Anyway, my sisters and I are kept at French all day—music and other studies, you know—but we sometimes get out to read. That's when we like to walk along the ramparts. But we're religiously marched home at half past eight to supper and bed."

"A well-regulated life for a well-regulated young lady!" Burton tossed off his second cup of punch.

"*Pooh!* There's not a bit of fun in it. We're like a parcel of prisoners. But we make the best of it, I s'pose. Anyway, who wants to frown when we ought to be smiling? They say Boulogne is the home of the stranger who's done something wrong. Now, lieutenant, you must tell me what brought you here, what you've been doing these past weeks, and—" she winked, "what you've done wrong."

"Well, Allah be praised!" he howled, dipping his cup in the punch bowl. "What mettle you hide under all that modesty! 'The home of the stranger who's done something wrong.' *Ha-ha!* With apologies to the Book of Common Prayer, I have left undone those things which I ought to have done and I have done those things which I ought not to have done. But there's a damn-sight more health left in me than in those who wrote that passage!"

Isabel snickered, sipping her punch. It was a Protestant parody, so she couldn't have cared less. "But what have you been doing in Boulogne, lieutenant?" she repeated.

"Fencing, my dear Miss Arundell. Fencing. I've thoroughly mastered the art, vanquished all opponents, earned my *brevet de pointe,* and am now a full-fledged *maître d'armes.*"

"Oh how wonderful! I've heard so many people say that 'Burton is an awfully clever young fellow, a man of great mark—in fact, the coming man.'"

"You'll find that man easily flattered, Miss Arundell. I fear you've overdone it." He set down his cup, took her hand, and kissed and squeezed it in such a sensational way that Isabel shivered with mixed emotion. His words were soft and exciting, and his hypnotic eyes searched deep into her soul. "I'm truly grateful to you for the dance and our little *tête-à-tête.* I'm sure you've had some fun. I know I have. Well, Miss Arundell—Zoo—" he grinned, "I must now bid you *adieu sans adieu*."

He left her dazed and trembling, thanked cousin Louisa for her hospitality, and stalked out without another word to anyone. That was the last she saw of him for five fateful years. Burton soon forgot all about her, but Isabel would always remember that rapturous night of nights as long as she lived.

2 : The crucial experiment

"Fools rush in where Angels fear to tread!" Angels and Fools have equal claim
To do what Nature bids them do, sans hope of praise, sans fear of blame!

"Burton, you must be mad! If they found you out they'd slash you to ribbons and hang you up like jerked beef on the door of some bloody mosque."

Sir James Hogg, chairman of the Court of Directors to the Honourable British East India Company, pounded his fist on the huge round conference table in the council hall of the Royal Geographical Society of London on Saville Row.

It was late autumn, 1852.

"And think how you'll have to live," Hogg thundered, "in constant fear of being discovered—a civilized European amongst savage Orientals, existing like an animal in a hellhole of filth and deprivation. Utter madness, I say!"

Sir James Hogg was a big and boisterous man. His voice rumbled and reverberated like drumfire in the hollow hall. He stomped around the table, thumping his fists on its ebony surface.

"I'll not allow it! Nothing but a string of fatalities has resulted from the travels taken in that region. No, I refuse to sanction such insanity!"

Lieutenant Richard Burton followed him with one glowering eye. He sat back with his arms crossed, chin in hand, lips pursed and tapped by an indefatigable index finger. He was thinking: *Poor bugger. If he only knew what they call him out in India. Sir James Sūar—Sir James Pig.*

Burton leaned forward and laid his hands on the table. "I'm ready for it, both physically and mentally."

"Impossible! I daresay you'll never do it and come back alive. They'll nail you to the gates of Mecca."

"Now hold on, Sir James," said Colonel William Sykes, a prominent member of the R.G.S. "I think it's only fair that we hear the lieutenant out. Don't you think you've done enough talking for the time being?"

Sir Roderick Murchison, president of the Royal Geographical Society, cleared his throat.

The secretary, Dr. Norton Shaw, stood up. "Hear! hear!

It's Burton who's come to talk, so let's all be gentlemen and listen to what he's got to say."

"Very well," growled Hogg, anchoring his hulk in a chair. "Proceed, lieutenant."

"Thank you, Sir James," Burton said, rising from his seat. Hogg listened with surly looks and a grunt of disapprobation here and there. "First of all, gentlemen, I want to continue and complete my exhaustive study of the inner life of the Muslim. I've always wished to see what others have been content to hear of. After my first year in India, when I knew enough Persian and Hindustani to read, write, and converse fluently, I began a systematic study of the Islamic people."

Hogg let out a loud *"Hhrrumph."* Lieutenant Burton was notorious in government circles for his secret investigations of Muhammed's children in Sind.

"The first difficulty was to pass for an Oriental. And this was as necessary as it was difficult! The European official in India seldom if ever sees anything in its real light, so dense is the veil the prejudiced and superstitious natives hang before his eyes. And the white man lives a life so distinct from the black that hundreds serve their term of exile without once being present at a circumcision or a wedding, or even a funeral." Burton shot a sharp glance at Hogg.

"Or even a bawdyhouse, lieutenant?" Hogg rasped in return.

"Well, gentlemen, after trying several characters I found the easiest to be assumed was that of a half-Arab half-Irani. Thousands of these 'Ajemis are met with along the northern shore of the Persian Gulf, especially in and around Bushire. So I set out as Mirza 'Abdullah of Bushire, a long-bearded cloth merchant in authentic costume. Being a *bezzāz*, a clothier, fast and fashionable dames let me display my wares even in the sacred harem."

"God forbid!" Hogg snorted.

"But I showed my stock in trade only when absolutely necessary."

"Why?" smirked Hogg. "Because it was uncircumcised?"

Burton bared his teeth. The other gentlemen, especially Murchison, twitched and fidgeted in their seats.

"*Heh-heh-heh,* Sir James," Burton said, twisting his mustachios, "you're to be commended on your cleverness." His eyes flashed fiercely as he sat down again, grinning like a wolf. "Well now, let me continue in this most intriguing vein. Perhaps you'll come up with another gem—eh, Sir James? You see, gentlemen, I could walk into most men's houses quite without ceremony. Even if the master dreamed of kicking me out, the mistress was sure to oppose such measures with might and main. I was flooded with invitations, was proposed to by several papas with marriageable daughters, and I won—or at least I thought I won—a few hearts. I came as a rich man, stayed with dignity, and departed exacting all the honors. No one, as far as I could see, held the slightest suspicion of my being other than what I wanted 'em to think I was. People collected in crowds to see the rich merchant riding into town. Every evening I wandered among 'em, gathering all kinds of information."

Hogg snorted again. "Tell us, lieutenant, how you carried out your orders as an intelligence officer. In other words, how did you handle the enemy's secrets?"

"*Touché!*" Burton replied. "Sir James has scored another hit! Well, hear me out. Now and then I rented a shop. But since the Intelligence Department of the Bombay Army is a rather impecunious organization, I had to rely on funds supplied by the old chief himself."

"You mean Sir Charles Napier, I expect," Hogg said dryly. "Well it should now interest you to know, lieutenant, that the commander-in-chief is not authorized by me or by the governor of Bombay to issue Company funds for masqueraders off on a lark."

"A lark, you say?" Burton roared, lurching out of his chair. "John Company be goddamned with all its twenty-four kings of Leadenhall Street! I was seven years in India working like a horse, volunteering for every bit of service, qualifying myself for all contingencies. I was Napier's right-hand man, the only British officer in the whole goddamned army who could speak more than six words of Sindi. If it weren't for me we'd have never held the country. I was the only intelligence officer who ever reported anything close to the truth. Why? Because I became a Muslim. I saw and heard everything first hand. I went into the mosques and listened to the mullahs, the spiritual leaders of the Sindi army. I mixed with hemp smokers and opium eaters, pimps and pederasts, prostitutes and eunuchs—all the spies and secret agents of Sind. Sure I went into whorehouses. I lived in whorehouses! Yaas, and what scenes I saw—what adventures I went through! But who would believe 'em?"

Burton glared at Hogg. His voice was cutting.

"My career in India was a failure, but by no fault of mine. The wretched people of Sind were being bled to death by a band of bloodthirsty plunderers and cutthroats, the filthy-rich talukdars and emirs. It was Napier's policy to hang all the thieving landholders and moneylenders—'a humane piece of rascality,' he aptly called it—and then replace 'em with honest men. But this wasn't allowed by the twenty-four tyrants of Leadenhall Street. So the looters are still on the loose, levying piratical toll on the Indus river traffic and robbing and raping every poor bugger they can lay their hands on. The only thing that interested John Company was gaining control of the vital port of Karachi and the strategic Indus. To hell with the rest of Sind and all its suffering, bleeding humanity! That makes us no better than the dirty bastards we came to conquer. If we're not in India to build a healthy and happy empire, then what are we there for? I'll tell you what. For pounds, shillings, and pence! That's what. Rupees stained with Indian gore! And because I supported Napier's policy, I suffered accordingly. When I put in an application as chief interpreter for the Multani expedition, I was at once refused and replaced by that jackal Rigby. Ignorant upstart, he knew only Hindustani when I could speak every dialect spoken in Western India. But he also knew the inner circle —the Outramists, the Anti-Napierists. The demon Interest fought against me and won the fight as usual. Napier couldn't have chosen a better pun than *Peccavi*—'I have sinned'—when he telegraphed his success to Government. And I join him wholeheartedly in this confession."

Burton sat down, his face afire and taut with fury.

At this very second Hogg jumped up, slammed both fists on the table, and said: "You, sir, are the most impudent man in the Bombay Army!" He now began to bellow. "You, lieutenant, are hopelessly mad! You're a wild man,

I say—insubordinate and incorrigible—and it's no wonder your career has been a miserable failure."

"Yaas, yaas. No wonder indeed!" Burton answered, leaping out of his seat and glaring violently at Hogg. "I'm a dangerous man. I dare to tell the truth. I dare to do what's right. It seems you much dislike my impolitic habit of telling political truths, don't you, Sir James? Last year I submitted to the Court of Directors certain remarks on the forbidden subject of Anglo-Indian misrule. I need hardly say that publication of these remarks was refused with many threats."

"Liar! Brazenfaced liar!" Hogg's face was so red-hot and swollen that it seemed as if he were about to burst. "I'll see you cashiered for this!"

"By whom? Outram? He's only the C-in-C. Though you both shit in the same nest, and though I can thank him for breaking up my career, you still have the governor to contend with."

"Fiddledeedee!" Hogg waved his arm. "Elphinstone takes his orders from me. He's a Company servant, and I'm his lord and master."

"Well la-de-da!" Burton returned. "If it weren't for the fact that Elphinstone's a personal friend of mine I'd have been drummed out of the service a long time ago. What a terribly ticklish feather up Major Outram's ass, my remaining in the army. His jealousy and ambition nearly had their way with me, but his trumped-up charges and excess of outraged modesty weren't allowed—thanks to a few honest friends."

"Trumped-up charges, you say? How dare you, man! Why the record is quite clear. Instead of doing your duty

as a British survey officer, you were gadding about the
countryside disguised as an Indian. What unutterable
folly! A clear-cut case of irresponsibility and dereliction of
duty."

"I needn't stand here and argue with you," Burton said
calmly. "You can believe what you want to believe, and
I'll believe what I know to be true. I was doing secret
service work for General Napier—"

"Against Company orders."

"The Company be damned! I took my orders from the
'devil's brother.' "

"The 'devil's brother' indeed! Old Fagin, you mean. You
and Charley Napier nearly made yourselves emperors of
Sind. A pity he was recalled before that shameful dream
could be realized."

"My, how you sneer, Sir James. Did my undercover activities uncover any unpleasant truths about John Company's rapacious propensities?"

"I think we're all well aware of your activities, Lieutenant Burton." Hogg was smirking again. "You needn't
remind us, I'm sure."

Burton suddenly became like a wild beast. His look and
manner startled every man in the room. "Just what do
you mean?" he snarled, stalking up to Hogg.

"I mean, sir, that instead of doing your duty as a survey
officer you were out studying unnatural vice."

"And what does that indicate, may I ask?" Burton was
now cautious.

Hogg was scared half to death, but old age gave him
false courage. "It indicates," he sputtered, "that a man
who studies vice must be vicious."

Burton threw back his head and burst out laughing—a

sharp, satanic shout that rang and re-echoed around the room. Everyone, and especially Sir James Hogg, mopped his brow and heaved a sigh.

Hogg slumped into his chair, gathered his wits about him, and said sternly: "Lieutenant Burton, you have applied for three years' leave of absence on special duty from India to Arabia. We—the directors and I—have considered your application very carefully. This is our decision. Recalling the string of fatalities which of late years have befallen many soldier-travelers in the East, and convinced that your contemplated journey is of too dangerous a nature, we refuse our sanction." Burton was about to start up from his seat, but Hogg waved him down. "However, in compensation for the disappointment, I'm allowing you an additional furlough of one year in which to pursue your Arabic studies in lands where the language and customs are best learned." He then stood up. "Thank you, gentlemen. Good day."

And without bothering to shake hands with anyone, out he went—muttering to himself and cleaning his spectacles with a sweat-dampened handkerchief.

"Well, Dick, goodness knows we tried!" said Colonel Sykes, easing back in his chair. "Sir Roderick, Shaw, and Yorke and I stormed Leadenhall Street in support of your application."

"Yes," said Dr. Shaw, "but we were unable to prevail upon the 'honorable' chairman and his equally 'honorable' court of directors to give their sanction directly. Sir James was rather disappointed that you weren't with us, and I think he put off his decision in anticipation of crossing swords with you face to face. That's why he generously offered to come over here."

"And damned anxious he was too!" said Colonel Yorke.

"Yaas," said Burton, " 'cause he knew damned well I'd never come crawling to him!" He laughed, then looked at Sykes. "Will, how does it feel to be mortified by one of your Asiatic Society colleagues?"

"Pigheaded old devil!" Sykes mumbled.

"Oh well, gentlemen, it wasn't a total loss. He's given me a year in which to unburden John Company of my beastly life."

"That's what worries me," said Murchison. "We're giving you our most warm and liberal support. The R.G.S. thrives on its zeal for exploration and its readiness to encourage the explorer and supply him with the means of travel. But what you propose to do is almost certain suicide. What hope is there that you'll ever come back alive? You can't possibly imagine every little thing that might occur; and if you're not ready for it, God help you! One trifle slip—! You're an Englishman, lieutenant, whether you like it or not. It's bred in you. You can't just suddenly become a Muslim overnight."

"Overnight, Sir Roderick? You seem to forget that I've been preparing myself for this project for the past ten years. I go into it with my eyes wide open. What now remains is for me to prove by trial that what might be perilous to other travelers is safe for me. The crucial experiment is a visit to El-Hijaz, at once the most difficult and dangerous point by which a European can enter Arabia. D'you think I'd be blind or mad enough to attempt it if I weren't certain of myself?"

Murchison shrugged. "You know yourself better than I do, lieutenant. But will you have enough time to complete this 'crucial experiment,' as you call it?"

Burton shrugged. "I'd originally intended, had my three years' leave been granted, to land at Masqat. That's a more favorable and safer starting place. From there I would've applied myself slowly and surely to the task of spanning the deserts, my idea being to remove that huge white blot of unknown and uncharted territory from the map of Arabia. That's now out of the question. I could never cross the peninsula and chart the eastern and central regions in less than two years. But I intend to obtain all the information I can concerning the great wilderness, that vast expanse marked on our maps *Ruba'l-Khālī*—the Empty Abode. I also want to inquire into the hydrography of the Hijaz, its watershed, the disputed slope of the country, and the existence or nonexistence of perennial streams."

Sykes attracted Burton's attention by snapping his fingers and smiling.

"Ah yaas," Burton grinned, pulling at his mustachios, "and I'd especially like to try by actual observation the truth of a theory proposed by Colonel Sykes—namely, that if tradition be true, there must exist certain physiological differences in the population of the vast peninsula sufficient to warrant our questioning the common origin of the Arab family. And that reminds me. I want to find out if any market for horses can be opened between Central Arabia and India, where the studs are beginning to excite general dissatisfaction."

There was a rustle of laughter as the men lit their pipes and cigars.

Sir Roderick Murchison stood up and extended his hand. "Burton," he snapped, "we're all behind you one hundred percent."

"Hear! hear!" said Norton. And each of them stood up to shake Burton's hand.

"Well, Dick," said Sykes, slapping him on the back, "how do you feel?"

"I feel so damned good I could dash off to Arabia this very moment! You can't imagine how grateful I am to all of you—how much I'm in your debt—"

"Nonsense," said Murchison. "Come back all in one piece, having done what you say you'll do and with enough information to put every other geographical society in Europe to shame, and we'll consider the matter settled."

"Aye," said Norton Shaw, puffing furiously on his pipe. "Remember, Dick, only the R.G.S. shall claim as its most distinguished member the only European ever to make the pilgrimage to Mecca as a born Muslim. And we'll see to it the first slice of roast pork you see when you get back to England will come off the arse of Sir James Hogg!"

3 : The circumcision of Mirza 'Abdullah

Cease, Man, to mourn, to weep, to wail. Enjoy your shining hour of sun.
We dance along Death's icy brink, but is the dance less full of fun?

Early the following evening, Richard Burton left his flat in St. James Place and headed for the Welbeck Street residence of an old bachelor friend, Dr. George Bird.

Alice or "Lallah," the doctor's charming young authoress-sister, was out on a social engagement; so the two men retired at once to Bird's office. When the door was locked, Burton stripped off his trousers and drawers, unbuttoned his shirt, and lit up a long black trichinopoly.

"Have a cheroot?" he said.

"Oh, don't mind if I do." Bird laughed to see him standing there, half-naked, puffing away at a huge cigar. "For Christ's sake, Burton, why the hell couldn't you let me do it at your place?"

Burton winked, grinning wolfishly through the haze of

smoke. "*Heh-heh,* my dear Bird. What better excuse than that of seeing your perfectly delightful sister, eh?"

"Lecher!" Bird chortled. "You should hope to Christ I don't castrate you. Then what would you do?"

"Spoilsport! Isn't it enough you sent Lallah out with some beardless boy? You also want to rob me of my precious jewels, the only valuable things I have left in life?"

Having rolled up his sleeves, washed his hands, and laid out his instruments and dressings on a dumb-waiter, Bird said: "I expect you'd better lie down on the couch."

"Ah hell, pull up a chair in front of me. We'll do it sitting—y'know, Eastern style."

Bird shrugged. "Have it your own way. But don't think you can just hop up and dash off after this. You're what— thirty, thirty-one? You must stay put for at least a week. No running about, mind you. In infants this is only a nick, but after puberty it becomes a devilish proposition."

Burton sat down on the edge of the seat, leaned back in the chair, and spread his thighs wide apart. Bird then applied a local anesthetic and began to perform the operation. Burton watched all the while, puffing away on his cigar and talking almost continually:

"That's it. You've got the right idea. Pull the skin forward as far as it'll go. There. Watch you get the cord clear of the tip of the glans. I don't want part of my head cut off! Here, let me clamp the skin while you—there, tie that damned cord as tight as you can. Reduces the bleeding to only a few drops. Now y'know there's a difference between the Hebrew and Muslim methods. The Jewish technique—which is your common European method—is supposed to heal in a kindlier way. But I'm no Jew, and I've got to make this look good."

"For Christ's sake, Burton," Bird laughed, thrusting an arm across his sweaty forehead, "what the hell's the difference how you're circumcised as long as you're circumcised? I never heard of any two ways about it. Circumcision is circumcision!"

Burton scowled. "Yaas, but Muslim circumcision doesn't prevent the skin retracting. The Jewish operator, after snipping off the foreskin, tears and turns back the inner layer to join the outer fold. In this way the external skin doesn't retract far from the internal mucous membrane, and the healed wound shows a narrow ring of cicatrice. This tearing isn't done by Muslims. They just slice off the prepuce, apply styptics to the open edges, then remove the cord. When the integument freely retracts beyond the rim of the glans they then apply the poultice."

"An insignificant difference! In either case the prepuce is amputated, the glans exposed."

"Yaas, but the difference is one of appearance—a difference between suspicion and acceptance as well as life and death. The Arabs observe everything, even circumcision scars."

Bird nodded, wiped his brow with the back of his hand, and proceeded according to Burton's prescription. A single stroke of the scalpel removed the betraying and unbeloved skin in a second. When the constricting cord was clipped off, the foreshortened sheath of Mirza 'Abdullah's Islamized sexual organ slid back and laid bare the glans penis and cervix. Richard Francis Burton was now a Muslim in the flesh.

Gnawing on his cheroot, Bird said: "I noticed your prepuce covered the corona. How did you get away with it in Sind?"

Burton cackled. "By sleeping with Hindu women, who don't give a goddamn if you're circumcised or uncircumcised as long as you've got a tool and know how to use it. Even Muslim whores won't go to bed with an uncircumcised man, no matter what he offers, so strong is the taboo against the 'filthy foreskin.' But that's custom for you. *Abū ghulfeh*—father of foreskins—is a sore insult, the mark of an unclean infidel. The danger of my journey would be doubled by noncompliance with the custom. In bigoted Muslim countries it's considered a *sine qua non*. Even acknowledged infidels aren't safe unless they've somehow submitted to the rite. Any Christian passing a mosque is liable to be seized and circumcised—perhaps even buggered besides. I'd be as good as dead if I set foot in Arabia with a foreskin. It's like being caught with a Bible instead of a Koran. When I was playing the part of Mirza 'Abdullah I never dared show my privates in the presence of Muslims, male *or* female, for fear they'd make a eunuch out of me."

"I see you still keep your pubic hair shaved," Bird said as he began to bandage his friend.

Burton chewed his cigar butt, eyeing every move the doctor made. "Yaas. It's another custom, and a damned good one. Sanitary, y'know. The women do it more than the men, but that's according to the country. Esthetically speaking, there's nothing more exciting than a smooth slit."

"Keep this compress on till I drop over and redress the

wound. You'll have a few bad nights till the thing cica-
trizes, but I doubt that involuntary erections will do any
damage. When the circumcision heals, your penis will be
tender and sore for a few weeks till the glans hardens.
This hypersensitivity may result in repeated erections, say
when the corona rubs against your clothes. After three
weeks these erections shouldn't be what you would call
painful, but you won't be able to masturbate for at least
a month."

Burton burst out laughing. "Indeed! Shan't or can't?"

"*Shan't*—unless you like to torture yourself! But of
course, man, vaginal intercourse will be entirely within
your means."

"Yaas, yaas," Burton drawled, fingering his mustachios.
"Come to think of it, the Arabs ascribe healing attributes
to copulation. Curative acids in the vagina, y'know. Syphi-
litics believe that by penetrating female animals and
Negresses they can cure their tortured tools."

Bird chuckled and sat back in his seat. "By Jesus Christ,
Burton, you're the most fantastic man I've ever met. Now
tell me—be honest with an old chum—why in the name of
hell are you doing all this?"

"You couldn't have asked an easier question!" Burton
laughed. "I'm fed-up with 'progress' and I'm sick of 'civilization.' I'm itching to see with my own eyes what others
are content only to hear of, Muslim inner life in a really
Muslim country. The truth is that I'm absolutely aching to
set foot on that mysterious spot which no traveler or vacation tourist has yet described, measured, sketched, or
photographed. And I'm resolved to resume my old character of a Persian wanderer, a dervish—Mirza 'Abdullah

—and to make the attempt come hell or high water."

Bird reached over to the dumb-waiter and poured Burton and himself a glass of brandy. "Why not travel under your English name? Now that you're circumcised, consider yourself a convert."

Burton tossed off his brandy like a drink of water. "Never. And for this reason. To pass through the Muslim's Holy Land you must either be a born believer or have become one. As a born believer you may demean yourself as you damned well please, but as a proselyte a path is ready prepared for you. My spirit can't bend to own myself a renegade—to be pointed at and shunned and catechized, an object of suspicion to many and of contempt to all. It would defeat my whole purpose! The convert is always watched with Argus eyes, and this would obstruct the very aim of my wanderings. Men don't willingly give information to a new Muslim, especially a hateful Frank. They suspect his conversion to be feigned or forced, look upon him as a spy, and let him see as little of life as possible. No, by heaven and hell, firm as my heart is set on traveling in Arabia I'd rather give up the whole damned project than purchase a doubtful and partial success at such a price. I have no choice but to appear as a born believer."

Bird refilled Burton's glass. "Well, old chap, a disguise may do wonders; but Christ only knows, it's when the beak opens that the parrot stands confessed."

"Arabic is like a second mother tongue to me. In two months I had the neck of the language broken. Did it all myself. Mostly a work of pure memory. When I came across some difficult sound like the guttural *ghayn,* I trained my tongue to it by repeating it so many thousand times a day. I always read out loud, so my ears might aid my memory. Whenever I talked Arabic with anybody, I took the trouble to repeat their words inaudibly after 'em. That's how I learned the trick of pronunciation and emphasis."

Bird became even more curious and fascinated. "I don't think you ever told me what got you started on all this."

Burton swallowed his second brandy. Bird was still sipping his first. "Mingling with the Muslims in Sind, I s'pose. That's when I first wanted to visit Mecca. My Persian munshi and I opened three shops in Karachi. Sweetmeats, tobacco, hashish—we sold a lot of stuff exceedingly cheap to those who deserved it. That's where I laid in a stock of native experience, especially concerning such matters as pederasty and prostitution. Y'know," he chortled, thrusting a fresh cheroot between his teeth, "behind the respectable front of those three shops we were running a highly profitable pandering service on the sly. Employing three good pimps, we were mobbed with customers. That gave us an opportunity to expand our business and turn the three tobacco shops into first-chop pukka whorehouses."

Bird howled with laughter and gulped down his drink.

"But naturally, while every Muslim in Karachi was banging away and buggering it up right before my eyes, I the dispassionate proprietor was plunged in more ascetic pursuits with my chief procurer, Mirza Muhammed Husayn. It was under him I began a systematic study of practical Muslim theology, learned about a quarter of the Koran by heart, and became a proficient at prayer. My brother officers started calling me the 'white nigger.' Except for my being uncircumcised, I'd all but 'turned Turk' in their eyes!"

"And that's how you became interested in the Arabs— by observing their Persian cousins?"

Burton shook his head in a mist of smoke. "That was only an impetus. I was sick of all our make-believe progress, sick of the slavery of civilization, long before I even went out to India. That's why I began to study Arabic at Oxford. When they gave me the gate I decided to get the hell out of Europe altogether, so I bought a commision in the Bombay Army and said good riddance to 'Merry Old England.' It only took me a couple months in Anglo-India to find out what a stupid mistake I'd made. There I was fed a dull and disgusting diet of meaningless parades, tiresome courts-martial, official squabbles, dislikes, disapprobations, and allusions to superior authority—gup, gossip, and all the scandals of small colonial circles—enough to make any sane man sick to death. I thirsted for freedom, and when Napier offered to make me his personal spy I jumped at the chance. My official capacity as assistant in the Survey of Sind gave me the liberty and opportunities I wanted, but my unofficial duties gave me even greater freedom. How I loved to get out of that goddamned blistering-hot monkey suit and slip into some cool pajamas and a loose robe! Then I could wander free."

"Then you first got the idea at Oxford."

"Yaas, more or less. You might say it was always my desire to visit Mecca during the pilgrimage season. Written descriptions of its rites and ceremonies are common enough in every European language, but none of 'em satisfies me. They're full of contradictions, 'cause they're all hearsay. None of 'em seems to know anything genuine about the matter. So to this preparation I'm devoting all my time and energy—not forgetting a sympathetic study of Sufiism, the Gnosticism of El-Islam, which will raise me high above the rank of a mere Muslim." Burton grinned. "I already have a murshid's diploma in the Qadiri Order of the mystic craft *Et-Tesaowuf*, making me a Master Sufi."

"How many men—Europeans, I mean—have done what you're about to do?" Bird said, lighting his pipe. "You know, made the pilgrimage to Mecca as a born Muslim—not as a convert?"

"Quite a few have tried, but none of 'em ever really succeeded. They were all known to be infidels, and many of 'em were killed. John Burckhardt entered Mecca disguised as a Mameluke, but he never saw the sacred Ka'abeh. He later confessed he was so damned nervous he was unable to take notes for fear of being detected. That was in 1814. Muhammed 'Ali Pasha, then governor of the Hijaz, knew who he was. He gave the Bedawin orders that Burckhardt wasn't to be touched, but that he also wasn't to see any of the sacred and jealously guarded sanctuaries. The Swedish orientalist Dr. Wallin performed the Hajj in 1845, but his perilous position and what he called 'the filthy company of Persians' were effectual obstacles to his taking notes. Wallin reached Mecca dressed as an Irani, but the minute he got there he heard that two Jews had just been nailed alive to the gates of a mosque for impersonating true believers. Needless to say, Wallin took the hint and soon made himself scarce!"

"So no European has ever gotten into the Forbidden City except as a known convert, never as a born believer."

"Exactly. Any Jew, Christian, or pagan who publicly

professes and embraces Islam before the Muslim authorities has a right to perform the pilgrimage in all safety and assurance. He needn't worry too much unless a few bloody fanatics doubt the sincerity of his conversion and decide to flay him alive—especially if he's uncircumcised, a condition allowed in most converts. The only European I ever met who entered Mecca without apostatizing is M'sieu Bertolucci, the Swiss consul at Cairo. He persuaded some Bedawin camel drivers to introduce him in disguise. These scoundrels do anything to get hold of a handsome flute, and Bertolucci certainly had a wicked mouth. As soon as he got into Mecca he tried to get rid of his enamoratos. That's when they betrayed him to the local governor. Bertolucci was seized, stripped, and unmercifully abused. I was told by a homecoming haji in Cairo that the Grand Sherif and his three sons took turns repeatedly buggering and otherwise abusing the poor devil. They then ran him stark-naked through the streets and out into the desert, where he was later picked up and saved by the same rascals who had turned him in. The haji also said he was forcibly circumcised by the Grand Sherif. A fitting injury to insult! But Bertolucci may already have been 'customized.' When I saw him in Cairo he naively owned that his terror of discovery prevented his making any observations in Mecca. Indeed, what little he saw of the place wasn't worth a damn remembering!"

"Did he ever mention his misadventures?"

"No. But he laughed at the luck of the Spanish Jew Badia, who entered Mecca as a spy of Napoleon. His disguise was against him, and before he left he was simultaneously sodomized and onanized by all the black eunuchs in the sherif's harem. The same fate befell his two Turkish slave boys, but they were rather used to being forcibly masturbated and buggered. So, my dear Bird," Burton added, cracking a wry grin, "if I come back with a sore anus and perhaps an equally irritated penis, you needn't add insult to injury by asking why."

4 : To Africa's burning shore

Life is a ladder, infinite-stepped, that hides its rungs from human eyes.
Planted its foot in chaos-gloom, its head soars high above the skies.

It was on the foggy and chilly Sunday evening of April 3, 1853, that Burton left London by train for Southampton. On the advice of another old bachelor friend and fellow officer, Captain Harry Grindlay of the Bengal Army, he got into his disguise before leaving town. Entering Grindlay's apartment as Lieutenant Richard F. Burton, he soon emerged as Mirza 'Abdullah-i-Hichmekani—Mister 'Abdullah of Nowhere.

With shaven head, huge black mustachios, white blouse,

blue bag-trousers, red cummerbund, green robe, and sandaled feet, Burton climbed into a waiting cab while Grindlay ordered the cabby and his Negro boy to load the luggage on top. Then the captain and his strange-looking traveling companion drove off to the railway station.

"Y'know, Dick," Grindlay said as their carriage clattered through the streets of London, "this impersonation will multiply the difficulties of your task. What I mean is, in the new convert a lot might be excused on the grounds of unfamiliarity with the customs, the ritual, the language —you know? But the born Muslim has no such refuge. He must be circumspect in every act and word—ever on his guard for fear some trifle lapse in ordinary behavior, some slight deviation from prescribed religious observations, might betray him at once."

"Harry, I can will myself to be whatever I damned-well please. I've done it before, and I'll do it again. It's a kind of self-hypnotism or auto-reincarnation. The Hindus call it dhāranayōga—recollective re-embodiment. You exercise dynamic concentration and convince yourself that what you want to be and what you must remember will never be erased from your mind. In other words, you'll never inadvertently stray from the path you've chosen to follow. I learned it from sadhus and sannyasis in Sind. That's when I was studying to become a Brahman, a yogi. When I actually believe I'm what I want to be, I know I'm perfectly safe. No one can touch me. I've trained my mind to make myself one of 'em. Yaas, once I'm reincarnated as Mirza 'Abdullah, Dick Burton is as good as dead."

"Grim thought!" Grindlay snorted. "Well I daresay you certainly look the part. Must be the gypsy blood in you. If you don't pass as an 'Ajemi, by God Almighty I'll eat my hat!" Grindlay suddenly knit his brow. "Egad, Dick, what does your family think of all this?"

Burton laughed devilishly. "Be damned if I know what they think now, and be damned if I know what they'll think when they find out!"

"You mean to say they don't know—you haven't told them?"

"*Ha-ha!* No, this afternoon I sent off a letter to my mother and sister. They're staying at Bath, y'know. I told 'em not to worry—I was going to Mecca as a Muslim— and I wrote out my will, leaving what little I have to them if I'm not back in a year's time."

Early the next morning an Eastern bird of passage, accompanied by his guide Captain Grindlay, stalked aboard the Peninsular & Oriental Company's plush three-thousand-ton steamer *Bengal*.

No sooner had they left the gangplank than Burton came face to face with a rawboned Turk in blue regimentals and black fez. The man had the face of a corpse. His sunken eyes lit up like red-hot coals, and he twisted his red-dyed mustachios with nervous fingers. A fiendish grin crinkled his sallow parchment complexion. "*Sbāhhel-khayr, yā effendi,*" he said in a sepulchral voice.

Burton answered his "good morning" with a sharp and scowling "*Yis'id sbāhhek.*"

The Turk flashed a huge signet ring as he lit his yellow cigarette. "Don't I know you, effendi?"

For a few seconds Burton stood glaring into the man's hollow face. He stared till his fierce and forbidding expression wiped away every trace of a smirk of assumed recognition, leaving the Turk with a vapid and vacant look.

Then he spat on the deck and walked away, Grindlay close behind him.

When the *Bengal* was about to steam out of the Southampton harbor, Mirza 'Abdullah unrolled his prayer rug, dropped to his knees, and recited the traditional *fātihheh* or brief "opening chapter" of the Koran. It was a prayer of *bon voyage*.

Grindlay, the leering Turk, and several gaping European passengers watched him as he shut his eyes and raised his hands, palms up and right forefinger outstretched, and intoned the invocation in a strident voice: "*Bismillāher-rehhmāner-rehhīm!* In the name of Allah the Merciful, the Compassionate! *'Lhhamdulillāh!* . . .

"Praise be to Allah, who all the worlds made!
   The Merciful, the Compassionate, King of the Day of Faith!
Thee alone do we worship and of Thee we ask aid.
   Guide us to the path that's straight,
   Of those for whom Thy love is great,
   Not those of hate who deviate.
Amen, O Lord of jinn and men!"

Squatting in a leeward corner of the deck, for a couple weeks Burton whiled away the time by training his mind and body to respond to Muslim manners and customs.

"Y'know, Harry," he said one evening in the privacy of their cabin, "both Easterns and Westerns perform the same offices of life, but each in a widely different way. Take for example a true believer guzzling a glass of sherbet. With us the operation is simple enough, but his performance involves at least five separate ceremonies." Burton began to count out on his fingers. "First of all he grabs the glass as if it were the throat of an infidel. Secondly, before wetting his lips he spouts 'In the name of Allah the Compassionate, the Merciful!' Thirdly, he gulps the liquid down like a dose of salts, heaves out a rasping sigh, then erupts with a belch of satisfaction. Fourthly, before tossing his empty glass away he grunts 'Praise be to Allah!' And fifthly, he croaks 'May Allah make it good for you!' in answer to his friend's polite 'Here's laughs and long life!' What's more, he carefully avoids the infidelic act of drinking sherbet or even water in a standing position. The only water one swigs on his feet is that of the Holy Well Zemzem, water given in charity, and what's left after the *wudzū'* or pre-devotional ablution."

The *Bengal* plowed effortlessly through choppy waters and misty weather, cutting straight through the stormy seas around Cape Trafalgar, till the rough and rainy Atlantic smoothed out into the mild and radiant Mediterranean. Like released rats that had been trapped in a hole, all the passengers swarmed up on deck to breathe in the balmy breeze.

Burton now began to break the monotony of this eventless voyage by competing with a Roman Catholic priest the day after they passed under the Rock of Gibraltar.

While the young Father William Strickland sat in a deck chair and recited the rosary and breviary with bated breath, Mirza 'Abdullah crouched across from him, told his beads in a trumpet-tongued monotone, and read the Koran in an ear-piercing whine. When Strickland murmured *"Avé Maria,"* Burton howled *"Allāhuakber!"* It was Christ Jesus versus the Prophet Muhammed, a sweet whisper against a sour wailing.

After a couple days of this cacophony, Father Strickland lurched out of his seat. "Oh my God, I can't stand this any more! It's enough to raise the dead!" He never again appeared on deck to say his prayers.

Five years later, much to his amusement, Richard Burton would learn that William Strickland was none other than Isabel Arundell's favorite cousin.

On the evening of the thirteenth day after their departure the big bearded pilot steered his mighty screwship toward the hazy-red harbor of Alexandria and put in off Ras et-Tin, the Headland of Clay.

Burton shook hands and said good-bye to Harry Grindlay, who was journeying on to rejoin his cavalry regiment in India.

"Well, Dick, good luck and Godspeed on your perilous enterprise. I'll be keeping my fingers crossed, and let me hear from you the minute you get back to civilization. Hey, you know it's one encouragement to see that with a short beard and a shaven head you've succeeded in fooling even your most eagle-eyed observer."

Burton laughed. "You must be referring to that mean-looking Turk."

"I am indeed! D'you know him?"

"Know him? I know him only too well! Rashid Bey of the Egyptian Army. A sneaking, treacherous polecat. He was educated in Paris. That's where I first met him. Called me an uncircumcised pig, so I challenged him to a duel. He laughed in my face, said he was too much of a gentleman to accept such a 'barbarous proposal,' so I knocked him ass over head with a solid right. That's the last I ever saw of him till now."

"Y'know, he's kept an evil eye on you ever since we left Southampton. A regular jackal!"

"Yaas, I know. And something tells me Rashid Bey and I are going to meet again one of these days, but on his own ground and at his own convenience. Then we'll try who's the better man—Burton, who likes to fight at a disadvantage, or that hyena Rashid, whose only prowess is in his prick."

Burton assumed a wild and withering look as he stepped onto the dock and started to plunge through a silent but sinister-looking mob of scowling spectators. When he raised his right hand and growled "'*Lhhamdulillāh!* Praise be to Allah!" all the people began excitedly murmuring "*Muslim! Muslim!*" among themselves.

A path was instantly cleared for the unfaltering and fierce-looking Mirza 'Abdullah-i-Hichmekani. The preadolescent population spared him the usual insults addressed to wandering dervishes. Everyone, even the untamed Arab children, stood aside in awe or admiration to let the fiery stranger pass.

But a grubby little boy, hoping to open the hand of handouts, suddenly popped up in front of him and brazenly blurted "*Bakhshīsh!* Freebee!" Burton shook his head and snarled "*Māfīsh!* I'm broke!", which caused the wide-eyed kid to run like mad and convinced a few bystanders in the open-mouthed crowd that here was no man to be dealt with lightly.

Having hired a donkey cart to convey his baggage, Burton forced and fought his way through a bellowing herd of merchants and pack mules and penetrated a stifling veil of clay dust and powdered dung. In half an hour he had found refuge in a cool and aromatic café, away from the stink and the glare.

With chibouk in mouth and coffee cup in hand, Burton languished in the luxury of a soft divan. He then opened his journal and began to write:

> Startling the sudden change from *presto* to *adagio* life! In thirteen days we had passed from the clammy gray fog, that atmosphere of industry, through the loveliest air of the summer sea, whose sparkling blue and purple haze spreads charms even on North Africa's beldam features.
>
> Now I'm sitting silent and still, listening to the monotonous melody of the East—the soft night breeze wandering through starlit skies and tufted trees with a voice of melancholy meaning.

He stopped for a moment, inhaling the heady Persian tobacco and sipping the bittersweet Egyptian coffee. He penciled feverishly:

> So this is what the Arabs call *kayf*—the savoring of pure animal existence, the passive enjoyment of voluptuous sensation. The delicious languor, the dreamy tranquillity, the airy castle-building—in Egypt all these lethargic pleasantries seem to take the place of the vigorous, intensive, passionate life of Europe.

But then Britannia was never noted for her cultivation of relaxation, he now thought what he did not care to write. *If she had, she wouldn't be mistress of the seas and ruler of one-sixth of mankind!*

> *Kayf!* It is the result of a lively, impressionable, excitable nature—an exquisite sensibility of nerve. It argues a facility for voluptuousness unknown to northern regions, where

happiness is placed in the exertion of mental and physical powers, where anxiety is the life, where niggard earth commands ceaseless sweat of face, and where damp chill air demands perpetual excitement, exercise, or change—or adventure or dissipation, for want of something better.

In the East, man wants but rest and shade. Upon the banks of a bubbling stream, or under the cool shelter of a perfumed tree, he is perfectly happy—smoking a pipe, or sipping a cup of coffee, or drinking a glass of sherbet, free from the cares of body and mind—the trouble of conversations, the displeasures of memory, and the vanity of thought being the most unpleasant interruptions to his *kayf*.

No wonder *kayf* is a word untranslatable in any European tongue!

Kayf! It isn't a word; it's a state of mind and body. Burton found it to be one time physical, one time mental, another time psychophysiological. To the unrefined sensualist, *kayf* is an orgy of inebriation and copulation. It is the prolonged erection and frenzied lust produced in some by the smoking of hashish. To the refined hedonist, *kayf* is a feeling of inner peace and well-being. It is never a cheap thrill, but an ecstatic experience in otherworldliness. It is *nirvāna* and *samādhīyōga*. It is the "absolute union," the "perfect orgasm."

Burton soon lodged himself in a large shack along the muddy Mehmudiyeh Canal, where he was free to pursue his exhaustive studies of Muslim life and culture. Although a certain Turko-Egyptian army officer tagged Mirza 'Abdullah an Irani whorehound on the loose for Arab meat, no one of Eastern origin had any idea of the part he was playing.

A few fanatics charged him with apostasy and demanded to see his circumcised *zubb,* but having gotten their kicks they abandoned their allegations. Many devout Muslims called him an *'Ajemī* or freethinking Persian, a halfhearted true believer—not a good one like themselves, but a bad one as far as the Faith is concerned. But all in all, no one knew his secret or had the slightest suspicion that he was other than what he claimed to be—a wandering dervish from Bushire to Nowhere.

Burton lost little time in hiring an intelligent and trustworthy old *shaykh* or scholar, and plunged once more into the depths of El-Islam. The white-bearded shaykh revived his recollections of religious ablutions, he repeatedly read through and memorized much of the Koran, and again he became proficient in the practice of prostration.

Burton's leisure hours were spent in prowling through the cool baths and smelly coffeehouses, in roaming around the turbulent bazaars, and in shopping about for nothing in particular—an amusement which amounted to his sitting on some shopkeeper's counter and smoking, sipping coffee, and telling his beads for a half hour or so—to show he wasn't one of the slaves for whom time is made. In fact, Burton delighted in pitting his patience against that of the merchant—a test of Oriental impassiveness.

Mirza 'Abdullah also found time for a brief trip to a quaint country village on the banks of the canal, where he entertained a rare opportunity of seeing the traditional Egyptian belly dance performed by a troupe of big-breasted and broad-buttocked Fellahin beauties. It would be many months before he might again feast his eyes on such a luscious spectacle.

But never letting the sensual seduce the spiritual, Burton attended the mosque every evening and visited all the shrines in and around Alexandria. He was shown the tomb of the prophet Daniel by his venerable shaykh, and a money-hungry donkey boy led him to the exact spot where the bones of Alexander the Great were buried. Mirza 'Abdullah praised Allah for such a rare revelation, but the donkey boy mumbled rotten bones when he got no bakhshish.

Within a week the people of Alexandria began to eye Burton's collection of phials and pillboxes with a yen for their contents. An Irani doctor was quite a curiosity to them. There was something strangely alluring about a magician, physician, and mystic who was able to make "heap big medicine."

Ever since 1842, when he went out to India, Burton had been a dabbler in medical and mystical knowledge. He now found this know-how extremely useful in establishing himself as a respectable Muslim.

Men, women, and children besieged Burton's shack from dawn to dusk; but at last he was able to examine the Arabs intimately and exhaustively. Mirza 'Abdullah was especially intrigued by the fair sex of El-Islam, of which Europeans usually knew only the worst specimens since Alexandria was overrun with veiled and unveiled nymphomaniacs.

Even skeptical natives, after witnessing a Burtonian performance of medico-mystical magic, opined that the fierce-eyed stranger was some sort of holy man gifted with supernatural powers and knowing just about everything. One old fortune-hunter offered his daughter in marriage; but since he said nothing about a dowry, Burton thought it best to refuse the flattery. Then a middle-aged dame

with that come-hither look handed him a hundred piasters
—about five dollars—and begged him to stay in town and
miraculously accomplish the curing of her blind left
blinker; but Burton suspected that her widowed vagina
was more in need of treatment than one of her bedroom
eyes.

Mirza 'Abdullah was invaded by young and old with
anal and genital ailments. He cured constipation and diar-
rhea; he treated hemorrhoids and anal itch. He doctored
swollen testicles and inflamed vaginas; he remedied syph-
ilis and gonorrhea. In dozens of little boys and girls he
healed circumcision sores and inflammation of the clitoris,
cuts and scratches and fly-festered eyes, by applications of
boric acid. He dealt with worms, bed-wetting, and menstrual disorders. He killed head lice with camel's urine,
served sprat soup to women who wanted to increase their
milk, tightened loose vaginas with infusions of alum, appeased priapism and prurient penises with divers and sundry drugs, and banished frigidity, sterility, impotence, and
premature ejaculation by administering liquid aphrodisiacs
and local anesthetics and by charming away the omni-
present evil eye with mesmeric magic. Hypnotizing pregnant females, he even helped deliver their babies. This
naturally led to his becoming a circumciser, and in one
week he clipped off fifty foreskins.

After a month's hard work at Alexandria, Burton took
down his shingle, closed his quack shack to all sickers, and
resumed the role of a wandering dervish.

From a mere "Mirza" he had now become "Shaykh"
'Abdullah, the scholarly Servant of Allah. While Burton
was in India, a Sindi agnostic initiated him into the esoteric order of *El-Qādirīyeh*. At that time he assumed the

occult sobriquet of *Dervīsh 'Abdullāh-i-Bismillāh Shāh,* Dervish King-in-the-Name-of-Allah, and after a short period of probation Burton was promoted to the proud position of *Murshid* or Master of the Mystic Arts.

Since he was wise in the ways of these Oriental Freemasons, no other character in the Muslim world was so apt for his exploit as that of the *qalander* or wandering dervish. A rugged individualist, the dervish comes and goes as he damn-well pleases; for his parts are brief upon the stages of life. A conscientious nonconformist, the dervish prays or doesn't pray, marries or remains single, lives and dies in an aura of self-sufficiency and cynicism. If anyone asks him, the licensed carpetbagger, why he comes or where he goes, their answer is a flash of spit and a harsh *"Allāh yenīk—Allah befuck you!"* The more he rants and raves, the more he's respected; and when the heat is on, he need only act like a lunatic to consider himself safe. A madman in the East, unlike a maniac in the West, is allowed to say or do whatever the evil demons demand. He may strip naked in the streets or sodomize a mule, and the most that anyone would do is to laugh and say: *"Mejnūn!* Jinn-ridden jerk!" And to this eccentric character a little knowledge of medicine, magic, and mysticism, and Shaykh 'Abdullah had the pull over all other peculiar people.

The dervish wants to wander, and he must do so, or he shall die.

Thus Burton wrote in his journal when he beheld the grim specter of boredom looming large before him.

A month had again made Richard Burton the most domestic of men. He smoked the pipe of permanence, he delighted in daily siestas, he enjoyed eating at a fixed hour, and he found a certain excitement in bull sessions and blabfests.

But now he couldn't eat, couldn't sleep, couldn't work. He stalked the lonely streets all night, feeling the fit of ennui gnawing at his insides like a ravenous rodent. Eerie winds of a wild and unknown world soughed the siren song—*Lebbayk, Allāhumma, lebbayk*—"Here am I, O Allah, here am I!"—and in the heat of anxiety he would plunge headlong into Araby's abysmal womb.

5 : The land of bondage

We live our lives with rogues and fools—dead and alive, alive and dead.
We die 'twixt one who feels the pulse, and one who frets and clouds the
head.

Although able to leave England with the greatest of ease, even under mysterious circumstances, Burton was not so lucky in Alexandria. He now found himself lacking an all-important necessity.

Shaykh 'Abdullah had to provide himself with a passport if he wanted to get out of Egypt, which was then like
a pig in clover under Turkish socialism. An Egypt teeming
with taxpayers was the Pasha's promise of a better life for
all Muslims, so nobody left the Land of Bondage without
a *tezkireh* or passport.

After several hours of sweating and swearing in broken
English, Shaykh 'Abdullah finally wangled out of Her
Britannic Majesty's Consul at Alexandria a certificate iden-
tifying him as a thirty-year-old doctor and Indo-British
subject named—Burton grinned—'Abdullah. For this favorable indulgence he was obliged to fork over a dollar.

"Oh the meanness of your magnificence! Oh the little-
ness of your greatness!" Burton lashed out in Arabic, spitting on the desk and on the floor, and causing the frightened officials to call for the consular guards to throw him
out. "Allah blister your anus that I should pay for the
shadow of your protecting wing!"

"*Yā q'wāseh, t'āleh!*" said the Armenian dragoman.
"Throw the dirty nigger out!"

"Pimps! piss-pots! pricks!" Burton howled as three strap-
ping kavasses hauled him out of the consulate. "*Māshallāh!*
I'm robbed of a dollar in order that these officers of the
Great Queen may not take too ruinously from a revenue
of seventy millions!" He hawked and spat. "*'Steghfrullāh!*
Satan blister your bungholes!"

When they had unloaded him onto the street, one of the
constables said in a more diplomatic demeanor than that
witnessed inside: "*Yā sīdī*, that new passport o' yours ain't
worth two whoops in hell without a visa—which means
the police commissioner's countersignature."

"Allah reward you for me!" Burton said, picking himself up.

So Shaykh 'Abdullah went to see the *dzābit* or police commissioner, who sent him to see the *muhhāfitz* or governor of Alexandria, at whose door he had the honor of squatting for at least three hours; after which a shifty-looking clerk handed him a hot tip that the proper place to apply was at the *dīwān khārigīyeh* or foreign office.

Burton took off at once for the 'Abdin Palace, which crowned the Headland of Clay. Through the dazzling white-hot haze he beheld a huge and hideous stucco-walled parallelogrammic structure glutted with government offices. Their whitewashed faces glared out on a central court where a few tortured trees, stripped bare of leaves, seemed struggling for the breath of life in a still-born atmosphere of choking clay dust and blinding sun.

As Burton approached the arabesque entranceway he saw the chief kavass stretched out in a strip of shade, dragging languidly on a gurgling narghileh. Burton strutted up to him and pulled out his passport. *"Slām 'alaykum, yā effendi,"* he snapped with a slight bow, touching the fingers of his right hand to his chest.

The kavass didn't bother to reply. He merely opened one eye and leered up at the bold young stranger, baring his yellow fangs like a vicious dog.

Burton scowled back at him. *"Inshallāh!* I'm Shaykh 'Abdullah bin Haji Yusef. I wish to leave Alexandria. Here's a consular certificate to prove my identity. They sent me here, saying a passport wasn't enough. How can I obtain a visa?"

"Mād'rī! Don't know!" he growled, and went on sucking the stem of his water pipe.

"*Inshallāh!* It appears they have little respect for dervishes in Alexandria. But perhaps you didn't hear me the first time. I said my name is—"

"*Rūhh!* Beat it!" The kavass now looked like a tiger poised to pounce upon its prey. His glowering eyes were wide open, his lips pressed tight against his teeth, his nostrils expanding and contracting.

Still Burton stood waving the passport in his hand and said: "Allah forbid that you should flout the brotherhood of El-Islam and forsake the mutual duties binding all true believers!"

"*Rūhh, yā kelb!* Beat it, dog!" he roared, lurching out of his disrupted *kayf*.

Burton sneered and spat. "Slutson muttson shit-eating abortion!"

The kavass snarled savagely and grabbed his kurbash, and Shaykh 'Abdullah would have been horsewhipped to shreds had he not swung around and swaggered off in double-quick time.

Burton made for the nearest market place and appealed to a dozen sources of information—policemen, peddlers, scribes, donkey boys, bums—but without any luck. At last, having lost all patience, Burton approached a young soldier and said: "Here are some pinches of hashish. Lead me to where I can get a visa and I'll give you this piaster."

The bashi-bazouk took the hemp and eyed the silver coin. "Okay, *yā saiyid*," he said, laying hold of Burton's hand, "let's get going!"

Without asking any questions the bashi-bazouk led Shaykh 'Abdullah through a webwork of reeking alleyways, in the deep shadows of which Burton saw half-naked children practicing the sexual intercourse they so often watched their parents perform. The rotting carcasses of dogs, rats, and donkeys made Burton dizzy with their sickening-sweet, suffocating stench. The inebriating aroma of garbage was offset by the sight of a bunch of Arab boys raping a Jewish girl, by scrapping curs and homosexuals hot at work in a dark doorway, by screams and crashes and curses. The bashi-bazouk laughed lightheartedly; but like a good Muslim, his grim-faced companion gasped "*'Steghfrullāh*—Allah forgive us!" in sheer disgust.

A few moments later, after this circuitous and unsavory excursion, Burton stomped up a grand staircase and stalked into a long, bare, wide-windowed room. He blinked and squinted, blinded for a few seconds by the sudden shift from glaring light to semidarkness.

At the far end of the hollow hall, sprawled out on a calico-covered divan, Burton saw a squat, tallow-faced, black-bearded Turk.

The soldier nudged him and whispered: "That's 'Abbas Effendi, deputy to the governor."

With head held high, Burton strode up to 'Abbas Effendi and made a flamboyant obeisance—touching forehead, lips, chest, and genitals with a brisk flourish of the hand. "*Slām 'alaykum, yā effendīna!*" His voice echoed sharply.

With head lolling and a listless, affected look on his face, the *nā'ib* or deputy governor did not trouble himself even to nod in answer to the proud stranger's flowery salaams. He leered at Burton with venomous eyes, then with curling lips he lisped: "*Mīn ent!* Who are you?"

"Shaykh 'Abdullah bin Haji Yusef, dervish and doctor." Burton bowed slightly, his hands clasped deferentially in front of him.

"*'Á-izay!*" 'Abbas hissed. "What d'you want?"

"If it please Allah, I've come for a visa, *yā effendīna!*"

'Abbas Effendi snorted contemptuously and looked away with a disdainful flick of the hand. A long gray lizard, which had been basking in the shimmering bolt of sunlight that shot through the nearest window, suddenly scurried across the floor a few inches from Burton's feet. 'Abbas Effendi eyed it with savage scorn. "*Tehht! tehht!*" he rasped, waving Burton away. "Below! below!"

"Come, *yā saiyid,*" the soldier muttered to a scowling Shaykh 'Abdullah. "Let's go below."

"Below! What in the name of Allah is below?"

"The customhouse, *yā saiyid,* and the foreign office."

"Well Allah be praised!" Burton said, flipped him the piaster, and darted out of the room and down the steps. But finding the door beneath the staircase bolted, he sat at least two hours in the sizzling afternoon sun waiting for someone to come and open up.

"Give up and go home, *yā sīdī,*" someone said with a frown. It was the assistant customs official, back from his midday *kayf* or siesta. "The *gumrukgī* won't be in today. He's being promoted by the Pasha. All business will be done tomorrow."

Burton stood up and grinned. "Ah, but effendi! If it please Allah, I need only a few seconds of your most precious time. You say your superior is being promoted by the Pasha. *Māshallāh!* That means you're now the new customs officer. *Yā sa'dī!* I have here a passport signed by the British consul. It now wants your signature to make it good."

"*My* signature?" the man blurted. "Allah knows, I have no authority! Get out of here before I call a kavass!"

Hawking and spitting, an angry-faced Shaykh 'Abdullah

marched over to a raucous band of Anatolian Turks. With horse pistols and yataghans stuck in their broad yellow sashes, red tarbooshes coiled with blue turbans cocked rakishly on their heads, and wearing knee-length green bag-trousers and short black-and-gold jackets, these rough and robust bashi-bazouks were lounging about and laughing it up in the shaded front of a coffeehouse across the street.

Seeing Burton approach, one of them lurched up and boomed: "Hey, by Allah, is that the customs officer?"

"*Slāmun 'alayk!*" he greeted them.

"*W'alaykes-slām!*" they rumbled in reply.

"No, *yā effendi*," Burton answered the accost, "that's his assistant. The chief won't be in till tomorrow. But that beardless bugger thinks he has no duty to perform just because the boss is away!"

"*Bismillāh!*" said the Turk with a ferocious look at each of his hard-faced companions. "We'll soon see what his duty is! By Allah, if he doesn't have any we'll ram our rods up his rectum till he does his duty one way or the other!"

With Burton and the head bashi-bazouk leading the charge, the Turks jumped to their feet and stormed the customhouse.

"Hey, by Allah," the soldier thundered at the startled official, "we've been waiting all afternoon! Where've you been?" He grabbed the cowering Egyptian by the collar and slammed him against the wall. "We all want visas— *now!*"

"But—but, effendi—" the man sputtered.

The Turk grated like a wild beast and whipped out his longknife. "By Allah, if I have to cut off your balls we're not leaving here without visas. You and that drag-assed master of yours are nothing but a pair of good-for-nothing goldbrickers. Now get busy and earn your bread and butter or I'll gouge out your guts and sell them to the tripemonger!"

Within a half hour the bashi-bazouks had picked up their passports and jogged out, swearing red-hot into their shaggy beards. A few moments later Burton had obtained written permission as Dr. 'Abdullah to leave Egypt whenever he pleased, and to retain possession of his dagger and pistols. Before leaving, he spat in the doorway and said "*Yā menyūk*—O befucked!" to the terrified official. "*Yā menyūk w'yā mezlūq!* O beferked and bejerked!"

Having cut the red tape, Burton heaved a sigh of relief. Arabia now lay wide open before him, beckoning like a seductive courtesan—*Here am I, O Allah, here am I!*— luring men into her secret parts. In a heat of wanderlust, Burton prepared to penetrate her.

6 : Shaykh 'Abdullah and Haji Wali

What endless questions vex the thought—of Whence and Whither, When
and How.
What fond and foolish strife to read the scripture writ on human brow!

At the end of May, 1853, Shaykh 'Abdullah boarded the
Little Asthmatic with all his belongings and steamed up
the Nile River to Cairo.

For three days Burton glared at muddy waters and a
milky sky. The furnace-blast breeze churned up burning
mists of fine sand from salty banks which glistened white-
hot in the broiling sun. Through a seething veil of dust
and vapor he saw the Pyramids rearing their majestic
heads above the skirt of the desert.

For a moment, standing on deck, Burton imagined himself in Sind. Once more he seemed to be sailing down the
Indus. He beheld the same morning haze and noontime
blaze, the same heat clouds driven by a scalding-hot wind,

the same dust giants and sand devils sweeping across the desert, the same fiery sunset and eerie afterglow.

Along the glittering banks he gazed at villages teeming with human and animal life. Little brown boys and girls, some stark naked and others in nightshirts, ran with barking dogs at their heels, shouting and slinging stones at the storms of wild birds. Brilliant green blankets of palm and sugar cane lay outspread to the glaring yellow desert; and he saw the fields swarming with blue-robed, chocolate-skinned Fellahin men and women.

Having taken a third-class or deck passage, Burton felt that roasting sun pierce the canvas awning like boiling water through a piece of gauze; and at night the cold dews fell raw and thick. Squatting alone in an empty corner, Shaykh 'Abdullah eased his tortured nerves by smoking constantly, telling his beads, and reading the Koran aloud. He gulped the muddy river water, scooping it up in a leather bucket, and he munched his own bread and garlic for want of better to eat.

In the scorching afternoon of the third day, with the soaring minarets and pearl-white mosques of Cairo glimmering into view, a big-bellied Syrian merchant plopped down on the deck next to Burton.

"*Wallāhī!*" he groaned, mopping his face and neck with a crummy handkerchief. He stank like a dungheap.

Burton scowled and laid his smoldering pipe down next to the man's pantaloons.

"*Bismillāh,*" he cried, his fat face red with rage, "I'll have you horsewhipped for this!"

Burton slipped a hand into his robe, pulled out his dagger, and began to finger it curiously. Although the dervish didn't remove his pipe, the merchant forgot his threat. He struggled to his feet, grunting and snorting, and waddled away scratching his ponderous posterior.

At that moment a handsome middle-aged Muslim with shaven head and a thin red beard, seeing Burton crouched alone and seemingly lonely, strolled over and sat down by his side.

"Peace be upon you, brother," he said, smiling.

"And upon you peace," Burton replied cautiously. He noticed the man was wearing a green turban wrapped around a red skullcap, meaning that he had made the pilgrimage to Mecca.

"My name's Haji Wali. What's yours?"

"Shaykh 'Abdullah."

"Allah prosper you, Shaykh 'Abdullah!"

"And you, Haji Wali!"

"I'm a Daghestani by birth. I'll bet you're Irani."

"You're right—I am. A Daghestani, eh? Now I know that red hair of yours is real."

Haji Wali laughed heartily. "You flatter me, brother. I'll tell you what gave you away—your piercing eyes."

Burton grinned. "As many Persians have penetrating eyes as Lezghians have flaming hair!"

"*Ho-ho!* Is it modesty or cunning that makes you so interesting? Allah alone knows the hidden things! I run a slave market in Alexandria. Am off to Cairo on private business. How about you?"

"I'm a doctor. And if it please Allah, I'm making a pilgrimage to the Sacred City."

"Thank Allah for doctors! And thank Allah for pilgrims! I was once a pilgrim. Now I'm only a half-assed merchant.

But aren't we all phoney-baloney? You doctors—what d'you do? A man goes to you for ophthalmia. It's a purge, a blister, and a drop in the eye! Is it for fever? Well! a purge and quinine. For dysentery? A purge and extract of opium. By Allah," he added with a broad grin, "I'm as good a physician as the best of you—if only I knew all the *drāhim-brāhim*, drams and drachms, and a few breakjaw Arabic names of diseases!"

Finding no room at any *wekāleh* or hotel in Muslim Cairo, which was then mobbed with pilgrims, Shaykh 'Abdullah and Haji Wali were obliged to put up at a cheap caravanserai in the *Gemālīyeh* or Greek quarter, which was swarming with drunken Christians.

Living under the same roof and sleeping side by side, the shaykh and the haji soon became fast friends. They ate together, prayed together, and smoked the forbidden weed *hheshīsh* together. Its effect upon Wali was a violent and prolonged erection and a savage lust, but 'Abdullah experienced a furious increase in appetite accompanied by alternating fits of drowsiness and nervous energy.

Wearied of repeated masturbation, Wali hired a hot-blooded Egyptian dancing girl on whom he performed continuous copulation for well over an hour—till the effects of the hemp finally wore off—while Burton, watching their wild sport with scientific detachment, hired a Greek caterer and amused himself by eating like a horse.

In their more sober moments, when they passed a quiet evening in the mosque, Shaykh 'Abdullah and Haji Wali talked off the record about that world of which both of them had seen so much.

"I've done a lot of traveling in my time," Wali said,

"and in my wanderings I've cast off most of the prejudices of my people. For instance, I no longer swallow alchemy, angels, and magicians—and I *don't* believe in miracles. I believe in Allah and His Prophet—nothing else."

A little later he said: "You've traveled in the lands of the Franks, you've seen many men and their cities, yet you call yourself a *hhekīm*—a doctor. Brother, y'want some good advice? Give up medicine—give up all this hocus-pocus—and make bread by honestly teaching languages. We're doctor-ridden enough as it is! And here's some better advice, O my brother," he added emphatically. "Get rid of those dervish duds—those blue bag-trousers and that short shirt and robe you're wearing—in fact, all connection with Iran and the Iranis. If you keep on being an 'Ajemi, you'll get yourself in a lot of trouble. In Egypt you'll be cursed, but in Arabia you'll be beaten because you're a heretic. You'll pay three times what other pilgrims pay, and if you fall sick you'll rot by the roadside."

"Then what would you suggest?" Burton said.

"I'll leave that to you, brother. Be what you will, only don't be what you are—a Persian!"

"Then I'll be the next best thing. I'll be a Pathan, an Afghan!"

"Allah protect us!" Wali groaned, repeating an old proverb: "*Slaymānī hhrāmī*—The crafty Pathan is a crooked man! But he's always welcome in Arabia, so I guess you could get away with it."

"If it please Allah, I know I can!" Burton grinned. "Let's see now. Born in India of Afghan parents, say at Delhi. There's a whole community of Pathans in Delhi. Educated at Rangoon, then sent out to wander from early youth—as men of that race frequently are. I'll dress like an Afghani scholar, but I'm still going to call myself a dervish and frequent the places where dervishes congregate."

Haji Wali frowned. "What've those cynical saints got to do with politics or statistics, or any of the information you're interested in? Call yourself a religious wanderer if you like, but be sure you let everybody know you're under a vow to visit all the holy places in El-Islam. Then if anybody asks you why you do so much traveling, you'll be able to persuade them that you're a man of mark under a cloud—and you'll get a lot more respect than you probably deserve," he added with a dry laugh.

Haji Wali thanked Shaykh 'Abdullah for his agreeable disposition by advertising him everywhere as the very phoenix of physicians. He drummed up a lively and lucrative business, and Burton was soon swamped with patients.

His first success came in the caravanserai.

"*Yā sīdī hhekīm!*" sputtered the Arab slave dealer who lived in the next room. "What man will bed with such thunder? The devil has cursed me with a bunch of snoring bitches! I'll only get half-price for these nocturnal noise-makers—even though they're nutcrackers, and nutcrackers are at a premium!"

Burton knit his brow. "Nutcrackers? What in Allah's name are 'nutcrackers'?"

The Arab cracked a wicked smile. "*Yallah, yā sīdī!* Don't tell me you never heard of a nutcracker woman? And you a doctor!" He howled with laughter.

"Allah blacken your body! What's a nutcracker woman?"

"A nutcracker woman, *yā sīdī*, is she who milks a man's

tool with the muscles of her slit. But who can describe such an exquisite sensation? By Allah, I'll let one of my girls give you a demonstration!"

"That won't be necessary," Burton snapped. "When did Allah will that I should suffer a strangled penis?"

"Ah, but sidi! It is like a velvety, slippery hand their sucker—squeezing and milking ever so skillfully—"

"*Bah!* Allah preserve us! I once stuck it in a hot-blooded Hindu whore, and a few seconds later I nearly fainted from strangulation."

"Ah, but an Ethiopian slut never squeezes too tight—only just right, like your own hand."

Burton laughed. "Allah my witness, I've treated too many swollen peckers to know better! Some of these she-demons get so hellishly hot they're struck with a violent and painful convulsion of the sheath, fitting punishment for such vicious lust. But about the snoring—"

"I pray Allah for a cure!"

"A cure you shall get, my good man! *Bismillāh,* bring 'em here."

A moment later and Shaykh 'Abdullah was hypnotizing them dosing nearly a dozen lean-limbed, broad-bottomed, black-skinned Ethiopian wenches with flabby lips and pointed breasts. They went around absolutely naked, were all avid prostitutes, and yet they retained a quaint modesty that made them seem more natural than the so-called civilized courtesan.

Finding them coy and coquettish, Burton began to tease the youngest girl: "How beautiful you are, O Meryem! What eyes! what—"

"Then why don't you buy me?" she giggled.

"We're of one faith, of one creed—formed to form each other's happiness."

"Then why don't you buy me?"

"Conceive, O Meryem, the blessing of two hearts—"

"Then why don't you buy me?"

"Aye, by Allah, why don't you buy her?" Haji Wali came in laughing.

"*Ha! Me?* Allah, you're the meathound around here! Buy one of these babies and you won't have to hire that Egyptian whore any more."

"I wish I could, but Allah knows I can't," he said sadly.

"Why can't you?" the girl bantered. "Have you no prickle?"

"Allah forbid! Don't look at me—look at him!"

"Oh, but he cured me of my snoring. You must cure me of my itch!"

So saying, the girl spread her spindly legs wide apart and revealed a gaping vaginal orifice looped by ashen scar tissue. Like all other females of her race, Meryem's clitoris and labia minora and majora had been excised in early girlhood.

"I seek refuge with Allah!" Haji Wali gasped, breezing out of the room with a half-hidden erection, much to Burton's amusement and Meryem's confusion.

Wishing to continue his theological studies, Burton hired a rawboned old teacher by the name of Shaykh Muhammed el-'Attar.

"*Subhhānallāh!*" he barked, wagging his grizzled beard. "Allah be praised, what words are these? If you're right, *aiwallāh,* throw away your drugs; for it's better to cure men's souls than destroy their bodies, O 'Abdullah!"

Lounging in the local bathhouse, sipping coffee and savoring their pipes, the two intellectuals were heatedly contesting a controversial question.

"*Aiwā! aiwā! aiwallāhī!*" the graybeard rasped. "Even so! even so! by Allah, even so!" Like the proverbial absent-minded professor, Shaykh Muhammed el-'Attar's pregnant mind suffered frequent miscarriages. "You're always writing, O my brave! What evil habit is this? Surely you've learned it in the lands of the Frank. Repent! There's no majesty nor might but in Allah the Glorious and Great! Be ashamed, O my son! Seek refuge with Allah from Satan the Stoned! The doctors of Egypt never write without reward. Better go to the desert and say your prayers day and night! What words are these, O 'Abdullah? Don't you ever say 'Guard us, Allah, from the sin of extravagance!'? Now the waters of ablution being of seven different kinds, it results that—d'you have a wife? No! Then you must buy a female slave, O youth! This conduct isn't right, and men will say of you—I repent and take refuge with Allah!— 'For sure, his mouth waters for the wives of other Muslims!' Fear Allah, O man!"

June was the *Ramedzān* or fasting month of El-Islam; and from dawn to dusk all true believers were forbidden to eat, drink, smoke, deliberately swallow saliva, or ejaculate semen voluntarily. Undesigned swallowing of saliva and involuntary seminal emissions, such as during a wet dream or at the sight of a beautiful woman, did not violate the fast; but sexual intercourse and masturbation were absolutely unlawful.

During the day, when the parching wind wafted a dusty haze and the furnace heat of the desert seeped over the city, the streets of Cairo were virtually denuded of all human and animal life. But in the cool, crisp, moonlit night a sleeping *El-Qāhireh* came wondrously awake; and all the streets were flooded with people.

Shaykh 'Abdullah and Haji Wali passed their eyes over an awe-inspiring orgy of eating, drinking, and merrymaking. Attracted by the twang of lutes, the whine of flutes, and the rattle of tambourines, they looked into a large coffeehouse and beheld a pair of bare-bodied Arab prostitutes performing the *reqs es-surreh* or belly dance amid a pandemonium of clapping and cheering and lusty shouts of laughter. Their bobbing breasts and pouting lips, wriggling rumps and writhing hips, aroused a rage of lust in the all-male audience. While Haji Wali stood gaping and sighing, Burton eyed their quivering bellies with scientific curiosity. The muscles rippled from their navels to their vulvas, which were smooth-shaven and large-lipped, simulating a convulsive series of orgasms.

"*Henī'en!* Cheers!" boomed a long-mustachioed, fierce-eyed Turk as he raised his cup of raki. "May it do you good!"

"*Allāh yhennīk!* Allah cheer you!" another responded, which someone else punned off as "*Allāh yenīk*—Allah queer you!"

"You drink for ten!" rejoined the Turk.

"I'm the cock and you're the hen!" came a tart reply, the common salute of *fā'il* or active to *mef'ūl* or passive homosexual.

"No, I'm the thick one and you're the thin!"

"But I'm the long—you've little in!"

And so the risqué repartee raged on over which penis gives the greatest pleasure, the thick or the long.

Suddenly, high above the hubbub, Burton heard the melodious wail of the blind muezzin, who from his balcony in the towering minaret rang forth the call to night prayer: *"Allāhuakber! Allāhuakber!* Allah is Almighty! *Ashheduan lā ilāha illallāh!* I swear there's no god but Allah! *Ashheduanna Muhhammeder-resūllah!* I swear Muhammed is the Prophet of Allah! *Haiya lislāh!* Come to prayer! *Haiya lil-flāhh!* Come to salvation! *Allāhuakber!* Allah is Almighty! *Lā ilāha illallāh!* There's no god but Allah!"

A tense hush fell over the city, and all good Muslims stopped what they were doing—even withdrawing from coition—to say their prayers.

Returning to their room in the caravanserai, Shaykh 'Abdullah and Haji Wali prepared to enjoy a quiet night of eating, drinking, and smoking.

"Say, did you see the two pistols I picked up this afternoon?" Burton poked a hand into his bedroll, pulled out the ornate weapons, and handed one of them to Wali. "Genuine Damascene barrels."

"Allah be praised!" Wali said, beaming.

A second later the door flew open with a crash and in stalked a strapping bashi-bazouk with scarred face, blazing eyes, and spiked mustachios drooping to a bare chest. His turbanless red tarboosh was cocked rakishly over a fiercely scowling brow, and his large *zubb* dangled from the opening of his dark-blue bag-trousers. A heavy swagger betrayed him as being half-drunk, and a vicious sneer marked him as an extremely dangerous man.

Flashing a fiendish grin, he snatched the pistol out of

Burton's hand and glared at it curiously. "What business have *you* with weapons?" he growled.

Not appreciating the Turk's curiosity, Burton wrenched it away from him and calmly said to Haji Wali: "Just look at the elaborate Damascus twist—"

But his profusely sweating friend was narrowly eyeing the terrible Turk, who now tapped Burton none-too-lightly on the back. He slowly turned around, and the two of them stared wildly at one another for several tense seconds.

"D'you know who I am?" the Turk drawled, shoving his tarboosh to the other side of his forehead in token of defiance.

"I couldn't care less," Burton said, twirling his mustachios in token of double-dare.

The Turk cackled like a grisly hyena. Had he been armed, he would have blown Burton's head off. "I'm 'Ali Agha, captain in the Albanian Irregulars, on leave from El-Hijaz!" He blew his stinking breath in Burton's face. "Hey, d'you have any raki around here?" he said with a smile, slapping Burton on the shoulder and leering about the room.

"No," was Burton's sharp reply.

The Turk sneered, hissing "*Hhmār! Ass!*" It wasn't exactly an insult, for "ass" is a slang synonym for "water-drinker" among liquor-loving Muslims.

Fancying a physician on the water wagon to be a perfect push-over, he seized Burton playfully with an eye to a test of strength. But for one who had studied and mastered *kushtī* or jujitsu in Sind, an opponent's brute strength was his own disadvantage. Burton caught him with a cross-buttock; and had the captain's bald dome hit the stone floor instead of the giant killer's bedroll, the

Prophet might have pulled him into Paradise by his pomaded topknot.

The fall had a good effect upon his temper. He jumped up, patted Burton on the head, and begged with bated breath for a pipe of tumbek and a cup of coffee. Burton obliged him as a merciful Muslim should.

So 'Ali Agha sat down to show them his battle scars and boast of his exploits, after which he stood up and said: "Come on over to my room and have a drink."

Shaykh 'Abdullah glanced at Haji Wali, and Haji Wali shook his head with a reluctant look.

"*Ho-ho!* So let your friend make faces. We'll make merry! Follow me, effendi!"

Burton shrugged. "What've I got to lose?"

"Only the virginity of your bunghole," Wali said dryly, "if it isn't already lost."

Burton got up, grabbed his pipe and tobacco pouch, slipped a dagger and a phial full of liquid cantharides into his cummerbund, and jogged out after 'Ali Agha.

"Welcome to my humble abode!" he captain said with a jazzy salaam. His implement was still hanging out of his pantaloons, and Burton saw him handle and dandle it unconsciously. "Y'see them bottles o' booze over there? Well watch your step, effendi," he half-grinned half-sneered. "Don't ever think an Albanian Muslim don't know how to drink! Here—come on—sit down next to me on the bed." He whipped his dagger out of his waistband and tossed it across the room. "You do the same, effendi, we'll get along a lot better." Burton obliged him, each eyeing the other with malignant satisfaction. "That's it, effendi. Now let's play the Greek and lap the gutter!"

Snatching up a shallow broad-brimmed tumbler, 'Ali

Agha gave it the squint, wiped out the inside with his forefinger, filled it to the brim with raki, then handed it to his guest with a respectful nod.

Burton received it with a salaam, swallowed it down like a shot out of hell, turned it upside down in token of fair play, set it down on the floor with a sporty flourish, belched loudly and bowed again, saying: "Help yourself. She's all yours!"

'Ali Agha grabbed the glass and fanatically followed Burton's ceremonious example. "*Heh-heh-heh!*" he showed his teeth, erupting a thunderous eructation. "Now it's your turn, effendi."

The glass passed rapidly back and forth till the first bottle was empty. Immediately after each drink they gulped a mouthful of cold water and gobbled a spoonful of *selāteh,* a salad of sliced cucumbers and curds, in order to cool their peppery palates. Lighting their pipes, they let out huge puffs of smoke—a sign language of the fast and free—and looked facetiously at each other, boozing it up being considered by Muslims a funny and fascinating sort of sin.

'Ali Agha, having been half-cocked when they began the bout, was now showing signs of what the Iranis call *bed-mestī* or 'lushy lust." He pawed Burton in a waggish and wanton way, croaking such ditties as "*Slaymānī sitānī—* The gay Afghan is a buggersome man!" and adding: "Hey, ain't you an Afghan, effendi? *Ha-ha! ho-ho!* 'The Arab likes a woman's crack; the Afghan likes the hole in back!'" He then picked up a flask of strong perfume, filled the palm of his right hand, and dashed it in Burton's face. "*Ya-ha-ha! hee-hee! ho-ho!* How sweet you smell, my pretty boy! Sweet as a pansy and pretty as a fairy!"

Burton jerked the flask out of his hand, poured some of the pungent stuff into his own, and flung it in 'Ali Agha's face. The captain was anxious to return the compliment in kind, but he had nothing left to throw at his cup companion except the following abortion:

"My pecker is big, and the Afghan said:
  'I'd rather eat that than my daily bread!'
  Said I, 'You'll choke!'
  Said he, 'What a joke!'
So I made him eat his words instead."

Burton was about to laugh, but 'Ali Agha clapped him on the thigh and said: "Hey, how about getting your respectable friend over here? There's nothing I like better than forcing some prickless hydropot to drink and get drunk!"

"Good idea!" Burton said with a devilish grin. "It's like making an atheist out of the Grand Mufti of El-Islam!"

So Shaykh 'Abdullah jumped to his feet and hustled to fetch Haji Wali, who growled when he saw his friend waving a hand for him to come over and join them.

"Oh, all right—if Allah will it," he said at last, picking up his pipe and pouch. "But it won't be for long!"

Burton laughed under his breath.

When the two of them returned, 'Ali Agha howled like a hyena. He lurched up, laid hands on Haji Wali, and forced him to the floor.

"Allah protect us! The bugger's goat drunk!"

In ecstasy at Haji Wali's horror, 'Ali Agha filled the tumbler brimful of raki, grinned grotesquely, and said: "Here, my good man, toss 'er off with the blessings of Allah!"

Haji Wali grimaced. "Allah forbid!"

Making a sour face himself, 'Ali Agha lifted the glass to his own lips and drained it dry. When he winced and berped, Wali muttered "Beast!" and "Bastard!" into his beard.

"I'll pretend I'm not insulted," the captain said. "Here! If you won't drink, have some hashish."

Haji Wali waved it away with a scowl, afraid of its superexciting effect upon his sexual apparatus while in the company of a lecherous Turk.

"Then smoke a few puffs of the less dangerous stuff," Burton laughed, winking at his friend.

After the three had enjoyed their pipes, 'Ali Agha said to Haji Wali: "Now, my good man, how about joining us in a drink?"

"No, by Allah, I never touch the stuff," Wali replied irritably.

"Why not?"

"Well, Allah willing, maybe tomorrow."

"Why not now?"

"In Allah's name, why should I?"

"And by the balls of the Prophet, why shouldn't you?"

"Because it's forbidden by the Prophet!"

'Ali Agha roared. "Indeed! Well you ought to read your Koran more carefully, effendi. The Prophet never said anything about raki. What he didn't like was wine! So stop eating shit and start drink shrab!"

"Satan gobble up your guts!" said Haji Wali.

"Drink!" said the wild-eyed Turk.

Haji Wali sprang to his feet, but 'Ali Agha caught him by the seat of his pantaloons. "Where d'you think you're going?"

"For the police!"

The captain snarled and tried to wrench the haji back, ripping out the rear of his bag-trousers. Wali took a belly flop. His fez flew off and his pipe clattered to the floor. Before he could catch his breath, 'Ali Agha had pulled off Haji Wali's pants and his slippers too, leaving him stripped bare below the waist.

By now, the dose of cantharides that Burton had dumped into what was left of the second bottle was having its ultra-irritating effect upon 'Ali Agha's genitourinary organs. A fierce itch evoked a violent erection, which he clutched and then cried:

"The round peg was made for a hole best to match it.
Were it made for a crack it would look like a hatchet!"

He would have raped Haji Wali right then and there had it not been for Shaykh 'Abdullah, who held the brute at bay just long enough for Wali to leap to his feet and lunge out of the room.

'Ali Agha pushed Burton aside, but didn't bother to pursue his spiritless guest beyond the doorway. "Anus-beaten ass! Whoreson! dogson! Lapper of bloody lesbians!" he said, stomping back to pollute Wali's fez, pipe, and slippers with a generous outpouring of forbidden wine.

Burton burst out laughing at the sight of his disheartened host, and for a moment it seemed that 'Ali Agha was in no mood for horseplay. "Hey," he bellowed, still clutching his enormous erection, "who spiked my drink with goona-goona?"

"I did!" Burton said, still howling to tears. "That wasn't meant for you, but you drank it!"

"What d'you mean?"

"I mean that Spanish fly was meant for my friend!"

"Oh, *ho-ho!* So that's why I'm so stiff and hot! By Allah, I'll need a whole troupe of dancing girls and dancing boys to soften this baby—*unless*—" he added, eyeing Burton wickedly.

"Unless what?" Burton didn't like the wolfish way he was grinning.

'Ali Agha began to wrench his erection, shouting:

"Let's eat of this and drink of that,
  Good booze and foods that make you fat,
  And serve each other, give and take,
  By seeing our tools both get a fair shake!"

"Oh no you don't!" Burton said, bracing himself for the assault. "Take on your troupe of dancing girls and boys, but leave me alone or I'll cut off your cods!"

"I can futter fifty women in one night!" the Turk said, his hand hard at work. "Have that fleaprick friend of yours find me some nice fat juicy piece of meat!"

"Would that he could! There are plenty of free pickings in Cairo, but such good eating isn't allowed here anymore."

"Is that so! And who put an end to it?"

"The Pasha."

"The Pasha, eh?" 'Ali Agha said with smoldering ferocity. He took off his tarboosh, brushed it off with his forearm, fitted it back rakishly on his forehead, twisted his mustachios to the sharp point of a single hair, thrust his pipe into his sash, and swaggered out the door swearing: "The Pasha, eh? Well I'll make the Pasha come here and dance naked in front of us!"

Burton foresaw a street brawl, feeling thankful for the

captain's sake that he had forgotten his dagger. Discretion told him to return to his room, bolt the door, and go to bed. But conscience whispered it would be unfair to abandon the Albanian 'Osmanli in his present condition, especially since he was partially responsible for it. So Burton ran out after him, grabbed him by the arm, and tried to pull him back.

Shaking loose for a few seconds, 'Ali Agha yanked out his long Turkish pipe and began beating a passing roomer over the head with it. Before Burton could stop him, he gave the man a catapultic kick and sent him flying head over heels down the stairs. "O Egyptians!" he howled after him. "O beferked and bejerked! O race of dogs! flutes of Pharaoh! embuggered butt-butchers! O Egyptians!"

He then burst open a door with his shoulder and reeled into a room where two old ladies sat basket-weaving. Both hens let out a bloodcurdling squawk and instantly veiled their beaks, especially when they saw the young cock with his hackle up. 'Ali Agha stood glaring at them, agitated his erection, and growled: "Yā 'ago-o-oz! Old hens!"

"Yā 'owr! O one-eye! Yā bin 'owr! O son of a prick!" they shrieked. "May Allah cut out your heart!"

"O desiccated coyntes!" he said, wielding his weapon. "I'll force my pizzle up your fundaments!"

At this the women screamed bloody murder: "Help! Police! Rape! rape!"

'Ali Agha barreled out of the room, shoved Burton aside, and stumbled down the stairs. Reaching the bottom, he fumbled and fell over the snoozing form of the night porter. "Allah burn out your eyes! I'll drink your blood for this!" He groped about on the floor.

The porter scrambled to his feet, more scared than hurt.

"Quick, before he gets up!" Burton said to him. "You grab his legs and I'll take his arms."

"Allah save me from such a task!" the porter gasped.

Burton was furious. His eyes flashed in the darkness. "Do as I say, or by Allah I'll break open your head like a watermelon!"

The man obeyed instantly; and they half-hauled, half-dragged the drunken bashi-bazouk up the steps to his room.

Still joggling himself, 'Ali Agha bawled at the top of his lungs: "O jerk-off Egyptians! O race of dogs! I've buggered all Cairo, all Alexandria, all Suez!"

"An extensive field of operations!" Burton chortled, as they dropped him down on his carpet-bed.

Haji Wali came rushing into the room. "You'd better start on your pilgrimage at once, my friend!" he said, smiling. "Those two old crones have sent for the cops, and the whole place is buzzing with how a bashi-bazouk and a phony physician are boozing and buggering it up on the second floor. O Allah, what a scandal!"

"*Ha-ha!* It seems I'm no longer considered a serious person!"

"Brother, you've lost your reputation. The sober-minded Afghan doctor turned out to be a hypocritical sot! By Allah, you'd better get out of Cairo while the getting's good!"

"Well, before they have to throw or carry me out I'll grab my luggage and hit the road right now!"

"Where will you be heading, brother?"

Burton chuckled. "Allah knows! Jidda—Mecca. Yembu' —Medina. Remember the old saying: 'Conceal your tenets, treasure, and travels!' "

7 : To Araby the blest

How Life is dim, unreal, vain, like scenes that round the drunkard reel.
How Being meaneth not to be—to see and hear, smell, taste and feel.

Seated high on a jouncing camel, his legs crossed in front of the pommel, Shaykh 'Abdullah crossed eighty miles of that natural blast furnace called the Suez Desert.

A billowy sea of yellow sand and sun-scorched rock sparkled from horizon to horizon. Reflected heat from the hard dry earth danced shimmering before Burton's kaffiyeh-shaded eyes, and burning sand sprays surged and floated in the fiery breeze. His senses were sharpened. The perceptive faculties, prone to sleep in the shell of a lively city, are jolted wide awake in the stillborn desert.

Burton opened his journal and began to write:

> To the solitary wayfarer there is a strange amusement in the wilderness—the effect of continued excitement on the mind, stimulating its powers to their pitch.

Above, through a sky terrible in its stainless beauty and the splendors of a pitiless blinding glare, the simoom—the poison wind—caresses you like a lion with flaming breath. Around lie drifted sand heaps upon which each puff of wind leaves its trace in solid waves, flayed rocks, the very skeletons of mountains, and hard unbroken plains over which he who rides is spurred by the idea that the bursting of a water-skin or the pricking of a camel's hoof would be a certain death of torture—a haggard land infested with wild beasts and wilder men—a region whose very fountains murmur the warning words "Drink and away!"

What can be more exciting? what more sublime? My heart bounds in my breast at the thought of measuring my puny force with Nature's might, and of emerging triumphant from the trial. This explains the Arab's proverb, "Voyaging is victory." In the desert there is present death—solitary, not in crowds, where (as the Persians say) "death is a festival." At night, in the drear silence, the solitude, and the fantastic desolation of the place, I *feel* what the Desert is.

And then the oases, and little lines of fertility—how soft and how beautiful! The mind is influenced through the body. Though your mouth glows, and your skin is parched, yet you feel no languor—the effect of humid heat. Your lungs are lightened, your sight brightens, your memory recovers its tone, and your spirits become exuberant. Your fancy and imagination are powerfully aroused, and the wildness and sublimity of the scenes around you stir up all the energies of your soul—whether for exertion, danger, or strife. Your morale improves; the hypocritical politeness and the slavery of civilization are left behind you in the city. Your senses are quickened; they require no stimulants but air and exercise. There is a keen enjoyment in mere animal existence. The sharp appetite disposes of the most indigestible food, the sand is softer than a bed of down, and the purity of the air suddenly puts to flight a dire cohort of diseases.

It is an ancient truth that Nature returns to man, however unworthily he has treated her. I will suffer real pain in returning to the turmoil of civilization, now that my tastes have conformed to the tranquillity of the wilderness. I anticipate with repugnance the bustle and the confusion of artificial life, its luxury and its false pleasures. Depressed in spirits, I will for a time feel incapable of mental or bodily exertion. The air of cities suffocates me, and the careworn and cadaverous countenances of their citizens haunt me like a vision of judgment.

Jogging into Suez, Burton found shelter in a scratch house swarming with flies, cockroaches, scorpions, ants, lice, gnats, and fleas. Although the crumbling walls were covered with mold and the sooty ceiling festooned with cobwebs, when Burton saw the floor black with bugs he bellowed for a broom and a bucket of boiling water. Then he swashed and swept out the room, much to the Coptic proprietor's scandal and shame.

After that long hard ride, every bone in Burton's body ached. His eyes burned, his head throbbed, his skin and scalp itched. Spreading out his carpet-bed, he immediately fell into a tense and turbulent sleep. All during the night, cats and rats crawled through the holes in the wall. Hideous noises broke the stillness—hissing, growling, caterwauling, howling—while storms of mosquitoes whined *ū'ā! ū'ā!*—beware, beware—from sundown to sunup. In the sultry morning Burton was greeted by a flock of cooing pigeons, a blathering billy goat that had notions of eating his knapsack, and a braying jackass that poked its head into the room, saw it was already occupied, then backed out again with dignified demeanor.

Hiring as his body servant a plump and beardless Meccan boy by the name of Muhammed el-Besyuni, Burton went browsing about the ramshackle bazaar, sat in the coffeehouse drinking brackish hot water imbued with burnt beans, prayed in one of the three dilapidated mosques, or squatted on the dock and lamented the lack of a bathhouse or *hhemmān*, which obliged them to bathe in the tepid brine.

One evening, when they returned to the caravanserai, Burton and the boy Muhammed ran into a half-dozen unveiled Fellahin females standing outside their room. The lovely young ladies, whom Burton knew to be foot-loose prostitutes masquerading as pilgrimesses, stopped their chatter as soon as they saw Shaykh 'Abdullah approach. The flirtation that followed was truly Egyptian.

"*Slām 'alaykum, yā hhekīm-bāshī!*" cooed the oldest and plumpest dove, who winked and called herself Fettumeh. The other playgirls ogled him fiercely. Burton returned their salaam with a salacious glint in his eyes. "We hear you're a great doctor, and we've come for some contraceptives and abortives."

"Allah be praised, how openhearted you are!" Burton caught the chaff and chucked it back: "Marry me, O Fettumeh! O daughter! O female pilgrim!"

Fettumeh tittered, wriggled her rump, and said with a toss of the head: "I'm mated, young man!"

Burton cackled and clapped his hands. "But surely you, being a person of polyandrous propensities, can bear the weight of at least three love affairs!"

"How dare you insult my secret parts, O son of an un-circumcised mother!"

"O daughter of sixty sires, your slit is too thick-skinned to feel insulted! It must be your loophole instead!"

"Allah tear off your tassels!"

"Or is it your mouth?"

A cloudburst of abuse now breaking, Burton and the boy Muhammed ducked and ran for cover.

In the fiery forenoon of July 6 the pilgrim ship *Silk edh-Dheheb* or *Golden Thread*, a fifty-ton dhow mobbed with Mecca-bound Muslims, darted down the Gulf of Suez and raced out into the Red Sea. Huddled on the narrow poop were Shaykh 'Abdullah, the boy Muhammed, and sixteen other souls.

As soon as they sailed out of the harbor, a gang of Maghribi cutthroats in brown and striped burnooses decided to storm the poop and make it their stronghold. Burton and the boy Muhammed drew their daggers when they saw a dozen lusty savages advancing with ten-inch blades in their teeth and palm rods in their hands.

Suddenly a giant Negro, who had been squatting silent and frozen-faced behind Burton and the boy, lurched out of his languor and stood towering upon the poop. A grimy red tarboosh was perched rakishly on his glossy-black poll; and a sleeveless, knee-length, dirty-yellow cotton nightshirt commonly called a *ghendūreh* or "fop frock" covered his statuesque nudity.

"*Yallah! yallah!*" he yelled, shaking a stick that was six feet long and thick as a man's wrist. "Come on, you sons of Satan! I'm Sa'ad the Demon! Come on, you sons of whores! I'm the holy terror of El-Medina!"

Bending over, he grabbed up a bundle of these ash staves and began to pass them out among the pilgrims on the poop. "Here, *bismillāh!* Defend yourselves with these if you don't want to be the meat of those Maghribis!" He then glowered at the ferocious foe. "Dogs and sons of dogs! Now you'll see what the children of Allah are!" He whirled the pole whistling over his head. "*Yallah!* I'm Sa'ad the Demon!"

Burton jumped up, waving his stick. "Come on, you pimps and pinpricks! I'm 'Abdullah bin Yusef!"

"Come on, you ass peddlers!" said the Meccan boy, his chubby face red with rage. "Flutes! butt-bruisers! I'm Muhammed el-Besyuni!"

The Maghribis scrambled up the high poop like a swarm of hell-roaring hornets, encouraging each other with the Muslim battle cry: "*Al-al-al-al-al-al-al-al-allā-huakber!*"

"*Lā ilāha illallāh!*" Burton replied. "*Yallah! t'ālū,* you *zubb* swallowers!" Gripping his staff with both hands, he swung it down with an awesome whir and smashed open the first head. The man fell dead to the deck like a sack of grain, splattering blood all over his frenzied companions. "*Allāh-t'āleh!* Come on, you *kus* lickers!"

Thwack! thwack! The clubs flew, singing a painful song, and heads were cracked and shoulders clouted right and left.

"Prick eaters! clitoris suckers!" said the boy Muhammed, poking the end of his pole into the wild eyes of the enemy. "*T'ālū! t'ālu! Lā ilaha illallāh!*" When one of the attackers battered his legs with a bamboo stick, howling "*Allāhuak-ber!*", the boy bashed out his teeth with a forceful jab.

Burton was still chopping away when the burly *mowlā*

or leader of the mob took a vicious swipe at him with his
razor-edged pigsticker. The glancing stroke nicked Burton's shins. "Satan sodomize you, you masturbated baboon!" Hoisting a huge waist-high earthenware jug full
of drinking water, he and the brawny Negro heaved it
down on the heads of the remaining Maghribis. Nearly
two hundred pounds of crockery and water bowled them
over like ninepins, leaving a heap of moaning and groaning Muslims lying upon the blood-speckled deck.

"Allah is Almighty!" the victors shouted, laughed heartily, and shook hands in the "slip me some skin" Arab
fashion by slapping palms together then touching the forehead with the fingers.

As the big lateen sail bellied out like a canvas crescent
in the warm wind of the gulf waters, all true believers recited the *fātihheh* or opening prayer with upraised hands
which they afterwards drew down over their faces to in-
still the bodily blessings of Allah.

The *Golden Thread* raced down the palm-dotted coast.
Still in sight of Suez, Burton couldn't help casting one
last wistful look at the British flag floating high above the
consulate. Images of home began to haunt him. For a
second the careworn, cadaverous faces of friends and family seemed alluringly smiling and carefree. The spoiled
child of civilization now sensed a native fascination in the
slavery of artificial existence, its luxuries and false pleasures, and in the suffocating atmosphere, the turmoil and
confusion, of civilized cities.

But the momentary regret was stifled by a stronger
sense of immediate reality. To give up and go back would
mean drifting once again into a suicidal nightmare. The
soul-stirring challenge of absolute life preordained that

he must seek his destiny in the womb of his reincarnation.

Sitting cross-legged against the rail, with the foam-flecked sprays soaking the back of his robe and a sizzling-wet weather-beaten umbrella propped up over his otherwise unshaded head, Burton opened his journal and dashed off in Arabic:

The sun bursts up from behind the main—a fierce enemy, a foe that will force everyone to crouch before him. He dyes the sky orange and the sea crimson where its violet surface is stained by his rays, and he mercilessly puts to flight the silvery mists and rosy haze and the little saffron-colored masses of cloud that were before floating in the firmament.

For the two hours following sunrise the rays are endurable; after that they become a fiery ordeal. The morning beams oppress you with a feeling of sickness. Their steady glow, reflected by the glaring waters, blinds your eyes, blisters your skin, and parches your mouth. You now become a monomaniac. You do nothing but count the slow hours that must minute by before you can be relieved.

The wind, reverberated by the distant glowing hills, is like the blast of a limekiln. All color melts away with the candescence from above. The sky is a dead milk-white, and the mirrorlike sea so reflects the tint that you can scarcely distinguish the line of the horizon. After noon the wind sleeps upon the reeking shore. There is a deep stillness; the only sound heard is the melancholy flapping of the sail. We're not so much sleeping as half-senseless. We feel as though a few more degrees of heat would be death.

The enemy sinks behind the deep cerulean sea, under a canopy of gigantic rainbow which covers half the face of heaven. Nearest to the horizon is an arch of tawny orange, above it another of the brightest gold; and based upon these a semicircle of tender sea-green blends with a score of delicate gradations into the sapphire sky. Across the rainbow the sun throws its rays in the form of giant wheel spokes tinged with a beautiful pink. The Eastern sky is mantled with a purple flush that picks out the forms of the hazy desert and the sharp-cut hills.

Night falls rapidly, when suddenly the appearance of the afterglow restores the scene to what it was. Again the gray hills and grim rocks become rosy or golden, the palms green, the sands saffron; and the sea wears a lilac surface of dimpling waves. But after a quarter of an hour all fades once more. The cliffs are naked and ghastly under the moon, whose light falling upon this wilderness of white crags and pinnacles is most strange—most mysterious.

The horizon is all darkness, and the sea reflects the spectral visage of the night-sun as in a mirror of steel. In the air we see giant columns of pallid light—distinct, based upon the indigo-colored waves, and standing with their heads lost in endless space. The stars glitter with exceeding brilliance, while the planets look down upon you with the faces of smiling friends. In communion with them your hours pass swiftly by, till the heavy dews warn you to cover up your head and sleep. And with one look at a certain little star in the north, under which lies all that makes life worth living through, you fall into oblivion.

The flaming red-hot orb melted simmering into a bloody sea. Burton and the boy Muhammed, still faint and dizzy from a mummifying afternoon on deck, opened swollen mouths and croaked for the water which before they had lacked the strength to drink. After everyone was bloated and belching, Burton passed a copper pot around. When it was filled with urine he emptied it out over the side, then offered with the others a drone of "'*Lhhamdulillāh*

—Thank Allah!" that he and they had lived through another day.

After passing the Gulf of 'Aqaba, Burton saw nothing but bright-blue sea and white-hot sky, weary faces and withered forms whose only entertainment or exercise was tossing to and fro upon the rolling waters—day and night, night and day—a maddening monotony.

After twelve days of torture at sea, the fly-infested port of El-Medina was a paradisaic blessing to behold. Burton's brief stay at Yembu', Gate of the Holy City, was uneventful except for the hiring of camels and cameleers.

On July 18, by the cool light of a crystal moon, a small caravan of Medina-bound pilgrims filed through the gates of Yembu' and cast its long undulating shadows across the eerie desert. Burton's resonant voice rang out sharp and clear in the crisp sweet air as he sang to the tinkling of camel bells the celebrated song of Maysuneh, the beautiful Bedawi wife of the Caliph El-Mu'awiyeh:

"Oh take these purple robes away,
  Give back my cloak of camel's hair,
And bear me from this pile of clay
  To where black tents flap in the air!
The camel's bells and limpid pools,
  The dog that barks at all but me,
Delight me more than feasts and fools,
  Than every art of luxury!
Now any nomad, poor but free,
Can take me, fatted ass, from thee!"

The Bedawin camel drivers listened with screams of joy; and scraggy-bearded Shaykh Hamid es-Semman, who was riding in front of Burton, suddenly turned in his saddle and said with a flashing grin: "For sure, O father of mustachios, I'll show you the black tents of my tribe this year!"

Thus Shaykh 'Abdullah got his nickname of *Abū Shewārib*—Father of Mustachios.

8 : The city of the prophet

*'Tis ours to pass with joy and hope, whose souls shall ever thrill and fill
Dreams of the Birthplace and the Tomb, visions of Allah's Holy Hill.*

Jouncing and jolting atop a jogging dromedary, Richard Burton gazed at an eternity of sun-scorched desert studded with ugly black rock and twisted brown scrub. A shimmery atmosphere made him sense how the ravenous heat was sucking up the vital sap of the earth, baking the hard crust till it cracked wide open and searing green tufts of grass a withered gray.

Burton and the boy Muhammed endured a steady diet of boiled rice and rancid butter, stale bread, date paste, bitter tea, and dried sour milk dissolved in goatskin-flavored water. For an Arab delicacy they occasionally consumed fried grasshoppers or locusts, which "tasty tid-bits" were popped into the mouth with a sip of "sweet" she-camel's urine—a universal tonic among the Bedawin. The scalding tea made Burton sweat so furiously that even his outer garments were soaked, but this excessive and continuous perspiration had a delightful cooling effect and soothing sensation in the dry heat.

In the blistering afternoon, huge black messengers blotched the face of the sun, bringing false promise of rain. Suddenly a blast of hot air like the breath of a volcano blew over the plain, blinding man and beast with a lashing, burning storm of sand—the satanic *semūm* or "poisoned wind" of Arabia.

In a few roaring-mad moments the evil jinni soared away, leaving his hideous cousin the mirage-making ghoul to make one's mouth water for the siren illusion that maddens the weak and unwary.

Burton cackled grotesquely, glancing at the boy Muhammed. "Allah knows, in discomfort man naturally hails a change—even though it be one from bad to worse."

On July 25, from the top of a basalt ridge, Shaykh 'Abdullah feasted his dazzled eyes on the Holy City of El-Medina. "O Allah," he cried, throwing out his arms, "this is the sanctuary of Thine Apostle! Open the gates of Thy mercy, and let us pass through them to the Land of Joy!"

All the others sang with one voice: *"Lā ilāha illallāh wa-Muhhammeder-resūlullāh!"*

Though sunsick and wayworn, the haggard pilgrims

were now fired with an electrifying excitement. They leaped from their camels, laughing and shouting in the wildest joy, and scrambled frantically down the black rocks to the blazing plain.

After having suffered nearly eight days in a torrefying inferno, Burton welcomed the cool oases of El-Medina. He was stirred to tears by the fervid spirit of his companions, and for those few impassioned moments his enthusiasm became as feverish as theirs.

Gazing eastward, Burton saw the demon sun peering over a misty horizon of rugged hills, staining the earth with a savage splendor of purple and gold. Sweeping streaks of violet haze, pierced and thinned by the violent rays, ribboned and wreathed the palm groves and gardens surrounding the white-walled city. The brilliant emerald green glared sharply at the drab ocherous surface of the far-flung plain, in the center of which stood the opalescent mass of box buildings, domes, and minarets that was *Medînet el-Munaowareh*—El-Medina the Illuminant —whose brightest gem is the flashing viridescent cupola under which the Prophet's remains rest.

Putting on clean white clothes, Burton and the boy Muhammed performed the *ziyāreh* or tour of the *Mesjid en-Nebî*—the Prophet's Mosque—and its neighboring shrines.

Passing through the *Bāb er-Rehhmeh* or Gate of Pity by a small flight of steps, Burton was astonished at the trashy and tawdry appearance of a place so universally venerated in the Muslim world. The Medina Mosque of Muhammed and the *Mesjid el-Hherîm* or Sacred Mosque at Mecca are the *hharemayn* or two most consecrated localities in El-Islam. Burton hoped to find the Meccan

temple grand and simple, the expression of a single sublime idea; for the longer he looked at the Medina mosque
the more it seemed to him like a museum of architectural
ornamentation, having neither beauty nor dignity, an old
curio shop full of elegant junk and poorly decorated with
gaudy grandeur.

While in the sanctuary, Shaykh 'Abdullah faced Mecca
and intoned a two-bow Koranic prayer, the *shihādet el-
Wehhdānīyeh* or declaration of Unity, beginning *"Qul,
'Hūwallāh!'* . . .

"Say, 'He is Allah!
    The Everlasting Allah!
    He begets not, nor is He begot!
    And unto Him the like is not!' "

Again dropping to his knees, in a position of prayer he
then enacted the *sijdeh* or forehead-to-the-floor prostration, thanking Allah for making it his fate to visit so holy
a spot.

Wending their way into the *hujreh* or sepulcher, above
which bellied the beautiful green dome surmounted outside by a large golden crescent and star, Burton and the
boy Muhammed beheld the marble tomb of the Prophet
of Allah.

Raising his hands reverently and telling his servant in
a stage whisper to repeat after him, Shaykh 'Abdullah recited the traditional supplication in a soft and solemn
voice that was faintly vibrant in the hollow mausoleum:
"Slām 'alaykum, yā nebīyullāh! Peace be upon you,
O Apostle of Allah! *Slām 'alaykum, yā resūlullāh, w'er-
rehhmetullāh w'en-ni'ametullāh!* Peace be upon you, O

Prophet of Allah, and the mercy and blessings of Allah!
Allah bless you as often as mentioners have mentioned
you and forgetters have forgotten you, and Allah bless
you among the first and the last with the best of blessings
ever bestowed on man! *Ashheduan lā ilāha illallāh, w'ashheduanna Muhhammeder-resulūllāh!* I swear there's no
god but Allah, and I swear Muhammed is the Apostle of
Allah! We your friends, O Prophet of Allah, appear before you—travelers from distant lands and far countries
—through dangers and difficulties, in times of darkness
and in times of light—longing to honor you by a prayer-
ful visit and longing to obtain the blessings of your inter-
cession; for our sins have broken our backs! *Bismillāher-
rehhmāner-rehhīm!* In the name of Allah the Merciful,
the Compassionate! I leave here with you, O Apostle of
Allah, my everlasting profession of faith from this moment even unto the Day of Judgment! *Āmīn, yā rebb el-
'ālemīn!* Amen, O Lord of the Universe!"

Having performed all the duties of a good *zā'ir* or visi-
tor, Burton prepared to leave the City of the Prophet. He
had secretly sketched and made plans of El-Medina and
its shrines, cut the drawings and maps into small numbered squares, and hid them in the tin canisters that contained his medical supplies.

Burton was extremely careful not to let any superstitious Arab catch him sketching the holy places. For this
infidelic indiscretion he ran the risk of being burned alive
as a European spy or a Persian sorcerer. However, while
mumbling the *fātihheh* in the *Musalla en-Nebī* or Prophet's Place of Prayer, Burton couldn't resist the temptation
of pulling out his pencil and scrawling a cryptogram on
the whitewashed wall of the mosque:

ا A

الله ALLAH

عبد 'ABD

عبده 'ABDEH

سنة SENEH

١٢٦٩ 1269

"A" is monogrammatic for "Allah." The rest of the cipher reads: "'Abdullah, Servant of Allah, year (A.H.) 1269 (A.D. 1853)."

In the early morning of August 31, Shaykh Hamid es-Semman, the head guide and host of Burton's small party of pilgrims, came running back from the bazaar. Excited and sweating, he seized Shaykh 'Abdullah's arm and said: "You must make ready at once, effendi! There won't be any 'flying caravan.' All hajis start tomorrow with the Damascus cafila. Allah will make it easy for you! Have your waterskins filled, effendi. You'll be traveling through the Nejd Desert, where you won't see water for three days!"

The boy Muhammed looked horror-struck, but his master was grinning with joy. No European had ever journeyed down the deadly *derb esh-sherqī* or eastern route, made famous by the Caliph Harun er-Reshid's fabulous pilgrimage in which he and Queen Zubaydeh walked from Baghdad to Mecca on costly carpets of crimson and gold.

Although the sudden change in plans was welcomed by one who wanted to do what no other *kāfir* or infidel had done, Burton was still curious about the *qāfilet et-taiyāreh* or "flying caravan." He said to Shaykh Hamid: "Not that it matters—Allah knows!—but what happened to the *t'yāreh?* It was supposed to leave two days after the Damascus caravan by the *derb es-sultānī* western route."

"Aye, by Allah, it was! But Shaykh Sa'ud el-Jibal, that prince of thieves, threatened he'll slit the throat of every haji who comes down the *derb es-sultānī*."

"Why, in Allah's name?"

"Because he hates the Sherif of Mecca, and the western road happens to run through his 'sacred' territory."

"*Hah! 'Steghfrullāh!*" spat Sa'ad el-Jinni, the black Demon. "If I ever catch him I'll cut off his cullions and send the sherif a new eunuch!"

"A gift for which he'd make you *shaykh el-hherīm—*head of the harem!" Hamid laughed.

Burton understood the remark as much as Sa'ad the Demon, whom he had seen naked on numerous occasions. The giant Negro wasn't ashamed to show that he had a penis but no testicles. When a boy in Somalia, he had been captured and castrated by Arab slavers, who sold him to the Sherif of Medina to serve as a slave in the royal household. When he had been later set free, Sa'ad the Demon took three wives and started to travel.

"I'm as good as any man," he once said to Burton. "In fact, I'm better! Women go for me because I get no sperm. But that ain't all! Because I get no sperm I can keep it up stiff for a long time—say for an hour or so of continuous futtering—like a boy before puberty. Sure I get a feeling! But it lasts longer than yours. It tickles me half to death, and makes me even harder and hotter. Sometimes it never stops, and when the woman can't take it any more I make her use her hand or mouth on me. I'm called the *Jinnī* because I fight and ferk like a demon. By Allah, I bugger and kill every man who calls me a codless one—a *tewāshī* or a *khessī!*"

9 : Here am I, O Allah, here am I!

Wend now your way with brow serene, fear not your humble tale to tell:
The whispers of the desert wind, the tinkling of the camel's bell.

As a fierce ball of fire glowed through purplescent mists, seven thousand Mecca-bound pilgrims of the Damascus caravan—on foot, on horses, camels, mules, or litters— crawled snakelike southward over the split and searing crust of the *Baydā Nejdī* or Highland Desert.

The wilderness reeked with sandy vapor blown out and about by the blistering breath of the simoom, and the air became cloyed with a glaring milky-white haze.

Seated cross-legged atop a plodding dromedary, Richard Burton watched bleary-eyed as pack animal after pack animal dropped dead along the roadside. He then glanced up. Clouds of vultures hovered overhead, gliding back and forth in continuous eddies, silhouetted against the opaline bowl of the sky. Now and anon a half-dozen would dip to the ground, attacking a swollen carcass. They would pick it apart with sepulchral squawks, hobbling away too bloated to fly. These grisly scenes reminded Burton of the oft-quoted Arab proverb: "The world is a carcass, and they who seek it are vultures!"

In the boiling afternoons, soaring devils of sand rode the wings of the whirlwind over the plain. Burton eyed these treacherous twisters with the same grim-faced fancy and fascination as his Arab companions. He had seen them in Sind, surging pillars of yellow grit churned up by the heat and high electrical tension of the wasteland. Now these monstrous shaitans and pisachees of India had followed him to Arabia, where they shot across the desert as evil jinn—ghouls and 'afreets.

The fiendish *zōba'ah* reared up its head with a terrifying roar, bending its towering body backwards and forwards as it raced wildly around the plain, tormenting its human observers with fitful onrushes that dashed down fear-maddened camels and mules as they bolted out of line. Whenever the demon darted towards them, superstitious Muslims pointed at it and said: "*Hhdīd! hhdīd!* Iron! iron! *Hhdīd, yā meshūm!* Iron, O ill-omened one!" Jinn are supposed to be afraid of iron, but Burton added a pious "*Allāhuakber!*" for good measure.

After the 'afreets had turned away and fled, the devil's breath was felt like an open oven. The pilgrims choked and croaked with disgust: "*Allāh! Allāh! Yā letīf!* Oh for God's sake! *Lā hhowla walā qūwetilla billāhi'l-alī'l-'atzīm!*

There's no majesty and might but in Allah the Glorious and Great!"

Burton gagged in the volcanic air, covering his nose and mouth with the skirt of his kaffiyeh. It was torture to speak, and merely opening the mouth was to inflame hotter agonies of thirst. The more he drank, the more he wanted to drink—till it made him sick. His skin was dry and leathery. He couldn't perspire—the simoom seemed to suffocate every pore—but he urinated constantly. This he did in a copper pot. His camel was less finicky. Jogging on to the jingle of bells, its supercilious head held high, *el-jeml* sprayed the sand with steaming torrents and splattered its neighbors by arrogantly whisking its dung like scatter-shot with the whirling flick of a wicked tail.

After the first two hours of agonizing abstinence, Burton mastered the overpowering feeling of thirst. It then became easy not to think of water—the triumph of *'aql 'ala asl,* mind over matter.

When the ships of the desert moved slowly into the *behhr el-milhh* or sea of salt, the white-hot glare and a ribbonlike reek of nitrous efflorescence made limpid pools of shimmering water appear across the plain.

"Allāhua'lem! Allah knows!" the pilgrims moaned, pointing wearily. *" 'Alīmallāh!* Allah is All-Knowing!"

Burton saw that the animals weren't fooled by this reflection of the sky, for no mirage ever wafted the scent of water. An acrid stench poisoned the air, and the strangling powder of the salt flats stung his eyes and seared his nostrils and throat. Hour after hour he listened to the dull crunching sound of the camel's padded feet upon the large curling flakes of potassium nitrate that crusted the hard bed of cracked clay.

A few stagnant water holes offered what seemed at first to be a sickening-sweet liquid, but which later tasted brackishly bitter. To Burton, the niter-tainted water excited the same cooling sensation as peppermint. He gulped it down in handfuls; but his parched mouth soon perceived its saline flavor, which left him gasping and retching.

"*Uff! tfū!*" Heaving and coughing, the boy Muhammed spat his out. "Allah befuck this hole!" he rasped.

"Allah indeed!" Burton sighed.

The both of them staggered back to their grunting and growling camels. Back to the barren sea of salt, the huge black *hhejr el-jehannem* or hell-stones of basalt, and—the fiery thirst in a fiend-stoked inferno.

Leaving the *behhr el-milhh* behind them, they ascended a rocky plateau where the water ran clear and cool. But this taste of paradise in a feast of hell was relished only for the time it took to refill the waterskins.

The Damascus caravan now descended into a desert peopled only with echoes—a place of death for what little there was to die in it, where a searing sun heated the brain to madness—a wilderness where, as the boy Muhammed said, "there is nothing but He."

Burton cackled, and his eyes flashed satanically. "*Yallah! yallah!*" he said, waving his arm. "Come on—*ha-ha! Lā siwa Hū!* There's none but He! *Hūwallāh!* There's none but Allah! *Allāhhūwallāh!*"

"*Lā ilāha illallāh!*" his servant responded, frantic with fear.

Burton glowered at the forbidding *baydā lā-siwa-Hū*. Nature scalped and flayed bare the "land where no one lives but He." The horizon was a sea of mirage. Gigantic sand shaitans whirled over the plain, and on both sides of the road huge piles of flesh-pink rock stood as sentinels of the barren waste.

Burton jotted in his journal:

> In these drear wastes of sea-born land,
>   These wilds where none may dwell but He,
> What visionary pasts revive,
>   What process of the years we see!
>
> Gazing beyond the thin blue line
>   That rims the far horizon ring,
> Our saddened sight why haunt these ghosts?
>   Whence do these spectral shadows spring?

Darkness fell upon them like a pall. It was a wild and uncanny scene. The spongy-footed camels paced along with silent tread, looming like phantoms in the midnight air. Boys running back and forth with long flaring cressets threw a passing glow of eerie red light on the black desert and the ghostly caravan. The hot wind moaned, whipping flakes and sheets of flame and smoke from the torches, while the tinkling of bells seemed unusually weird.

The camels fumbled and stumbled over stones and furrows, tossing their loads like houseboats in a choppy sea. It was every man for himself.

Burton cautioned his camel with shouts of *"Hai! hai!"*, then urged the bawling beast on with *"Yāhh! yāhh!"* and an occasional switching. The boy Muhammed resigned himself to Allah over rough ground by repeated cries of *"Ya sātir! yā settār!* O Veiler! O Protector!"

In the early hours of September 9 the Damascus caravan threaded its way through Ez-Zeribeh, a rolling moss-green valley embraced by high granite hills, at the southern mouth of which the pilgrims pitched their tents and prepared to perform the sanctification ceremony of *el-ihhrām* or assuming the outward appearance of pilgrimage.

In the blazing mid-day sun a Syrian barber shaved Burton's head completely bald, clipped his nails, depilated his pubic hair, and trimmed his beard and mustachios. When the boy Muhammed had grumblingly undergone the rite of *el-hhelq* or tonsure, he and his master bathed themselves in a spring-fed pond and perfumed their bodies with attar of roses.

Having enacted the *ghusl* or over-all religious ablution, Burton and the boy Muhammed slipped into *'lehhrām*—the haji's ascetic habit—which consisted of two snow-white cotton sheets, six feet long by three and a half wide, with thin red stripes and narrow fringes. They flung the so-called *ridā* or serape over their backs, leaving the right arm and shoulder bare and knotting it on the side, then wrapped the so-called *izār* or loincloth around their naked bodies from the waist to below the knees, knotting it in the middle. Their heads and feet were bare, traditionally exposed to a burning and blistering sun—the better to make humble saints out of haughty sinners.

Burton slung a canteen and a pouch over each shoulder, fingering his prayer beads in his right hand. Dropping to their knees, he and the boy Muhammed faced Mecca and performed a two-bow prayer: "I pledge this *ihhrām el-hhajj* to Almighty Allah!" Still kneeling with arms uplifted, they said the *nīyeh* or declaration of intention: "O Allah, I aspire to the Hajj! Enable me to accomplish it, and accept it of me, and make it a blessing to me!" Then, rising to their feet, they joined their seven thousand fellow pilgrims in a thunderous *telbīyeh:*

"Lebbayk, Allāhumma, lebbayk!
Lā sherīka laka—lebbayk!
Inna'l-hhemda w'en-ni 'ameta laka w'el-mulk!
Lā sherīka laka—lebbayk! . . .

"Here am I, O Allah, here am I!
No partner unto Thee—here am I!
Thine the majesty, the mercy, and the might!
No partner unto Thee—here am I!"

"Remember the taboos, O father of mustachios!" said
Sa'ad the Demon as they marched on foot towards Mecca.
"We're now heading into *el-hharem,* the sacred territory.
No fighting, killing, swearing, lying, stealing, kissing, ferk-
ing, buggering, fluting, spitting, scratching, farting, belching, bleeding, perfuming, scrubbing, snipping, cutting, shav-
ing—Allah be praised, I ain't even begun!—and *no* jerking
off." His eyes bugged fiercely at the boy Muhammed, who
grinned when he added, "unless you get no juice and are
just like me. But no jumping any girls or licking any tarts,
or you'll sacrifice your camel for doing like the devil in the
Holy City."

"How about after the Hajj?" the boy said slyly.

"*Inshallāh,* after the Hajj you can do anything—even
bugger a beast of burden! Here's what they say: 'Finish off
the pilgrimage by futtering your camel!' "

A torrent of pilgrims streamed southwestward through
the wadies and ravines toward *Mekkeh el-Mukarrameh,*
Mecca the Magnificent. Burton glanced behind him and
saw lustrous waves of white-clad Muslims cascading over
the billowy bed of the valley, their newly-shaven heads
glistening in the radiant sunlight. The rocks rang with vol-

leys of *"Lebbayk! lebbayk!* Here I am! here I am!" and the hollow rumble of a hundred kettledrums.

In the predawn darkness of Sunday, September 11, Shaykh 'Abdullah and the boy Muhammed heard heated murmurings of *"Mekkeh! Mekkeh!"* up ahead. They looked up with a thrill of excitement, straining their eyes, and saw by the starry light the shadowy outlines of a large city lying on the tableland of a winding crag-crested wady.

In a few seconds thousands were aroused to an awe-inspiring crescendo of spiritual fervor. Passionate outbursts of *"El-hherīm! Yā'l-hherīm!* The Sanctuary! Oh the Sanctuary!"* were broken by sobs, and a jubilant chorus of *"Lebbayk! lebbayk!"* was dampened by violent weeping.

"O Allah," Burton cried, "this is Thy stronghold and Thy sanctuary! O Allah, save me from the pains of hell-fire! *Lā ilāha illallāh wa-Muhammeder-resūlullāh!"*

Before the first faint flushes of Aurora swelled from below the eastern horizon, seven thousand pilgrims surged through the last defile and poured into the womb of *Umm Medīneh*—Mother of Cities.

10 : The house of Allah

Perhaps the Law that rules the world allows to man the widest range;
And haply Fate's a Theist word, subject to human chance and change.

At daybreak, Shaykh 'Abdullah and the boy Muhammed bathed in the *Shāmīyeh* or Syrian quarter of Mecca, put on their ihrams, and proceeded to the Sanctuary.

They entered the immense *Baytullāh* or House of Allah by a northern gateway, descended two long flights of steps, walked down a dazzling-white marble colonnade to the innermost court, and stood in sight of the sacred Ka'abeh.

There at last it lay, the symbol of Richard Burton's long and laborious pilgrimage, realizing the hopes and plans of more than a decade. *El-Ka'abeh*—a gray cube of stone, stark in the uterine circle of the majestic Mother of Mosques, the most revered structure in the Muslim world.

Of all the worshipers who clung weeping to the *kisweh*, the brilliant gold-embroidered black shroud that veiled

the "Bride of Mecca," few felt for the moment a deeper
emotion than did the haji from the far north. Of all who
pressed their burning lips to *hhejr el-aswed,* the celestial
Black Stone given to Abraham by the archangel Gabriel,
few looked upon that forbidden shrine in an ecstasy of
gratified pride. For a magic second it seemed to him as if
the poetic fables of Araby spoke wondrous truth, and that
the waving wings of angelic jinn—not the sweet breeze of
early morning—were stirring and swelling the sable covering of the Ka'abeh.

The boy Muhammed gazed in admiration and awe. His
was a high feeling of Islamic enthusiasm, a passion bred
in the bone of every hot-blooded Arab baby, a spirit of
racial superiority aggravated by a fatalistic religious fanat-
icism.

Stalking through the *Bāb es-Selām* or Gate of Salvation
and stepping out into the bright sunlight, they raised their
hands and repeated "*Lebbayk, Allāhumma, lebbayk! Allāhuakber! Lā ilāha illallāh wa-Muhhammeder-resūlullāh!*",
passing their palms down over their faces to receive the
blessings from above.

They now entered the mosaic building which enshrined
Zemzem, the hallowed well of El-Islam, where Haji 'Abdullah and Haji Muhammed dipped their tin cups into
leather buckets full of fresh but tepid salt-bitter holy
water.

Having sipped the nauseous nectar of Hagar and Ish-
mael, who discovered Zemzem cool and sweet during their
desert wanderings, Burton and the boy Muhammed walked
in silent solemnity towards the Ka'abeh and prepared to
perform the ancient ceremony of *tewāf* or circumambulation.

Haji 'Abdullah made certain his ihram was well knotted and that his *'ōreh* or private parts were completely concealed. To expose the genitals during this devout rite was to commit a paganistic sin reminiscent of the pre-Islamic days of phallicism, when men and women danced naked around the Ka'abeh—a womb symbol—practicing ritual masturbation and sodomy.

He and Haji Muhammed then placed their calloused feet on the hot pavement of polished granite surrounding the sacred structure, lifted their arms in prayer, and said the *nīyet et-tewāf* or declaration of circumambulation: "*Bismillāh w'Allāhuakber!* In the name of Allah, and Allah is Almighty! I pledge seven circuits unto Almighty Allah, glorious and great!"

Pressing their way into the mob of pilgrims moving in a massive circle around the Ka'abeh, Burton and the boy Muhammed circuited counterclockwise three times at a slow pace and four at a brisk trot, repeating aloud: "*Subhhānallāh!* Praise be to Allah!" When passing the Black Stone, they kissed their fingertips and proclaimed at the top of their lungs: "*Bismillāh w'Allāhuakber!*"

Having enacted the *tewāf*, Haji 'Abdullah made several attempts to touch and kiss the Black Stone. But each time he plunged into the surging procession at the southeast corner of the Ka'abeh, Burton was shoved off the pavement—a penalty for having lost his place in line. For several moments he stood glaring at the swarms of impassioned pilgrims that besieged the stone, awaiting the opportunity that seemed beyond all hope, until Haji Muhammed came strutting up with six stalwart Meccan friends of his.

The boy said: "O Allah, I do this in Thy behalf and in

belief of Thy Book—get out o' the way, you flea-bitten dogs!—and in obedience to Thy laws—scram, you pigs, O sons of a whoring sow!—and in following the example of the Prophet Muhammed, may Allah bless him and keep him—beat it, you long-bearded bastards!"

Burton howled with laughter to hear his servant spreading holy terror like an Irish priest: "Hail, Mary, full of grace—*arrah*, now don't ye be lettin' that pig at the pot!— the Lord is with thee . . ."

In only a few seconds they had plowed a path through the crushing crowd of pilgrims, who glowered and snarled like wildcats. Several savage Bedawin clapped their hands instinctively to their waists, but they had nothing with which to knife the intruders. Burton was ready to flatten a half-dozen of them singlehanded if they wanted to fight, yet no one felt the odds other than in 'Abdullah's favor.

The six stalwart Meccans formed a protective ring around master and servant, who knelt down on either side of the Black Stone and monopolized it for at least ten minutes amid shouts of impatience and growls of indignation.

"*Subhhānallāh!*" Haji 'Abdullah said, grinning.

"*'Lhhamdulillāh!*" Haji Muhammed replied, also grinning.

Burton touched his lips to the Black Stone, rubbing his hands and forehead upon it, and murmured: "*Bismillāh w'Allāhuakber!*" While kissing and fingering *hhejr-el-aswed,* and repeating the appropriate formula in a monotonous undertone, he eyed it closely.

The glossy-black stone, an irregular oval approximately ten inches in diameter, appeared to be a common aerolite. Partially imbedded in the granite wall, it was enshrined with a narrow inner circle of reddish-brown cement and a wide outer ring of gilded silver. Burton understood it at once as a sexual symbol or yoni. The pitchy stone itself represented the vaginal orifice, the slightly convex reddish-brown cement border the labia minora, and the broad gilt band the labia majora of Venus' vulva—a remnant of ancient Arabian phallicism.

With scorched feet and a burning head, Burton strode over to the Zemzem enclosure, where three bucketfuls of holy water were dumped over his body by a vulture-faced old man.

The heat was stagnant, the sun blurred in a blinding haze. He saw no fewer than five men stagger, drop to the dust, and die after a quick convulsion—each a *shehīd ed-dīn*, martyr of the Faith.

Burton could now twirl his mustachios and stroke his beard as a full-fledged haji. It was late morning, and he stood watching the circumambulation ceremony till his clothes were dry.

At midday, while Haji 'Abdullah was sitting on the wall of the sacred well, telling his beads and savoring the shaded coolness, the boy Muhammed came rushing into the mosaic reservoir. "Quick, effendi—follow me!" he said, his eyes wide with the wildest excitement.

Burton felt a chill of suspense race through him. He jumped off the well and followed Haji Muhammed out into the open court, where the dead heat turned it into a crematorium and where the sharp glare dazzled his eyes.

Burton squinted, his lips pressed tight against his teeth in a grotesque grimace. But before he could see clearly through the glimmering veil, Fate spun the threads with startling speed. He heard an explosion of voices:

"*Bismillāh! Yallah! yallah!* Make way for the haji who enters the House of Allah!"

Without warning, two strapping black eunuchs seized Burton by his arms and thighs and hoisted him up on their broad shoulders.

"*Billāh! billāh!* Open up for the haji who would enter the Holy House!"

With Burton still perched on their shoulders, the terror-striking castrates—one of whom he now noticed to be Sa'ad the Demon—stalked straight through the murmurous throng of gaping pilgrims and stopped abruptly at the entrance of the Ka'abeh. A sudden, frightening hush fell over the crowd.

At the silver-plated, gold-embossed door of the Ka'abeh sat several dark-skinned Meccan officials. One of them, a mean-looking youth in green turban and white caftan, held in his hand the huge gilded padlock of El-Baytullāh.

"*Es-slāmun 'alaykum!*" the young Bedawi shrilled. The three officiating Mekkawis merely stared stone-faced, not moving a muscle.

Burton was nervous, his mouth was dry, and his flesh crawled with a hot sweat of anxiety. *Now they suspect me!* The thought flashed tingling through his system. But after all this time—could it be possible? *They're putting me to the test. They want me to crack.* Did he think the worst, that they were trying a suspect, or were they traditionally honoring a meritorious true believer?

There was no time to analyze. There was only time to assume a savage expression of self-esteem, and to snarl an instant response of "*W'alaykum es-slām!*"

"What is your name, O such a one?" the youth snapped.

"'Abdullah bin Yusef!" Burton snapped back.

"Where is your home, O 'Abdullah bin Yusef?"

"I have no home!"

"Then where were you born?"

"In the city of Kabul, in the country of Afghanistan!"

"*Hmmm.* An Afghani, eh?" The Bedawi leered wolfishly. The Mekkawis sat like corpses, their arms crossed and faces blank.

Burton gave them each a scowling look, hoping to arouse some sort of favorable reaction, but they were cadaverously cold.

Suddenly the youth grinned, flashing a fine set of ivories. "*Wallāhī, yā hhājj 'Abdullāh, ahlen wesahlen alf ahlen wesahlen!* Well, by Allah, O Haji 'Abdullah—welcome, a thousand times welcome!"

"*Marhhebā! marhhebābek!* Hail! hail to you!" the officials droned impassively.

"*Allāh yisallimek, merhhabtayn!*" Burton answered, smiling. "Allah save you! Greetings!" His eyes blazed, and he no longer felt afraid.

"O Haji 'Abdullah," the youth said, "I'm 'Othman bin Talheh of the Benu Shaybeh! My noble tribe has kept the keys to the sacred Ka'abeh ever since they were first entrusted to us by the Apostle of Allah himself. Enter, therefore, in the name of Allah and with the blessings of His holy Apostle!" He then glared askance and shrieked: "In Allah's name, O Muhammed el-Besyuni, I order you to guide Haji 'Abdullah into the Sanctuary and recite the prayers with him!"

The boy Muhammed salaamed, said "*Aiwallāhī!*", and leaped partway up onto the ledge of the entranceway, which was about seven feet from the marble-inlaid pavement.

As he was hanging by his upper arms and bellowing for one of the eunuchs to give him a boost, 'Othman bin Talheh grabbed the seat of his ihram and said: "Are you circumcised, O son of a flea? By Allah, no uncircumcised boy can enter the Ka'abeh!"

"'Steghfrullāh!" Haji Muhammed grunted. "Y'want me to stick out my prick and prove it? Sure I'm circumcised! I was circumcised when I was three. What about you?"

These insults inflamed the thoroughbred sensitivity of the fifteen-year-old 'Othman, who had recently suffered the Bedawin puberty rite of es-selkh—the flaying. As Burton understood it, selkh is a barbarous method of circumcision in which not only the prepuce but also the entire sheath of the penis are severed and stripped off, leaving the male organ like a skinned eel.

"Yā zelīq! Masturbator!" the Bedawi hissed.

"Ha! By Allah," the boy Muhammed replied, "I'd call you a 'jerk-off' yourself, but you have no skin left to jerk! And I can't call you a 'prick,' 'cause that's what a man like me has! So I'll honor you as a son of an uncircumcised bitch, O shitface of Shaybeh!"

With that, Sa'ad the Demon shoved Haji Muhammed up into the entranceway before an enraged 'Othman could lay hold of him again. Burton was then lifted onto the ledge, assisted at the door by a red-turbaned attendant who slammed it shut once he had handed the haji in.

Looking around at the windowless walls of the stifling candlelit interior, glancing once or twice at the armed official at the closed door, and faintly hearing the mob of excited fanatics outside, Richard Burton—alias Haji 'Abdullah—felt like the proverbial trapped rat.

To a born believer, *El-Ka'abeh* was the House of Allah. But to a born infidel it was the abode of Azrael, angel of death. However safe a European might be at Mecca, nothing could have saved him from the ever-ready daggers of rabid Muslims if detected in the sanctum sanctorum. Jews and atheistic Persians were flayed alive, stabbed to death, burned, or impaled for polluting the holy places. Burton would surely die a much slower and more imaginative death.

But these macabre thoughts did not prevent him from carefully observing almost every inch of the Ka'abeh during his long prayers. And unbeknownst to the boy Muhammed or the guard at the door, he even made a rough plan and several small sketches with a pencil inside his white ihram, sitting and saying his beads all the while.

Compared wth the Prophet's mausoleum in El-Medina, the Ka'abeh of Mecca was a masterpiece of majestic simplicity. Burton found the walls and floor tessellated with multicolored slabs of the finest marble engraved with Koranic inscriptions, while the ornate carved-wood ceiling was draped with gold-embroidered crimson damask.

There he sat in the position of prayer, with the sweat streaming down his skin and soaking through his ihram, the only infidel ever to enter the Holy House. He thought for a moment how sublime it was—the temple of the One and Only God, expressing by all the eloquence of unsophisticated fancy the glory and grandeur that vitalized El-Islam—this the symbol of its spirit and strength, a cube of stone.

"*Bismillāh,* make way for the great haji from Hindustan!" the boy Muhammed said as he and Burton strode up to the door, which was now open for the receipt of payment. "Seven dollars, effendi," he whispered with a suggestive nudge.

Burton scowled, thrusting a hand into his pouch.

When helped down from the doorway by the two brawny eunuchs, Haji 'Abdullah was greeted by none other than 'Abdel-Muttalib bin Ghalib, the Grand Sherif of Mecca. He was bald and beardless, with the face of a hawk and a tanned-leather complexion, dressed in a simple white ihram. The only sign of his rank was a big gold-embroidered green satin umbrella held over his bare head by a black slave boy.

He eyed Burton aggressively, and Burton thought with a piercing stare and a slight curl of the lip: *So you're the hyena who raped M'sieu Bertolucci, and the devil knows how many others.*

The haji handed the sherif seven dollars.

"*Mā bess!* Not enough!" the sherif said, slapping the money back in the haji's hand.

Expecting something of the kind, Burton had been careful to carry no more than eight dollars in his pouch.

"In Allah's name," screeched the Shaybeh youth, "is that all you brought with you?"

Burton looked stupid and pretended not to understand by shrugging his shoulders, shaking his head, and holding out his hands.

The sherif growled impatiently and said to the Bedawi: "By Almighty Allah, make him see the light of generosity!"

"*Aiwallāh, yā s'ādtek!*" 'Othman reached into his robe and pulled out a gold-embroidered green silk sheath attached to a cord around his neck. Revealing the quatre-foiled knob of the large golden key of the Ka'abeh, he rubbed it lightly over Burton's closed eyes in an effort to brighten them with benevolence.

Haji 'Abdullah swallowed the hocus-pocus with a goodly grace, put on a kind and enlightened face, slipped a hand into his pouch, and pulled out the last dollar.

His excellency took it with a hopeless glance; and much to 'Abdullah's satisfaction, 'Abdel-Muttalib didn't care to hold out his hand to be kissed.

"*Wallāh,* effendi," the boy Muhammed said, patting his master on the back as they left the *Baytullāh,* "you escaped better than anybody I ever saw! Some men have left their skins behind!"

Burton laughed halfheartedly. What a sick pun! He thought of 'Othman bin Talheh and his flayed phallus, of Consul Bertolucci being sodomized and circumcised, and of dozens of infidels being skinned alive for desecrating the Holy of Holies. He shuddered, while Haji Muhammed shook with laughter.

11 : The transformation of Haji 'Abdullah

The chill of sorrow numbs my thought; I think I hear the passing knell,
As dies across yon thin blue line the tinkling of the camel bell.

Having performed all the rites of pilgrimage, Haji 'Abdullah entered a bathhouse and washed with henna and warm water to relieve the pain of sunscalds on his exposed flesh.

A few days later found him riding westward over the wasteland towards Jidda, the great seaport of the Holy City. That night he wrote in his journal:

I longed to leave Mecca. I had done everything, seen everything. The heat was unendurable—120° in the shade— and the little room where I could enjoy privacy and jot down my notes was a perfect oven. All through the worst part of the day, from noon to sunset, I used to lie reading, dozing, smoking, or writing completely stripped. During the heat of the day clothing is unendurable at Mecca.

Riding into the open plain, I felt a thrill of pleasure—such joy as only the captive delivered from his dungeon can experience. The sunbeams warmed me into renewed life and vigor, the air of the desert was like a perfume, and the homely face of Nature was as the smile of a dear old friend.

I contemplated the city without any of the sadness usually suggested by a parting look. Those who find danger the salt of life should visit Mecca. I have been exposed to perils, and I have escaped from them. My heart is happy that I have been able to accomplish what I set out to do; but if asked whether the results justify the risk, I'll reply in the negative. I shall strongly dissuade anyone from making the attempt. Woe to the unfortunate who happens to be recognized as an infidel—a choice thrice offered between circumcision and death.

Arriving in Jidda, Burton found it necessary to cash the emergency letter of credit given to him by the Royal Geographical Society. He was now flat broke, without a cent to take him back to Cairo. So being an Indo-British subject, liable to European protection, Haji 'Abdullah went at once to the British consulate.

"Who are you and what d'you want?" The salaaming Pathan from Delhi presented his passport to a surly Turkish dragoman. " 'Abdullah bin Yusef, eh? Well, what d'you want?"

"I wish to see his excellency the consul, *yā sāhhibī!*"

"Is that so? Well you can't—he's sick."

"Let the dirty nigger wait!" rasped an Armenian on the other side of the room. "Who is he and what does he want?"

"An Indian. He wants to see *Khwājeh* Cole."

"Well let the dirty nigger wait! The *khwājeh* has a fever. He isn't here."

"Then where can I find him, *inshallāh?*" Burton roared, fiery-eyed.

"*Bismillāh!*" the Turk said hotly. "I didn't like your looks the second I saw you. Now I don't like your tone of voice!"

Burton bared his teeth in a vicious grin. "Yaas, by Allah, but you're going to hate my fist even more when it knocks those yellow teeth down your throat!" He then made a menacing move as if to punch the dragoman right in the mouth. The Turk lurched back with alarm. Burton cackled, pulled a folded slip of paper and a pencil out of his sash, and dashed off a note. "Here, you scum of a pissing skunk, take this to the English consul. And if you dare read it before he does I'll cut out your heart and feed it to the pigs!"

When the Turkish dragoman ran upstairs with 'Abdullah's note, his Armenian co-worker on the other side of the room burst out laughing. He was soon put to silence by the Afghan's savage stare.

The note read:

Don't recognize me. I'm Dick Burton, but not safe yet. Give me some money and take no notice of me.

Haji 'Abdullah heard a welcome sound from above: "Send him up, you bloody fool, and be quick about it! That man is my old friend from India!"

In another moment Charles Cole met Richard Burton, and an exclamation of astonishment was soon followed by hearty shouts of laughter.

"Good God—sit down, man! Here—have a cigarette, cigars—I'll call for coffee. How 'bout a brandy-pawnee whilst we wait? Well good God, I shouldn't believe it! Y'know, dear fellow, every time I get together with a group of Muslims I always like to remind them there isn't anything an Englishman can't do. Keeps up respect and prestige—call it fear, Anglophobia, if you will. Well, anyway, they always reply favorably to the fact that we British can do everything—everything, that is, except pilgrimage to the Holy City. That, by the scented beard of the Prophet, is an absolute impossibility! Well, by God, I promise myself a laugh at their beards over your fluke, dear man, which proves the fact!"

On September 26, Haji 'Abdullah stalked aboard the Bombay Steam Navigation Company's little screwship *Dwarka,* bound for Suez. The moment he stepped on deck, Burton was hailed as the Pasha of El-Medina by a mob of Turkish pilgrims en route to Istanbul. The boy Muhammed, who was there to say good-bye, chuckled with devilish delight. None other than he had "borrowed" the fancy clothes for his famous friend.

The deck was so jammed with Turks that Burton and the boy Muhammed were obliged to squat on either side of the companionway, and just when Captain Wolley and Commander Taylor were coming up from the hold. Taylor gave Burton a slight kick and said: "Get out of the way, you dirty nigger!"

Burton wanted to kick him back, but he dared not betray himself in the midst of fanatics armed to the teeth. So he sneered, spat, and snarled instead: *"Yā Nesrānī, kelb 'awānī!* O Nazarite, dog sodomite!"

'Abdullah thought it advisable to move; so he and the boy Muhammed edged their way over to the rail, where several young officers of the Bombay Army were standing, smoking and chatting.

"What a clever, intellectual face that Arab has!" one of them remarked. And though each was staring straight at him, not a single lieutenant recognized him as their fellow officer.

"*Ha!* You always were a nigger lover," another retorted. "The only intellect that Arab has is in his arse, and as for being clever—well, if you call buggering clever!"

Burton grinned into his beard, and considered these insults a compliment paid to his disguise.

As Haji 'Abdullah and Haji Muhammed strode past the Anglo-Indians and approached the gangplank, the loose folds of Burton's flowing green jubbah brushed against one of the officers.

"Damn that nigger's impudence! If he does that again I'll kick him!"

Haji 'Abdullah suddenly stopped, swung around, and growled: "Well damn it, Hawkins, that's a fine way to welcome a fellow after four years' absence!"

"By Jove, it's Ruffian Dick!"

The boy Muhammed stood dumbstruck for a few seconds. Then he frowned, and his plump cheeks flushed with anger. "Now I understand! That was English you spoke. You're a burra sahib from India! Allah forbid, you've laughed at our beards!"

Before Burton could catch him, the boy Muhammed shot down the gangplank and disappeared into the crowd.

"I'll be right back," Burton said, grinning. But he didn't

go after Haji Muhammed el-Besyuni. That friendship was finished.

Haji 'Abdullah bin Yusef took Captain Wolley aside, procured a first-class passage, and disappeared below deck. Having washed, shaved, and changed his clothes, he came up from his cabin as Lieutenant Richard F. Burton of the 18th Bombay Native Infantry—so transformed that none of the Turkish hajis ever took notice of their late pilgrimage companion. He then joined his old army buddies.

"Well, Dick, I expect you'll be heading home now to reap the glory."

"Home? Like hell! England's the last place on earth I'd even be seen dead in. *Bah,* glory! What glory?"

"Come now, Dick, you must be joking. When the world finds out what you've done, the name Burton will be a household word from one end to the other. So get a move on, man! Hurry home as fast as you can. You'll be a national hero! I wager they'll boost you to captain—hand you a staff appointment and a pukka hike in pay. What're you waiting for? Don't be such a damned ass all your life! Now's your chance to be champion of the day. Go back to London and everyone'll itch to death till they hear your story."

"The devil go home! I've got better things to do than go back to that prison and lock myself up again. I'm heading for a long rest in Cairo. Then I'll write a book they can read. But I won't be around to answer any of their stupid questions, to be flattered and fawned over like some sort of freak. All my other books I wrote in India and sent back to England to be published. So why not another? How does this title sound? *Personal Narrative of a Pilgrimage to*

El-Medina and Mecca. After that it's back to Bombay. My leave's up in March, and if I don't return—*phffft,* no commission. Six months'll be just enough time to throw a book together and get some rest—unless these Turks find out who I am and toss me overboard with a knife in my back!"

In 1855, three marbled volumes astounded the world with the adventurous tale they told. Burton's pilgrimage to the sacred and forbidden cities of Arabia was universally hailed as the most daring exploit and dangerous undertaking of modern times.

But the author and adventurer was less enthusiastic. In fact, he was nowhere to be seen and congratulated. Though honored as the most fearless and famous explorer of the century by the R.G.S., Burton turned his back on London and refused to be lionized. He infuriated Sir Roderick Murchison with a curt telegraph reply from Aden:

I WANT HONOR, NOT HONORS.

Isabel Arundell repeatedly read and cherished those three fabulous volumes by Lieutenant Richard Burton. She hoped for him, prayed for him, and waited for him— thinking and dreaming always of the frightfully fascinating man who had forgotten her.

12 : A tempting of providence

How sore the burden, strange the strife; how full of splendor, wonder, fear:
Life, atom of that infinite space that stretches 'twixt the There and Here.

"I'm going to Harar!"

"You're what?"

"Harar—next to Mecca, the most forbidden and unknown city in the Muslim world."

Richard Burton was seated in a fanback chair on the cool verandah of Dr. John Steinhaeuser, civil surgeon at Aden. It was October, 1854.

The doctor, a stout stone-faced Anglo-Indian, puffed aggressively on his cheroot. "But Dick, no white man has ever gone into Harar and come out alive. Why it's worse than Timbuktu used to be before the French Army opened 'er up."

"John, I don't give a goddamn *what* other white men have or haven't done. So no European has ever come out alive!

So the Hararis have penetrated the disguise of every infidel who got in or tried to get in *à couvert!* So they've
tortured a few travelers to death, castrated and cut up a
few Catholic missionaries! Is it any more dangerous than
my pilgrimage to Mecca, where they string an unbeliever
up by his balls and chop him down the crotch till all his
guts jump out?" Flicking away his cigar butt, he laughed
roughly. "By Allah, I'll make it even if it kills me!"

Steinhaeuser snorted. "Yes, well I fear it might just do
that! Y'know, Dick, they don't call it the Whiteman's Grave
and the Abode of the Dead for nothing. But you're not
going as yourself, are you?"

"*Ha-ha!* Heavens no!"

"Well thank God for that!"

"Damn it, John, you ought to know I'm not *that* crazy!
Now what made you think Dick Burton would be mad
enough to go to Harar? The only daredevil for that enterprise is Haji 'Abdullah!"

Steinhaeuser slapped his thighs and lurched out of his
seat. "Well by Moses' beard, let's have a drink to Haji 'Abdullah and hope for his success. *Hai,* punkah-wallah—put
some steam into that fanning! Where the damn-hell are
those wretched mallees? *Hai,* water down those tatties before it gets like *jahannum* in here! *Koī hai,* khidmutgar!
Brandy-and-soda *lāo, jaldī-jaldī!*"

Burton cackled. "Well, burra sahib bahadur, you still
keep 'em jumping, eh? Just like out in Hindustan."

"*Ham dēkhta hai!* I keep a sharp lookout. Aden's my
own little India. The only regret is, I'm sick of looking at
syphilitic ulcers on the Arab genitalia."

"Why I should think the civil service would be a life of
ease! What better bundobust in the Indian Army? Cutting

off the infected foreskins of stinking Hindu sepoys! At least there's one encouragement. Gonorrhea's so common among the Arabs it's hardly considered a disease. It's the mark of a man, a dirty joke. *Dā'l-mubārek* they call it—the 'blessed ailment.' A young blade without at least one venereal sore on the glans or skin of his penis is laughed at as a masturbator."

The white-liveried Muslim khidmutgar came in with a laden tray just as the little dhoti-wearing durwaun poked his head through the beaded portiere and yelped in baboo English: "Ootrum Sah'b Bah'dur, huzoor!"

"Well, speak of the devil!" Burton muttered.

Colonel James Outram, political resident at Aden, stepped into the verandah and handed his pith helmet to the durwaun.

"Jamie!" Steinhaeuser greeted him. "You're just in time to join us for a drink."

"No, thank you, John," he said, wiping the sweat from his side whiskers and mustache with three smart flicks of the finger. Outram was short and broad-shouldered and square-faced, and he gripped a stout Malacca walking stick with which to beat "niggers" over the head.

Burton stood up, saluted, and sat down again.

Outram returned his salute as curtly and coldly. They didn't shake hands. Outram glowered at Burton, and Burton glowered back. For a few seconds there was tense silence. Then Outram spoke: "Well, Burton, we meet again."

"What a dishonor!" Burton was expressionless.

Outram scowled. His knuckles whitened as he tightened his grip on the stick. "You haven't changed a bit, have you? Still the most arrogant griff in the Bombay Army."

Burton chortled sneeringly. "Where've I heard that before? Ah yaas, the piglet protégé apes Sir James Hogg!"

"Insubordinate beast! You'd have never talked that way to me out in India and got away with it."

"*Ha!* How presumptuous! You, my dear colonel, never gave me a chance to tell you personally what I think of you and your lot. Where were you? Hiding back at Government House, ramming your nose up Elphinstone's ass, playing God Almighty—conveniently out of reach. Such poor mortals as Napier and I should be grateful we got away with our skins. You did a good job of bundling off the devil's brother, but the governor proved to be Satan himself when he sent the damnable Lieutenant Burton on sick leave instead of civilian hell."

Outram couldn't find words to express his rage, so Burton twitted him some more. "That notorious stick of yours," he pointed with the stem of his pipe. "How many 'dirty niggers' has it polished off in the past five years?"

"Be damned glad you're not one of them, or I'd have broke it over your skull by now! But enough of this nonsense! I didn't come here to skirmish over the past. Burton, they tell me you're at it again. But now you've got *me* to contend with, and it won't be so easy as before."

"If at first you don't succeed—" Burton drawled sarcastically. "Fate couldn't have chosen for me a more challenging Nemesis. Well throw down the gauntlet and I'll grab it up!"

Outram banged the end of his stick on the hardwood floor. "This insane expedition is a tempting of Providence, and I shan't allow it! How could any man in his right mind sanction such folly? What is this, the same sort of death-defying whimsicality that sent you to Mecca?"

"Call it what you will. I couldn't care less." Burton eyed Steinhaeuser, who finally got around to fixing his friend's brandy-pawnee. "I'll lead a government ass to water. Let's see if he drinks." Burton tossed off his glass in a manner that made Outram blink. "Here's an elementary lesson in strategic geography. Berbera is the real key of the Red Sea. It's the center of East African traffic and the only safe place for shipping from Suez to Guardafui. It's backed by country capable of cultivation, and by hills covered with pine and other valuable trees. It enjoys a relatively temperate climate with a regular, though mild, monsoon. I needn't tell you this seaport has been coveted by many a foreign conqueror. Circumstances have thrown it into our arms, but the position is too shaky to be held for long. If we refuse a chance to strengthen and secure our footing in Somaliland, another nation won't be so blind. Don't think our rivals the French wouldn't like to grab it up! And don't forget the Italians. They're all licking their chops, waiting for us to slip and fall into the gulf. The local sultan need only give us a gentle shove, and in we'll go! In 1825 the crew of the *Mary Ann* brig was treacherously murdered by the Somalis. And mark my words, if tomorrow a P. & O. steamer happened to fall into their hands it'd be the same old bloody story. We need to civilize as well as govern. You can't do business with a bunch of savages."

"That's all very well," Outram said with a smirk, "but how do you propose to civilize Somaliland?" He shook his stick. "The only sort of civilizing I ever heard of is that done with the sword—and not by one man, but by an army of men. Well let me tell you, the E.I.C. has no intention of annexing that Godforsaken place; and as for our position at Berbera, I and the Company consider it far from shaky—in fact, quite solid indeed."

"Yaas, yaas. Well Outram & Company have been proven wrong before and shall be proven wrong again. Harar is scarcely three hundred miles from here. It's cousin-germane to the ill-famed Timbuktu. A tradition exists that with the entrance of the first infidel the city will fall. So all who tried it have been foully murdered. Well, it's a point of honor with me to use my title of Haji by entering this so-called forbidden stronghold, by visiting its so-called bloodthirsty ruler, and by returning in safety—after breaking the guardian spirit's spell."

"And by whose authority do you propose to carry out this madbrained scheme of yours? Certainly not by mine or the Company's!"

"Wrong again, my dear colonel! Presumption begins in ignorance and ends in—oh well, you've been away too long. Things aren't what they used to be, y'know! In fact, things have never been quite the same since you left—or rather since Elphinstone got rid of you, advised Hogg you'd do better dirty work here in the coalhole of the East. Well anyhow, whether you know and like it or not, the Bombay Government and the R.G.S. have long desired an exploration of the unknown and uncharted Somali country. But up till now they haven't found anyone able to undertake such a dangerous and deadly enterprise. The land held captive by the tyrant of Harar may be one of rich resources, and the safety and security of Berbera for the Red Sea trade is dependent upon our establishing friendly diplomatic relations with the emir. He controls all the tribes. One word out of him and there'd be a wholesale slaughter at Berbera. You know how these barbarians like to play cat-and-mouse. He's just biding his time right now, but one snap of the fingers would set off a general massacre and strangle all traffic into and out of the country."

"Yes, and that's exactly why I shan't allow this insane expedition of yours. The Somali tribes are in a state of feud as it is. There's bad blood between the emir of Harar and the sultan of Zeila, and all this madness of yours might very well provoke an uprising. Such an event would jeopardize our position and prestige at Berbera, which is now quiet—thank God! So hear me well and take fair warning, lieutenant. No expedition to Harar will originate from here so long as I'm in charge. As political agent I take my orders from the Court of Directors, and those orders are to maintain and protect British interests and free trade in the Gulf of Aden. Suffice it to say, your madbrained scheme is detrimental to our African interests."

Burton lit a cheroot. "The vested interests of Outram & Company don't interest me in the least," he said dryly, blowing a torrent of smoke in Outram's direction. "While you bow and scrape to the twenty-four kings of Leadenhall Street, I find myself empowered to make you even more jealous and vindictive."

"Just what do you mean by that?" Outram thumped the floor with his stick.

Burton grinned demonically. "The Bombay Government approved my application for permission and assistance."

"By whose authority, may I ask?"

"By his excellency the governor's. Lord Elphinstone is personally patronizing the expedition. Funds have also been donated through the auspices of the Royal Asiatic Society. I'm afraid the odds are against you this time, my dear colonel."

"Not quite, my dear lieutenant! I don't give a tinker's damn what Lord Elphinstone has authorized you to do, much less the R.A.S. This isn't Bombay. You're out of his jurisdiction now. Aden is under E.I.C.protection, and I'm the burra sahib around here. Until I receive orders from London to the contrary, no expedition will leave here for Harar. When I'm informed that any such expedition has been organized and is ready to depart, I'll have every man jack of it placed under close arrest pending court-of-inquiry proceedings."

Outram, who had been standing all this time, suddenly swung around and pounded the floor. "*Arē*, durwaun! Topee *lāo!*" The little porter came scurrying in with the burra sahib bahadur's pith helmet. Outram flipped it on his head and tapped the rim with his stick. "Well, good day, John. Be seeing you again soon." He then cast a cursory glance at Burton and walked out into the dazzling sunlight.

Burton snatched the cigar out of his mouth and laughed aloud, accepting his second drink with a wink and a nod.

Steinhaeuser was grim-faced. "Well, Dick," he sighed, "what are you going to do now?"

"Go to Harar—what else! You don't think I'll let that jackass-in-office stop me, do you? He's been in my way before. A first-chop authoritarian. But he's not half so insolent as I am, and that's his great weakness. That's why he beats poor devil niggers over the head with that big stick of his. Who he's really beating are Hogg and the Leadenhall gang, but he doesn't know it. Poor devil, I should pity him. Ah well, when they don't stand aside you just walk around 'em!" Burton emptied his glass. "We anticipated this, so the four of us—Speke, Herne, Stroyan, and I—are going to pull a feint. I plan sailing over to Zeila and going inland from there—"

"Alone?" Steinhaeuser interjected.

"How else, except for a few Somali bearers and guides! After I'm gone, the three of 'em are going to head over one by one to Berbera, meet there, and survey the coast together while I'm in the interior. After I've opened up Harar—*inshallāh!*—I'll then make for Berbera and join 'em in a general exploration of that huge parched horn of *terra incognita* called Somaliland."

Steinhaeuser finished his brandy-and-soda and smiled shyly. "This may be an absurd question—knowing you as well as I do—but aren't you just a bit afraid?"

"*Kuchh dhar nahīn hai!*" Burton barked Hindustani: "There's no such thing as fear!"

"*Shābāsh!*" Steinhaeuser replied. "Well done! bravo! Now have another drink."

"Don't mind if I do. I s'pose I've earned it! Y'know, John, Harar is as difficult to enter as Mecca—even harder than Timbuktu used to be. It's the southernmost masonry-built settlement in North Equatorial Africa. The bigoted and barbarous population threatens death to the infidel who dares venture within its walls, some Negro Merlin having read decline and fall in the first footsteps of the Frank. I'll go as an Arab merchant. The inside of Harar has never been seen and studied by any European. It has its own language, its own unique history and traditions. I hold the people to be Himyarites. The Semito-Hamitic dialect is unwritten, but I hope to compile a grammar and vocabulary. And there's enough savage anthropology there to interest me," he added laughingly. "You know—things like nymphotomy and clitoridectomy, concubinage and polyandry."

13 : First footsteps in East Africa

Swift the Camel Rider spans the howling waste, by Kismet sped,
And of his magic wand a wave hurries the quick to join the dead.

Haji 'Abdullah left Aden for Zeila on October 29.

Colonel Outram watched Lieutenants Speke, Herne, and Stroyan of the Bombay Army embark for Berbera each on different days. He was suspicious, but powerless to act against what was certainly no organized expedition.

As for Lieutenant Burton, the kingpin of this perilous enterprise, he just suddenly disappeared under mysterious circumstances. Outram searched the whole city for him, but found not a trace. No one, not even Dr. Steinhaeuser, seemed to know where that daredevil had got to.

:

At Zeila, the sights and sounds of El-Islam filled Haji 'Abdullah with feelings of passion and pride. He again thrilled to the melodious chant of the muezzin, more solemnly beautiful to him than any evening bell, and sensed a warm tingling in the mosque as he listened to the loudly intoned "*Āmīn!*" and "*Allāhuakber!*" more soul-stirring to him than any organ or choir. These things he understood. They allured him and he loved them.

Nightfall was celebrated with the singing and dancing of marriage festivals and circumcision feasts, and veiled *filles de joie* flitted seductively through the dark streets and deadly alleys.

Burton opened his journal and began to write:

The evening star hangs like a diamond upon the still horizon. Around the moon a pink zone of light mist, shading off into turquoise blue and a delicate chrysoprase green, invests the heavens with a peculiar charm.

The scene is truly suggestive. Behind me, purpling in the night air and silvered by the radiance from above, lie the wilds and mountains inhabited by the fiercest of savages—their shadowy mysterious forms exciting vague alarms in the traveler's breast. Sweet as the harp of David, the night breeze and the music of the water come up from the sea; but the ripple and the rustling sound alternate with the hyena's laugh, and the jackal's cry, and the wild dog's lengthened howl.

This journey is to be through a ferocious, treacherous, and bloodthirsty land of people whose tribes are in a constant state of blood feud. Everyone weeps over me, and considers me a dead man.

I fall asleep, feeling once more at home.

Haji 'Abdullah was too much of an Arab to be bored or bothered by the mobs of Muslim visitors that besieged his room in the water-front khan, curious to see and eager to talk with the eminent scholar from Arabia. To break the monotony of these visitations, 'Abdullah would pick up his Koran and swagger into the local mosque. With his Somali servant carrying the prayer rug under his arm, and with three hundred pairs of eyes staring at him, he would then order 'Abdi-Abukir to unroll the *sejjādeh* on which his master would kneel and recite the customary two-bow prayer in honor of the mosque.

With 'Abdi-Abukir looking on attentively and piously, Haji 'Abdullah would now lay his scimitar and beads on the floor in front of him, sit cross-legged, open his Koran to the eighteenth sura, and read in a loud twanging voice:

"Allah! There is no god but He!
   Of slumber and sleeping He is free!
   The Living, Eternal One He be!"

On November 27, Haji 'Abdullah rode out of Zeila on a black stallion. He was elegantly garbed in a flowing white caftan with a yellow sash, a green muslin turban wrapped around a red skullcap, and thick leather sandals. A double-barreled shotgun lay across his lap, a scimitar was thrust through his cummerbund, and two Colt revolvers in home-made holsters were strapped around his waist. A canteen and cartridge pouch hung from either shoulder, and con-cealed inside his robe were a dagger and pocket pistol. Haji 'Abdullah had no intentions of being murdered in murderous Somalia.

That evening in the eerie desert, after he and his Somali

donkey boys had pitched camp, Burton sat by the glowing
fire and penciled in his journal:

> I now feel the die is cast. Placing my pistols by my side,
> with my rifle butt for a pillow and its barrel as a bedfellow,
> I seek repose with none of the apprehension which even
> the most stouthearted traveler knows before the start. It is
> the difference between fancy and reality, between anxiety
> and certainty. To men gifted with any imaginative powers
> the anticipation must ever be worse than the event. Thus
> it happens that one who feels a thrill of fear before engaging
> in a peril exchanges it for a throb of exultation when he
> finds himself hand to hand with the danger.

For a month Haji 'Abdullah and his small party of Somalis and pack mules traveled over desolate and deadly
terrain. The demon of thirst danced all around them, and
often they did not taste water for twenty-four torrefying
hours. The piercing sun paralyzed their brains, the ghoulish mirage mocked them every step of the way, and the
effect was a delirium of monomania.

As Burton jogged along with his eyes shut tight against
the fiery air, lurching and swaying in the saddle, no image
unconnected with the want of water entered his tortured
mind. Water ever lay before him. Cool water lying deep in
a shady well, icy water cascading over cold gray rocks,
sparkling water in limpid lakes inviting him to plunge
headlong into their refreshing depths. Now a monsoon
cloud showered upon him a liquid more precious than
molten pearl. Then an invisible hand offered him a cup
of that natural nectar for which in reality he would gladly
have given ten years of his life.

Shocked into hope, Burton opened his glazed eyes. He

opened them to a heat-reeking desert and a blazing pearl-blue sky. He looked desperately for huge purple messengers, but none came to him. All the hydraulic spirit of Indra was burnt out of the world by the crematorial incandescence of Surya. In a few more hours, Kali would be making the deathbed of day; and the blood-red sun would sink into an ocean of flame, leaving behind a sizzling iridescent glow soon to be smothered by the black pall of night.

Burton tried to talk, but couldn't. He could only croak like a deaf-mute. His leathery tongue gagged him. It was a swollen hunk of dehydrated tissue, gorging a numbed and mummified mouth, forcing open dry cracked lips. Burton felt and looked like a corpse. His cheeks were hollow, his eyes sunken. He tried to think, but evil jinn were driving white-hot spikes into his head. Every brain storm saturated his soul with one eternal image—*water!*

What kept him alive? What kept him staggering on ahead of a half-dead horse he had to drag by the halter, his bleary eyes trailing the sun-split earth, stumbling and sprawling and gasping for—*water!*

Twelve hours in a fiery, waterless wasteland could not kill man or beast with a furious will to live. The fiends of hydromania lashed them on. Burton had never suffered so severely in all his life. The deadly Arabian desert "where none but Allah dwells" was a paradise compared with this African purgatory.

After thirty-six hours without water they could go no further. Frozen in their tracks by a paroxysm of despair, they dropped to their knees and waited indifferently for the agonizing onslaught of Death—that Bedawin wraith riding over the desert on a skeleton camel.

Burton heard the sepulchral sound of tiny bells. The opalescent vault above was speckled with vultures whose hovering shadows traced weird patterns on the dust below. *Die! die! die!* they seemed to squall.

Suddenly Burton caught an even stranger but more lively noise, a shrill piping of *kettā! kettā! kettā!* He looked up and saw a pin-tailed sand grouse streaking across the slowly reddening sky. *"Māshallāh!"* he breathed, pointing to where the bird darted down among massive black rocks about a hundred yards away. *"El-qetāh! el-qetāh!"*

"Māshallāh! What a wonder!" the Somalis echoed, stumbling to their feet. *"Qetāh! qetāh!* Grouse! grouse! *Mā! mā!* Water! water!"

The pack animals scented the blessing from afar. They raised their heads and pricked up their drooping ears. With distended nostrils and bulging eyes, they paced after their wild-spirited masters.

Circling the rocks, man and beast sighted a huge water hole. Laughing and shouting, Haji 'Abdullah and his Somali servants threw themselves with a belly flop into the muddy liquid. The surface was alive with tadpoles and insects, but it could also have been poisoned for all they cared. Burton dashed the ambrosia over his burning face, dunking his head and wallowing bodily in a delirious delight. He drank and drank till he could drink no more, scooping the water up in his hands and gulping it down till he sickened and retched. Burton vowed that he would never again shoot a *qetāh*.

The closer they got to Harar, the more they were approached and stopped by scouting parties of ferocious-looking Somali Fuzzy-Wuzzies. Some rode away to report evil of the Arab intruder, and many threats were uttered. Finding Burton heavily armed and apparently unappalled by their presence, these spear-toting Galla and Falasha tribesmen shook their fists and flung heated taunts in his face.

"A thousand curses never tore a shirt!" 'Abdullah always replied, raising his rifle and setting off a deafening discharge that sent half of them scattering in every direction.

"*Heh-heh, wallāh!*" shrieked one old bird of prey. "They'll strip off that white skin of yours at Harar!"

"Let 'em try," 'Abdullah snarled, clawing his beard and fingering a revolver. "I'm hard as the heart of Harar!"

At the end of December they entered a large village several miles outside the Forbidden City. In only a few seconds flocks of jabbering and gesticulating Somali Bedawin had surrounded them. Tall, black, bearded and woolly-headed warriors in dirty yellow tobes, sporting bamboo spears and hippo-hide shields, their leathery feet bare and fuzzy hair pomaded with camel piss, glared wild-eyed at the unwelcome strangers. Big-breasted, broad-buttocked, and bald-headed women, whom Haji 'Abdullah deemed as homely as the men were handsome, gaped sullenly with little black scowlers perched on their naked hips. Bare-bottomed boys and girls ran about chattering like monkeys.

Burton threw a leg over the saddle and jumped off his horse. While loosening the bridle he happened to hear one of the warriors say: "What good is his barking-stick? Before he can fetch fire I'll send this arrow through him."

Burton swung around sharply, whipped out one of his revolvers, and blasted three shots over their heads. The resonant roars threw them into convulsions of terror. He then lowered the Colt, cocked it in the frightened Somali's face, and said: "This next thunderbolt won't be into the air. It'll be into your belly."

Burton's grisly grin announced new horrors of wonderment. "By Allah, put up one of your shields as a target and I'll blow a hole through it as big as your fist!" They laughed nervously and shook their heads. "All right then," he said, gazing about, "I hear you Somalis hate the vulture because he eats the dying and the dead. Well watch this!" Seeing a large brown vulture drifting in the air twenty yards away, Burton raised his revolver and shot it down.

"*Māshallāh! māshallāh!*" the Somalis screamed in amazement.

He then grabbed his scatter-gun, loaded it with swan shot, and aimed at a bird they all laughingly considered far out of range. *Bang!* Burton knocked it over flying.

Fresh screams followed this marvelous feat. "Lo and behold," they cried, "he brings down the birds from heaven!"

At that moment a strapping, shifty-eyed Bedawin came strutting up. "Show me this shaykh who brings down birds on the wing!"

Haji 'Abdullah faced about and confronted with a frown the headman of the village. The *jerrād* or chief extended his hand. Burton clapped palms with him and touched his forehead in the Muslim manner of greeting.

"I'm 'Adn bin Qaoshan! Who are you without that lightning-thrower?"

"Hand me a quarterstaff and I'll damn-soon show you!" Haji 'Abdullah said, spitting. "Where I come from, when dogs run at us we thrash 'em with sticks!"

"*Yāllāh! yāllāh!*" 'Adn bin Qaoshan howled in mock

trepidation. He thrust a forefinger in his mouth, praised Allah, and prayed to be saved from such a calamity. Then he handed the haji a long stout stick and wielded one himself.

"By Allah, I hope you're the best buck around here!" Burton said tauntingly. "I take on none but the best and the bravest!"

"O sucker of your mother's uncircumcised clitoris," 'Adn answered, "there's none better or braver than I am! Why even my erection is stronger than many a man's arm!"

"*Bismillāh!* Come and get it, O father of foreskins!"

"*Wallāh!* Here it comes, O son of a pecker swallower!"

Haji 'Abdullah let 'Adn bin Qaoshan swing and chop at him as much as he liked, easily warding off the blows with appropriate parries. After repeated failure, and much huffing and puffing, 'Adn fell off guard and received from 'Abdullah a resounding whack on the backside that sent him sprawling to the dust. The crowd laughed long and loud, applauding the "shaykh who knows knowledge," while the fallen tower of strength crawled away in confusion.

An hour later, after 'Adn bin Qaoshan had licked his sores, Haji 'Abdullah approached him in his hut and said: "By Allah, my good man, I want your best and bravest warrior to escort me into Harar and introduce me to the emir."

'Adn looked leeringly. "Ah, but what are you willing to pay for such a service?"

"Plenty, if it please Allah!"

"Then I'm your man, *inshallāh!*" he said, flashing his ivories. "My sister was married to the emir's father, so I'm well known in Harar. But that don't mean I'm welcome there. Nobody's welcome there. By Allah, I'd as soon walk into a crocodile's mouth as go into the walls of Harar! Allah put a curse on that dreadful city. He made it the black hole of Shaitan. No one is safe in the emir's clutches. He's the devil in human disguise! No—" he shook his head in false alarm, "Allah forbid, I'd rather step into a crocodile's mouth than set foot in that infernal city!"

'Abdullah eyed him suspiciously, then cackled. "Allah willing, perhaps if I kicked out the crocodile's teeth—?"

"Ah, *yā sīdī*," 'Adn grinned, "then it would make things a lot easier!" He shrugged and gestured. "After all—and Allah is All-Knowing!—I have but one life, and it ain't too easy as it is. I'm a humble man, wanting but little, yet Allah knows I'm a poor man too. Now being a tribal chief, a responsibility Fate thrust upon me unwillingly, I need certain luxuries befitting my authority. Otherwise people won't respect me, and—"

'Abdullah cocked his eye. "What d'you want?"

"Ah, but you are understanding!" 'Adn beamed, salaaming obsequiously. "I beg of you, *yā hhājj*, when you get back to Berbera, buy what I need and return here at once. Bring me a silver-hilted scimitar and two sets of silver bracelets, a gold-lettered Koran, a silk turban, two pairs of satin slippers and a satin jacket, a thousand dollars, some soap and snuff, about a dozen tobes—make them of indigo-dyed stuff—a scarlet coat embroidered with gold, twenty of those guns of yours with powder and shot, some poison that never fails, and—well, any other little article of luxury you think might suit me as headman here."

'Abdullah nodded, his arms crossed and face severe. "Take me to Harar, and you'll get what you want."

Several Bedawin drew rein outside 'Adn's huge hut.

lurched off their horses, and strode in shaking the dust off their robes. 'Abdullah was certain that for a few seconds black 'Adn turned gray in panic.

"*Allāh y'āfīk,* O 'Adn bin Qaoshan!" one of them barked with a sharp gesture of greeting. "Let's not waste any time and get down to business. We've been sent here by his royal highness the emir to settle a little matter of blood money."

Burton recognized these ill-mannered men as belonging to the Hebr Aowel clan, the emir of Harar's goon squad.

After coming to terms with 'Adn, the spokesman of the five enforcers turned his attention on 'Abdullah and said gruffly: "This Arab here. You say he's one who buys and sells? Jackass! jerk-off! He's a spy! O licker of your sister's enlarged clitoris, for a hundred dollars you should take him prisoner to Harar."

'Abdullah slipped a hand inside his robe and fastened his fingers around the haft of his dagger.

'Adn scowled. "*M'ādhallāh!* Allah forbid having been called an abuser of the *zubb* I should also be called an abuser of the salt! This man and I are *mālihhīn*—on terms of salt."

"So you've eaten salt together!" the Bedawi said in sarcasm, throwing up his arms. "'*Lhhamdulillāh!* Well in three days and three nights the salt won't be in your belly. Then perhaps you'll sell your silly honor for a hundred in reward money. As for us," he added airily, waving his hand, "we'd take him in ourselves, only—Allah forbid!— we wouldn't want to be called breakers of the salt bond. Y'know, being his excellency's royal guard, the sons of Hebr Aowel have a high reputation to uphold—*ho-ho-ho!*"

When the Bedawin were gone, 'Adn bin Qaoshan broke

out in a cold sweat. "Allah! Allah!" he wailed. "Now I'm really scared! I've never been so scared in all my born days! But you needn't fear—I won't betray you. I promise I'll send my salaams to the emir, but it's impossible for me to accompany you to the city. My brother was accidentally murdered in Harar. That's why those cutthroats paid me the customary blood money of atonement. Nobody likes to pay this price of blood, but it's the unwritten law and keeps down a lot of 'accidental' deaths. So now I dare not show my face in Harar, or the Hararis will slit my throat for accepting what the Hebr Aowelis would've slit my throat for refusing! But tell you what I'll do. So's to show you I'm a man of my word, I'll have my oldest son Sherwa guide you into Harar. They'll only spit at him. But me— Allah protect us!—they'd cut off my bat and balls."

No longer in the mood for taking any unnecessary chances, Burton dashed off in English a letter of intro- duction to the emir of Harar and signed it *Colonel James Outram, C.B., Political Agent at Aden.* Folding it up and tucking it into his shirt with other important papers, he intended to deliver it in person. It was neck or nothing.

Haji 'Abdullah took only what was absolutely necessary, leaving behind all his donkey boys, pack mules, and a load of supplies. He stuffed into his saddlebags some presents for the emir, a change of clothes, a Koran and an incom- plete copy of *El-Kitāb Alf Layleh wa-Layleh* or *Book of the Thousand Nights and a Night,* a few biscuits, ammuni- tion, and a little tobacco.

When Haji 'Abdullah and Sherwa bin 'Adn were ready to ride out, all the villagers assembled and recited the *fātihheh.* Everyone wept and wailed over them, for they were already considered dead men.

Burton's servant, 'Abdi-Abukir, had asked earlier if he could join them. At the last minute 'Abdi-Abukir changed his mind. "Do you think I'm a coward, O pilgrim?" he said, grinning like a Cheshire cat.

"Yaas, I do," Burton replied with a stony stare.

Without looking shamefaced, 'Abdi-Abukir said sternly: "What does a man have but one life; and he who throws it away, what is he but a fool?"

'Adn bin Qaoshan then came over, tears in his eyes, and consoled them with the sad old song that they were dead men.

"Then why do you send me, O father?" said Sherwa with a frown of suspicion.

"Because I am bound by the bond of salt, O my son!" he said, bursting out in a howling fit of crocodile tears.

Haji 'Abdullah had heard all he wanted to hear. *Bismillāh! inshallāh!*" he said, kicking away at full gallop. "*Yallah! yallah!*"

While on the road, 'Abdullah and Sherwa were hailed by an old Galla shaykh who stopped them and said: "Beware, you brave fools! If you escape the Benu Hebr Aowel, who will bury you alive in a man-eating anthill, it'll only be to die by the hands of the bloodthirsty emir of Harar, who will skin you alive with a scourge of scorpions. But first he'll bugger and abuse you, castrate you, and cauterize the wound with a red-hot spearhead. Then he'll doubly disgrace you by preparing and eating your penis and testicles, after which he'll have the potency of three men!"

Burton laughed in his face. "Allah knows, you don't believe that nonsense any more than I do!"

'Abdullah and Sherwa rode on—the haji cackling, the

chief's son crowing, and the shaykh cursing a blue streak as he galloped off in the opposite direction.

14 : Into the jaws of death

How lovely visions 'guiled my sleep, aye fading with the break of morn,
Till every sweet became a sour, till every rose became a thorn.

In the hazy afternoon heat of Wednesday, January 3, 1855, Richard Burton stood on the crest of a hill overlooking the Forbidden City of Harar.

The spectacle was an immediate disappointment to him. He expected to behold all the barbaric splendor of turreted and castellated walls, majestic domes, and towering minarets gleaming white-hot in the glaring sunlight. What he saw instead was a shock to one who now realized he had risked his life to win so paltry a prize.

Burton gazed glumly at the long drab line of mud that walled in a massive webwork of squat unwhitewashed adobes. Nothing conspicuous caught his eye but a crude-shaped pair of gray minarets and the imposingly nude palace of the emir, a large whitewashed cube.

But of all the infidels who had attempted it, none had ever succeeded in entering that somber pile of clay and stone. A shiver of anticipation and excitement flashed through Burton's body at the thought that he, in the role of Haji 'Abdullah, stood an even chance of being the first European to unveil the hardhearted virgin.

It was a sweltering 3 P.M. when the two intruders approached the gates of Harar, whereon Burton imagined he read an Arabic inscription of Dante's *Lasciate ogni speranza, voi ch'entrate*—All hope abandon, ye who enter here! Sherwa chuckled to hide his fears, for he read it also.

"Beware, intrusive dogs!" the gigantic gatekeeper growled, leveling his spear. "What d'you want?"

Sherwa answered at once: "In the name of Allah, we send our salaams to his excellency the emir! You know me as Sherwa bin 'Adn bin Qaoshan, and Allah knows I need no introduction to his most eminent majesty. This man is Haji 'Abdullah bin Yusef, a great merchant from across the waters. He has come all the way from Aden as a representative of the English *wekīl*, and he requests the honor of audience with his royal highness Sultan Ahmed bin Sultan Abibekr."

The *baowāb* shouldered his spear, shouted "Open the gates," and ushered them inside the city. "Wait here!" he said harshly, eyeing 'Abdullah as if he itched to impale him. 'Abdullah returned his vicious stare with even hotter ferocity.

While they were cooling their heels in the courtyard, an ugly bunch of Hebr Aowelis collected around them with scowls and snarls. Sherwa began sweating furiously. He licked his lips and tried to looked unconcerned, but the trial was sheer torture. Burton was sweating too; but arms firmly folded, he exchanged venomous glances with a coolness that confounded these members of the emir's elite corps.

"Why didn't you tell us your intentions of entering Harar?" they sneered.

Burton didn't bother to answer. He knew they were hinting that he should pay them protection money, and the threats that followed were intended to force his hand.

"Listen, stranger. Take our advice and get out while the getting's good. We have it straight you're going to be killed somewhere between here and the palace. But that don't necessarily have to happen, y'know. They say it's hard holding a knife in a well-greased hand!"

Burton remained unmoved. He understood the Oriental protection racket only too well. It was the reverse of being murdered and then robbed. Besides, he thought, no amount of money could save him from a death preordained by the Harari devil himself.

Without saying a word, and with a grotesque grin on his face, Haji 'Abdullah fingered his dagger suggestively. Now the Somalis understood him as well.

After waiting half an hour, the two intruders were accosted once again by the big *baowāb,* or gatekeeper, who shook his spear at them and said: "Advance and follow me, O suckers of ass pizzles! His excellency the emir is pleased to receive you!"

Sherwa looked at 'Abdullah, and 'Abdullah looked at Sherwa, and both of them smiled with assurance.

"*Phew, billāh!*" Sherwa heaved a sigh of relief.

'Abdullah leered and laughed. "*Inshallāh,* the worst is

yet to come! *Yallah!* Let's go, O son of 'Adn bin Qaoshan!"

Incensed by their cautious stroll, the gatekeeper roared: "Run! run, you dirty cunt-lapping dogs! No one walks to the palace of the prince!"

Sherwa was about to obey, but 'Abdullah grabbed his arm. "Keep right on sauntering," he said with teeth clenched tight, "and stop looking around you. Stare straight ahead, but be careful. Make that bastard respect you. He's the kind of cur that bites those who show him any fear. Don't give him an excuse to kill you."

Though too frightened to reply, Sherwa did what he was told.

Suddenly a gang of blue-robed Bedawin fell in behind them. Recalling their words of warning, Burton kept his hand clasped around the haft of his dagger, hidden inside his robe.

The *baowāb*, who was striding in front of and then beside them, now dropped back out of sight. "Keep moving!" he grated.

Burton acted at once. His blade flashed as he shot around and shoved it up to the hilt between the legs of a Hebr Aoweli. The victim let out a bloodcurdling yell as cold steel transpierced his scrotum and perineum. When Burton yanked the dagger out, the Bedawi dropped paralyzed to his knees and stared at the crimson-edged rip in his robe.

"When the guides go behind you, the destination is death!" 'Abdullah said, wild-eyed.

The gatekeeper gave a shout of laughter and stalked up in front of them again. "Put away your pigsticker!" he said. "Follow me and fear not! No one will attack you now that you've shown yourself hard as the heart of Harar!"

When they reached the open entranceway of the palace, a huge Negro standing guard outside rammed the spade-shaped head of his spear into the dust at their feet. "*Bismillāh,*" he bellowed, "take off your slippers!"

Burton knit his brow. "Why, by Allah? We're not entering a mosque!"

"Do as I say!" the Negro answered, snatching up his spear. "You go into the palace in your bare feet or you go out of the city in your bare bones!"

Burton grumbled as he kicked off his slippers. Sherwa, being a rural Somali, was already barefoot.

"Who ever heard of such a thing?" the haji muttered. "This must be the devil's domain! Where else d'you take off your slippers but in the house of Allah?"

"Now, throw down your weapons!" the Negro said with a savage scowl.

Two daggers clattered to the dust. Haji 'Abdullah made no fuss about this second and final order, not wishing to be searched or stripped.

"All right," the Negro said, "enter in the name of Allah!"

Haji 'Abdullah, with Sherwa close behind him, stepped into an immense hall at the far end of which sat his excellency the emir of Harar, Sultan Ahmed bin Sultan Abibekr.

The sudden change in light made Burton squint for several seconds, and he stopped for that length of time to prepare his mind for the most perilous but exciting trial of all.

Two long rows of half-naked Galla spearmen stretched from the entranceway to the throne, and it was between these lines that Burton was obliged to walk. He looked at them. They stood like enormous statues, each one holding a huge spear with a head the size of a pointed shovel blade. There was no time left to think. He must now act, and act fast. He must play his role perfectly.

Burton swaggered down the hall, leering at the fierce-looking spearmen whose bestial eyes followed him every step of the way. He had a six-shooter concealed in his cummerbund, and at the first sign of excitement he intended to run to the emir and put the gun to the ruler's head. Sherwa also played his part, and played it well, so there was no immediate cause for alarm.

Burton now fixed his eyes on the emir. Sultan Ahmed, for all his notorious reputation as the devil incarnate, looked to him like a harmless little Hindu rajah. At first sight, he too was a disappointment. But as Harar was a black hole of unspeakable horrors, Burton dared not pre-judge its ruler at a glance.

Ahmed bin Abibekr was an outwardly sallow and effeminate Himyarite between twenty and twenty-five years of age. His fuzzy beard and bulging eyes, small nose and thin lips, suggested to Burton a baby-faced paranoiac. The emir's bony nakedness was covered by a flowing crimson *khil'ah* or robe of honor fringed with snowy fur, and a narrow white turban was tightly twisted around a tall red tarboosh on the top of his shaven head.

Sultan Ahmed, who was reclining on a green couch, rested his elbow on a gold-embroidered cushion from under which projected the jeweled hilt of an Indian scimitar. Arranged in double rows on either side of the emir were all his male cousins and kinfolk, the so-called court of Harar, standing with right arms bared after the Ethiopian fashion.

"Peace be upon you, O prince of Harar!" Burton rapped out with a flamboyant bow.

"And upon you peace, O such a one!" the emir uttered graciously. He then snapped his fingers and put forth a bony yellow hand.

Two black eunuchs stepped forward, seized Burton by the arms, and assisted him in bending over the emir's ring-studded claws. Ahmed turned up his palm to be kissed.

"Well, what're you waiting for?" the royal youth snapped, as the fiery-eyed stranger stood staring at his palm without touching it.

"Where I come from," Burton replied firmly, "the only thing we Arabs kiss is a woman's mouth—the one on her face and the one between her thighs."

The emir chortled. "By Allah, what guts you've got, O father of fierce eyes!" He motioned the eunuchs away with a disdainful gesture. "What did you say your name is?"

"I didn't," Burton responded, "but now I do! It's Haji 'Abdullah bin Yusef."

"Well, Haji 'Abdullah bin Yusef, and who is that behind you?" The emir pointed a finger of contempt at Sherwa bin 'Adn, who came forward to kiss his excellency's hand. Finding him handsome, Sultan Ahmed ogled the scion of the celebrated Somali chieftain to whom he recently had paid blood money. He then said, pointing to the floor, "Well, gentlemen, be pleased to seat yourselves on these cushions in front of me."

Burton salaamed, and he and Sherwa sat cross-legged.

The emir cocked an eye and knit his brow. "Why did you come here?"

Burton reached a hand into his robe. The emir squalled

out, lurching upright on the couch. Several Gallas lowered their spears and sprang at the haji. Burton gave them a leering look, curled his lips, and slowly pulled three folded pieces of paper out of his inside pocket.

Sultan Ahmed scowled and waved the spearmen away. He then signaled one of the eunuchs to step over and take the haji's credentials. Burton handed them to the chamberlain, who in turn handed them to the emir, who after a brief glance threw them down on the floor at Haji 'Abdullah's feet. His eyes bulged larger and his frown became a smirk.

"So here we have a diploma signed by the Shaykh el-Islam of Mecca, which proves you're a man of faith; another declaring you to be a Master Sufi, which shows you're a man of wisdom; and a letter of introduction from the English agent at Aden, which means you're a man of mark." The emir stopped his drawling and suddenly lashed out: "But why did you come here?"

"If it please your excellency," Haji 'Abdullah dragged coolly, "by the goodly grace of Almighty Allah I've come all the way from Aden carrying with me the compliments of our most gracious governor. Since there was no greater friendship than that which existed between the English authorities and your late-lamented sire, Sultan Abibekr, it's only natural that your humble servant as a representative of the English agent should enter Harar to see the light of your excellency's countenance and bear to you the best wishes of the *wekīl*."

While the haji poured out a smooth flow of tongue oil, the emir kept nodding and simpering.

"In the old days, O excellency, your late-lamented sire sent his vizier with a present to the governor of Aden. Now

it is the wish of our people to re-establish friendly relations and commercial intercourse with Harar."

"*Khayr, inshallāh!*" the emir hissed. "Well and good, if
Allah will it!" He then beckoned to his steward, a pug-
nosed brute with angry eyes and bristly beard, and began
whispering sour somethings into his ear.

The steward, who had been ogling Burton with canni-
balistic looks, suddenly smiled as if he loved him and made
a sign for the two intruders to stand up. The audience was
now ended.

"*Ma'sslāmeh, yā s'ādtek!*" Burton said, bending over the
emir's hand—but without kissing it.

"*Ma'sslāmeh w'Allāh yisallimek!*" Sultan Ahmed replied
lecherously. "Farewell, and Allah save you!"

"*Allāh yihhftzek! Allah keep you!*" Haji 'Abdullah repeated, bowing and backing out of the audience hall.

"*B'hhaftzillāh! Allah guard you!*" the emir's high voice
echoed.

The steward led 'Abdullah and Sherwa to a spacious
room on the other side of the palace, and a short while
later he sent them a big dish of *shabteh* or dillseed cakes
soaked in sour milk and seasoned with plenty of red
pepper—compliments of his highness the emir.

Worn out with physical stress and mental strain, after
wolfing down his dinner Burton threw himself on one of
the divans and gazed thoughtfully at the hardwood ceiling. No one could be more profoundly impressed with the
irony of his position. He had expected and prepared for
the worst, fighting overwrought nerves and anxiety. He
was under the roof of a perfidious young fanatic whose
least word could mean death, among a distinct race of
eight thousand people who detested and despised all out-

siders. He was the only European who had ever passed through their forbidden threshold, and he was the fated deputy of their future downfall.

Haji 'Abdullah had unveiled the hardhearted virgin of Harar. Already he was thinking of a new book—*First Footsteps in East Africa*—and of a new exploit, the unveiling of Isis.

For ten days Burton was so closely watched that it was almost impossible for him to put pencil to paper. He saw as much of the city as the emir wanted him to see, and what he saw of its population didn't impress him favorably. They never spoke; they only spat. A stranger and a spy were one and the same to them. Harari was a language understood only by the Hararis, who kept many a dark secret, and Harar itself was like a jealously guarded jewel.

Every evening, soon after eating, 'Abdullah and Sherwa sensed an intense urethral itch resulting in persistent erections from which they achieved no relief for several hours. At first Burton thought this irritation was the effect of their superspicy diet, but it presently became apparent they were being drugged with powdered cantharides mixed in the red pepper.

Excessive sexual hospitality made the Harari guestright a red-hot scandal throughout the Muslim world. The animal lust produced by aphrodisiacs was appeased by indefatigable Ethiopian slave girls trained by harem matrons to milk a man bone-dry with repeated coital applications of internal dynamic tension. Their extravaginal specialties included oral stimulation and manual manipulation of the male organ.

Burton received the erotic treatment for ten nights in a row. He was copulated, masturbated, and fellated. To refuse such elevation of spirit on the part of Sultan Ahmed was tantamount to insulting his excellency's artistic taste, partial or complete castration then being in order.

A dozen lithe, long-legged black beauties took turns mounting 'Abdullah on the divan. They sweated out hours of exotic intercourse with him, till his burning thirst was quenched. Each morning he remembered almost nothing of the night before. Tempest-tossed in a seminal sea of delirium, Burton was solely aware of violent waves of stormy sensation lashing a stiffly straining masthead. By this he knew they were doping him with powdered opium pills.

Sherwa also suffered compulsory copulation. But he, being a hot-blooded hopped-up Somali youth, remained actively engaged long after 'Abdullah had lost his senses in passive ecstasy. Sherwa belonged to a lusty race of inveterate opium eaters, drinkers, and smokers; and the drug's effect on his genital nerves was now more anesthetic than hyperesthetic as in uninured 'Abdullah's case. This prolonged fit of rigid frenzy so inflamed Sherwa to seek the most vigorous excitation that he forcibly analized all the shrieking slave girls.

Their last experience was a harrowing nightmare. Though half-dazed with opium, Burton heard the emir and an unknown number of rutting savages burst into the room.

"With a hundred wives and five hundred concubines," the emir shouted, "I have more muscles in my pizzle than these pigs have in their arms! *'Steghfrullāh,* look at them wallowing in beastly passion! The one beats a girl's butt, the other is mounted and mouthed! *Inshallāh,* I should have sent them beardless boys and eunuchs for bottom-bumping and member-munching! . . . Let that one alone; but this one—*lā hhowla walā qūwetilla billāhī!*—he's the bastard abortion of that fetus 'Adn bin Qaoshan, to whom I had to pay the price of blood. *Yallah!* Four of you—hold his arms and legs! Make him bend! If he won't open we'll ram home a red-hot spearbutt! That'll open him up to Satan himself! *Yallah! yallah!* Come on—all of you—lay it on good and hard! . . . Keep battering away! Keep him yelling! Push in—pound without mercy—impale him to the heart! . . . *Yallah!* Keep shaking it! Faster! harder! I don't care if you wrench it off! I want him jabbed and joggled to death! . . . Now, throw him down! Hold open his legs! Here, hand me that knife! Behold, O dog beferked and bejerked, how you lose your precious jewels! This in payment for your father's greed, your uncle's curiosity, and your own folly! First I cut off your sack— *wallāh!*—then I slice off your tassel—*ah! Ha-ha!* Ready with the branding iron!"

Burton heard wild, spasmodic screams welling up out of the hollow depths of horror. He too was wailing, thrashing his arms and jerking his legs. The slave girl squirmed in an orgasm of bloodthirst. A paralyzing, paroxysmal pain gnawed through the numbness between his legs. It shot all over his body and exploded in his brain, hurling him into a howling whirlpool of convulsions. Retching and vomiting, Burton was riven with fiery trembling. He lurched up and sank his teeth in the hellcat's breasts, digging his fingers deep in her throat as she twisted and squeezed his testicles with murderous hands.

For a few feeble seconds he clawed and clutched her, then fell back limp and senseless. In a frenzy of sadistic heat, she kept on wrenching and crushing his scrotum until the emir dragged her away shrieking.

Haji 'Abdullah fled from Harar on January 13, taking with him on the same mule Sherwa bin 'Adn. His thighs tightly bound, the Somali sat sidesaddle in front—still in a state of shock—now a eunuch.

A grinding ache and swollen testes reminded Burton of what he had read in a prophetic footnote of *Les Abyssiniennes,* a rare erotic and anthropological booklet describing the harems and harem inmates of East Africa:

> *On dit que personne sorte la ville terrible d'Harrar sans souffrant l'émasculation dans l'un manière ou l'autre, soit par amputation génital (la castration), par l'onanisme forcé et outré, ou par la torsion et la compression des testicules à la main d'un concubine éthiopien.*

(They say that no man leaves the dreadful city of Harar without suffering emasculation in one form or another, either by amputation of the genitals [i.e. castration of the testicles and/or the penis], by forcible and excessive masturbation [which allegedly induces impotence], or by twisting and squeezing the testicles [i.e. mangling and crushing the spermatic vessels], done with the hand of an Ethiopian concubine.)

Mutilation of the sexual organs was the emir's memento to all outsiders. *Hhjār zay'l-qelb Hhrār*—Hard as the heart of Harar—would always hold a grim secret meaning for one who had experienced it.

Burton later wrote in his journal:

All African cities are prisons on a large scale. You enter by your own will, but you leave by another's.

How melancholy a thing is success! While failure inspirits a man, attainment reads the sad prosy lesson that all our glories are shadows, not substantial things. Truly said, "Disappointment is the salt of life"—a salutary bitter which strengthens the mind for fresh exertion and gives a double value to the prize.

15 : The battle at Berbera

Safely he jogs along the way which "Golden Mean" the sages call.
Who scales the brow of frowning Alp must face full many a slip and fall.

Richard Burton reached Berbera on February 5. Lieutenants Speke, Herne, and Stroyan were there to welcome him with shouts and handshakes and a bottle of brandy to celebrate his success.

"We almost gave you up for lost!" Speke said, after Burton had given an account of his adventures. "Reports kept coming in that an Arab merchant had entered Harar, but was destined to die there. We all held our breaths till we heard everything was all right and that the Arab merchant had left Harar with a whole skin."

Burton laughed. "Yaas—the whole skin of my teeth!"

"Well, Ruffian Dick," Stroyan said, slapping him on the back, "where do we go from here?"

Burton gritted his teeth. "Back to Harar!"

"Jesus Christ, you must be joking!" Herne said, gulping down his glass of brandy.

"No, I'm dead serious."

"*Ha!*" Speke threw up his arms. "You're dead *period* if you think you can get away with going back to that infernal hole! Whether you know it or not, the Somali Bedouins have orders to shoot you on sight."

"Hand me a cheroot and shut up for a second, won't you?" Burton barked, slamming the palm of his hand on the folding table. "I've listened to enough shit for the past couple months. Do I have to hear it from you too?"

"You haven't heard anything but good advice," Herne said. "Why the hell d'you want to go back?"

"Never mind why," Burton said with a vicious scowl. He bit off the end of the cigar Speke flipped him, spat through the doorway of the hut, and struck a match on the tabletop. "I have a score to settle with the emir."

Stroyan chuckled. "What'd you do, Dick, leave some nigger wench back there you'd like to smuggle out? The emir's wife, maybe?"

"The emir has a hundred wives, you laughing hyena!" Burton said with the hint of a grin.

"Well, if I know you, you'll steal the lot of 'em!" Stroyan retorted. "Why I'll never forget the time you ran off with that havildar major's booboo—"

"Yes, and he nearly cut your balls off when he caught you two in bed together!" Herne added admonishingly.

Burton kicked over the table and smashed his glass against the wall. "Goddamnit," he roared, crumbling the lighted cheroot in his fist, "what's all this gup got to do with my going back to Harar? Either you're with me or you're not! If you are, we'll shake on it and look for another bottle. If you're not, I'll get the hell out o' here right now." Burton glared at each of them.

"Well, I'm with you, Dick," Speke said, holding out his hand. Burton cracked a smile and grabbed it for a hearty shake.

"What've I got to lose?" Stroyan shrugged.

"Only your empty head, which you'll never miss!" Burton chortled, pumping his fellow officer's arm.

"Don't think I'm a spoilsport!" Herne said, extending his hand. "Count me in—last but not least!"

After a brief rest in Berbera, Burton went back to Aden. It was there that he first learned of his mother's death on December 18. It was there also that he again encountered Colonel Outram.

"You can't leave well enough alone, can you? You've won your laurels—now you want funeral ferns! I'm warning you, Burton. One of these days you're going to tempt Providence a trifle too far, and it'll be the death of you."

Burton cackled. "That's something to look forward to! You'd do better to assist than to frustrate me."

Outram rapped the side of the desk with his Malacca stick. "Very well, lieutenant, you've earned carte blanche to beard the lion in his den. So you and your three pot companions wish to make a new expedition into Somaliland, but this time on a larger and more imposing scale, eh? *Bahut achchhā!* You have my permission to organize and explore. I'll draw up a letter enjoining the Somali shaykhs and the emir of Harar to treat you with consideration and hospitality. You'll want a show of strength to impress these savages, so I'll commission Lieutenant King of the Indian Navy to take you over on board the *Mahi*. She's a pukka gunboat, and she'll command the Berbera harbor till you leave for the interior. You'll do well therefore, whilst you remain in port, to select the site of your camp in a place where you can appreciate the gunboat's protection. Of course I'll accept no personal responsibility as to your safety—all this is at your own risk, y'know—but Lieutenant King shall have his orders to open fire on the town in the event of a general uprising. However, I leave it to your discretion not to make the bombardment of Berbera an inevitable eventuality."

Between 2 and 3 A.M. on April 19, Lieutenant Herne dashed into Lieutenant Burton's tent with a saber in one hand and a revolver in the other. He was clad only in his underdrawers. "Jesus Christ, Dick, we're being attacked!"

Burton lurched off his cot and pulled on his pants. "How many of 'em?" he muttered, unsheathing his sword and snatching his revolver from under his pillow. "Take a couple men with you. Go tell King to start shelling the town. That'll damn-soon scare 'em off!"

"There's no hope for that! Outram recalled the *Mahi* over two hours ago!"

"Recalled it! How d'you know?" Burton's eyes blazed in the candlelight, and his teeth were bared.

"One of the crew came ashore and said they had orders to relieve another ship."

"Another ship! What ship? There isn't another gunboat within a hundred miles o' here! Goddamnation—" Burton swung his saber and split his campstool in half. "Y'know what we are? We're sitting ducks! That bastard Outram has left us in the lurch, and that's just what these fanatics have been waiting for. Well goddamnit, we'll make one hell of a noise that even Outram can hear! How many of 'em are there?"

"The sentries say three hundred and fifty."

Burton howled with laughter. "Y'hear that, Outram? Three hundred and fifty niggers! Yaas, and I'll live to tell you and the whole goddamned world about it!" He stared wild-eyed at Herne, who was more frightened of Burton than of three hundred and fifty savage Somalis. "We've what—fifty fighting men?"

"Fifty-four, to be exact."

"Yaas, yaas." Burton jabbed holes in his cot. "Well, half to three-quarters of 'em've run away by now. So consider yourself alone. It's every man for himself, and the devil take the hindmost!"

Suddenly they heard a volley of shouts and a rush of men. Burton and Herne sprang to the entrance of the tent. As they gazed into the vibrant blackness, Herne spotted wraithy forms flitting among the braying and bolting pack mules and the piles of baggage and supplies to the left of the tent. He nudged Burton, who was waving his sword to Speke and Stroyan in the next tent about twenty yards to the right.

Like a flash, a huge half-naked Somali darted from behind the boxes and came running at Herne, who raised his revolver and fired point-blank. The yowling native threw up his war club and took a belly flop to the dust, his bowels blown out by the infidel's "thunder-and-lightning stick."

Burton cackled. "One down and three hundred and forty-nine to go!" He beckoned to Speke and Stroyan. "Come on over! We'll take a stand in my tent!"

"D'you think it's safe?" Stroyan said quaveringly.

"What—my tent?" Burton gibed.

"No," Speke answered, "our making a run for it! We're the only ones that haven't made themselves scarce around here!"

"Come on!" Burton said, waving his sword. "Run like hell! We've got you covered!"

"Well what're we waiting for?" Speke muttered to Stroyan. "Let's get going."

The two men raced out of the tent. A second later Stroyan fell flat on his face with a spear through his back.

"Look out, Jack!" Burton yelled to Speke, took instant aim, and fired. The Somali dropped over dead. "There's no getting him now," he said when Speke reached his tent and glanced back at their brother officer's lifeless body.

"Poor chap, didn't have a chance—" Speke gasped.

"We've none of us a chance," Burton said sharply. "You'll envy him if we all die a slow death!"

A sudden, horrifying outburst of ululations broke the deadly stillness.

"Jesus Christ, here they come!" Herne said.

"Get inside!" Burton said. "Keep one of the flaps open! We'll hold 'em off from here!"

The Somalis swarmed like raving-mad hornets around the tent. Herne and Speke knelt on either side of the half-open entranceway, while Burton stood between them.

"*Al-al-al-al-al-al-al-al-allāhuakber!*" They wailed the war cry with intent to terrify, dodging and darting in front of the tent and hurling their clubs and spears at the narrow opening.

Burton and Herne with their Colt six-shooters and Speke with his Deane-Adams revolver blasted a continuous barrage of hot lead into the roaring waves of on-rushing Somalis. In less than three minutes the open area in front of the tent was heaped with dead and dying bodies. Warriors having fallen thick and fast in the initial attack, the rest were now more cautious and charged only in small spurts.

Burton, being a dead shot, picked them off by the dozens. A hailstorm of javelins and longknives was ripping the canvas to shreds. Covered with cuts and scratches, Burton kept shifting and ducking as he fired and reloaded and fired and reloaded.

In five minutes they were out of ammunition, having killed or incapacitated at least a hundred warriors. A tense lull followed, during which they heard a shuffling of feet around the sides and rear of the tent.

"We'd better get out of here, and fast!" Burton said, seeing how the ripped canvas was shaking. "They're cutting the ropes. When those poles come down we'll be caught like rats in a trap. It's an old Arab trick."

"Well Jesus Christ, we're all out of cartridges!" Herne

said, wiping the sweat from his brow with the back of his hand. "How the hell are we going to get out of here?"

"We're going to cut our way, that's how!" Burton rasped, holding up his favorite weapon in Herne's face.

"Well let's get going," Speke said in a weak and wavering voice. "I don't fancy being snared and speared to death! At least we have an even chance outside."

"You two stick close behind me. I'll cut a path and you keep it clear. Herne, you follow me and chop from side to side. Speke, you follow him closely and swing any goddamned way you want." Burton patted each of them on the shoulder. *"Inshallāh!* Let's go!"

About twenty Somalis were crouching among the dead bodies around the entrance to the tent, while other dusky figures stood farther off—waiting. When the infidels emerged, the feverish warriors sprang to their feet and came at them with war clubs.

Burton plunged straight through the screaming mob, slashing and hacking flesh and bone, with Herne and Speke sabering close behind him. Blood spattered and shot out in crimson jets, speckling their faces and spraying their bodies with its liquid warmth. Burton averted the battering, bruising clubs and with vicious saber strokes cut men down like stalks of corn. Dozens fell away in terror, but a few hashish-maddened ghazis remained to harass the infidels.

"Kill the Franks who kill the Somalis!" one of them shrieked, charging at Speke with an iron-bound knobstick.

Speke parried a sharp blow that snapped off the blade of his sword close to the handle. In the next instant he was stunned and beaten down by several well-delivered shocks, then jumped upon by three drooling natives who strapped his hands behind his back and jerked his trousers down about his ankles. Speke was still in a daze when one of them, pressing the flat of a longknife to his throat, lashed out in Hindustani: "Circumcision or death, you Christian dog!"

"Mussulman! Mussulman!" Speke gasped, half-crazed with fear.

The Somali cracked a fiendish grin. He pulled Speke's foreskin and stretched it tight, then sliced it off with his razor-edged blade and stopped the bleeding with a styptic powder. Speke fainted at once. Not bothering to bandage the infidel's Islamized penis, the Somali ran off triumphant with his prepuce trophy.

Suddenly aware that Speke had somehow disappeared in the darkness, Herne called out to Burton: "Jesus Christ, they've got Jack! Come on, before they get us too! I'm making a run for the city!"

Burton turned to follow him, but in that second a naked ghazi cried "Death to you, O son of Satan!" and cast his javelin. Burton was frozen in his tracks by a rending sensation as the slender spearhead transpierced his jaws, ripping across the roof of his mouth and tearing out four back teeth. He dropped his saber and grabbed the shaft with both hands, staggering a few steps and struggling to yank it out. It wouldn't budge. Every effort to twist and pull intensified the searing, pulsating agony. Warm blood streamed down his bare chest.

Dizzy and sick at first, Burton was now furious with frustration. An explosive strength sent him charging off towards the city. None of the Somalis dared touch him. They howled and ran horror-struck from this wild-eyed, gory demon racing through the night with a lance in his jowls.

Stumbling into the fresh-water creek that purled between Berbera and the camp site, Burton wallowed in the cool flow. He was burning with fever and thirst. Faint from loss of blood, he seemed to be sinking deeper and deeper into slow-swirling eddies of unconsciousness. The harrowing, hammering pain was dying away little by little to a heated numbness.

"Dick, is that you?"

Burton opened his eyes, slapped the water, and swayed upright out of his stupor. He gagged on his own blood, which he could not swallow.

Lieutenant Herne came trudging up the creek. Behind him were several of the runaway guards.

"Jesus Christ, I thought I'd lost you—hey! what the hell—?" Herne stopped, turning pale for a second, then splashed on and dropped to his knees beside Burton. "Jesus Christ Almighty," he whistled and shuddered, "they really got you but good! And me with only cuts and bruises!"

Burton scowled, grabbing the lance with a savage groan.

All at once Herne snapped out of his bewilderment. "Jesus Christ, can't you get it out? Here, one of you—give me a hand! Hold the sahib's head while I try and pull this thing out. Steady, old man," he added, taking firm hold of the javelin, "this is going to be a bitch! Sorry there's no easier way." He glanced at the Somali. "Now hold his head still! When I pull, you pull! Ready?" The Somali nodded, his eyes big and mouth agape with trepidation as he gripped the burra sahib's head. "All right then, here goes—!"

Herne tugged once, twice, then withdrew the weapon and broke it over his knee.

"Allah be praised!" the Somali sighed, grinning broadly.

Burton hardly felt a thing, his jaws were so numb. He retched and gasped, spitting out blood and teeth.

"Jesus Christ, what ugly gashes!" Herne said, examining the wounds in Burton's cheeks. "Well, we'll get 'em washed and dressed right away; and they'll close up like India rubber."

By the gray light of dawn, Burton and Herne found Lieutenant Speke lying where he had been clubbed, bound, stripped, circumcised, and spear-pricked eleven times in the shoulders and thighs. He was still very much alive, rolling his head and croaking for water. When he cried out in terror, it was because he imagined that the lustful blacks were again fingering his penis and severing his prepuce.

While the cannibals had left long before, taking with them all of Burton's pack animals and supplies, the vultures and wild dogs were now moving in; and a sickening-sweet stench of stagnant blood and bloating bodies glutted the morning air.

Having given Speke a drink and dressed his wounds, Burton and Herne tottered over to gaze at the livid corpse of Lieutenant Stroyan. The body had been battered with war clubs, the thighs and forehead stabbed and slashed with longknives. Spearholes riddled the chest and abdomen, and a ghastly mutilation between the legs made the two men turn away trembling.

The expedition had ended before it had begun.

16 : Home is the stranger

Why must we meet, why must we part? Why must we bear this yoke of
    MUST,
Without our leave e'er asked or given, by tyrant Fate on victim thrust?

"Well, look who's coming our way!" said cousin Louisa.

Isabel looked up, and her heart nearly stopped. She dropped her book. There was no mistaking that arrogant swagger, that iron stick, and that tall wiry figure with drooping mustachios.

It was August, 1856, in the Royal Botanical Gardens of Regent's Park.

"Well, well," Burton drawled, shouldering his stick and flashing a wolfish grin. "The Mesdemoiselles Arundell, I believe?"

"Why, Lieutenant Burton, what a marvelous surprise!" said sister Blanche, holding out her hand.

The fashion was now to shake a lady's hand; but being elegantly unfashionable, Burton bent and kissed it. "Beg pardon, Miss Blanche, but it's *Captain* Burton now. In recognition of services rendered," he added dryly.

"Good to see you again, Dick," said Louisa, offering her hand. "You know, the gentlemen don't do this much anymore."

"That's because there aren't any more gentlemen," Burton smiled, kissing her hand. "They all died gallantly in the Crimea. Only the cads came home."

"But weren't you in the Crimea, captain?" Blanche teased with a frown.

"No, I'm afraid not," Burton said, shaking his head sadly. "Hadn't you heard? After the charge of the Light Brigade the War Office was looking for volunteers to save Lord Cardigan's face. No one seemed equal to the task, so I arrived in Turkey and threatened to take Sevastopol singlehanded. That's when the armchair strategists at Whitehall deemed it advisable to bite their tongues and tie me up in official red tape."

The young ladies laughed.

"Poor Captain Burton was stuffed in Turkey!" Louisa said. Burton was about to turn his attention on Isabel when Louisa added: "You know, Dick, both Blanche and I are married now."

"Well, let me be the first of the last to congratulate you!" Burton answered with a slight bow to each of them.

"Yes," Blanche said, "and we've been working on Zooie here to hook herself a husband before she ends up an old maid."

"Oh, Blanche!" Isabel blurted, nudging her sister.

Burton cackled. "A good angler is always patient and persevering! Sooner or later along'll come the sucker— er, fish—that bites her kind of bait, and she'll have him hooked in a trice." He pressed Isabel's hand in his own, then touched it to his lips. There was a devilish glint in his eyes. "Pardon my impertinence, Miss Isabel. As I said before, all the cads came home."

Isabel blushed for a second, then smiled with self-assurance. "That's quite all right, captain," she said, her rapid pulse easing back to normal. "Everyone's been after me to get married, and I *will*—when the man I want is as ready as I am." She gazed up into those dark, feverish eyes that seemed to search her through and through.

"Yaas, yaas—I'm sure you will," he dragged, fingering his mustachios. The sudden painful expression faded into a faint smile. "We're a nation already overrun with old maids, most of 'em married men."

He had changed, she thought. Not in personality, but in his features. He was still the same Dick Burton who had swept her off her feet five years ago; but he was now harder looking, more gaunt—almost gruesome. She couldn't help staring at the hideous scars on his hollow cheeks. They made her shudder, and the very thought of how he had gotten them was an ever-recurring nightmare to her.

"I think you've dropped your book," Burton said, breaking the spell. He picked it up and handed it to her.

"Oh, thank you, captain! It was awfully clumsy of me, and I didn't even notice—" She reddened, which made her deep blue eyes even more brilliant.

Blanche and Louisa eyed each other with a look of disgust. Burton wasn't paying the least bit of attention to them.

"D'you come very often to the Gardens?" he said to Isabel.

"Oh yes," she quickly replied, lest one of the others snatch him away from her, "we always come and read and study here from eleven to one. It's so much nicer than staying in the hot rooms this time of year."

"Yaas, yaas. That's quite right." He was contemplating her hourglass figure, her rich flaxen hair and peachblossom complexion. He had never known a pure white English girl. "What are you studying?"

"An old friend—Disraeli's *Tancred*—the book of my heart and soul." She held it to her bosom. Isabel was now the fair Saracen maiden, and the bold Norman knight stood before her in all his shining armor.

"Ah yaas," Burton said, beaming. "There's a brilliant gem in it—'The East is a career.' "

"Well, Dick," Louisa interrupted, "I do think we'd best be getting on. It was very nice seeing you again."

"Likewise, likewise," Burton drawled, honoring each of them with an Islamic salaam. "Y'know, Lou," he murmured roguishly as the young ladies were about to move on, "your unattached cousin has grown quite charming. I never imagined the little schoolgirl of Boulogne would become such a sweet demoiselle." He glanced over at Isabel, who pretended she didn't hear him.

"*Ugh!*" Louisa uttered, and walked away with a deepened look of disgust.

On the following day Isabel came to the Botanical Gardens alone. There she found the man of her dreams sitting on a bench and smoking a long black cheroot. He was dashing off something in a pocket-size notebook. She hesitated, which made him look up.

"Why Miss Arundell!" he said, jumping to his feet and tossing away his trichinopoly.

"Oh, Captain Burton—am I disturbing you?" She smiled sheepishly.

"Not at all, not at all!" He took her hand. "Come and sit down." He then chuckled. "You won't chalk up 'Mother will be angry' now, will you—like you did when you were a little girl?"

"Oh, heavens no! But Mother found it, you know, and *was* angry. After that I was a stricter prisoner than ever."

"D'you think she'd still mind my talking to you?"

"Perhaps not. But she'll be angry all the same."

Burton burst into laughter—a sharp, wild-animal sound that startled her. "Well that's quite a conflict!" he said. "But I recognize no man's right to interfere between a woman and her conscience, so I'll say no more on the deadly subject."

"Oh, captain—before I forget—you didn't have to throw your cigar away because of me. I'm not as strait-laced as you think. Blanche and I always used to steal Daddy's cigars and go off somewhere and smoke them. It's a sin, I know—but how exciting! When Daddy found out it was *us* and not the servants who were taking his cigars, he laughed and said we deserved a good licking for getting into such a nasty and unladylike habit. We were scared stiff at first, but then we laughed too and made him promise not to tell Mother."

Burton grinned. "Ah, a conspiracy of sin! And did he keep that wicked promise?"

"Oh yes, Daddy's a real darling! He didn't dare betray us, but I think Mother knew anyway. Her nose was always twitching whenever we got close, and she gave us a lot of suspicious looks. One time she made a knowing smile and told Daddy to hide his cigars."

"Reminds me of what I used to hear—'The beast's in liquor!'"

"We've been regular smokers ever since. Of course Blanche now gets them from her husband, while I still borrow from Daddy. I think cigarettes are more ladylike, and I hope someday women will be able to smoke them in public."

"Well, what're you waiting for? Why not start the fad? Women have as much right to smoke in public as men. It only needs someone to kick over the traces and say 'Mrs. Grundy, be damned!'"

"Oh, I wouldn't dare! What will Mrs. Grundy say?"

Burton cackled. "'They eat and drink and scheme and plod; they go to church on Sunday. And many are afraid of God, and more of Mrs. Grundy.'"

Isabel blushed. "Oh, captain, may I ask what you were writing when I so rudely interrupted you?"

"A rather rude piece. Would you like to hear it?"

"Oh, indeed I would!"

"But only on one condition."

"What's that, pray tell?"

"That you call me Dick and I'll call you Zoo."

"Very well, Dick," she grinned.

"*Māshallāh!*" he winked, pulling out his notepad. "You asked for it, Zoo, and now you're going to get it:

"If all the harm that women have done
    Were put in a bundle and rolled into one,
    The earth couldn't hold it, the sky not enfold it;

It couldn't be lighted by the sun.
Such masses of evil would puzzle the devil
And keep him in fuel while Time's wheels run."

Isabel smiled and frowned at the same time. "Why that's kind of cute—in a crude sort of way."

"*Merci, merci!* But don't ask me to explain it! I wrote it for Lord Houghton—y'know, the poet Monckton Milnes. He's an old misogynist friend of mine. Would you like a copy?"

"Oh, thank you! Yes, Dick, I would. I'll treasure it along with all your books, which I want you to autograph for me when you come and visit us at Montagu Place. And remember five years ago when you waltzed with me at Louisa's party? That was a night of nights I'll never forget! I kept my sash, where you put your arm around my waist, and my gloves. I never wore them again. Oh, Dick, I've at least a thousand questions to ask you about the last five years. They must have gone so fast for you— you did so much—but to me they seemed an eternity. I was almost ready to give up everything and go into a convent, when suddenly I realized that destiny was still in my favor—still struggling to fulfill its promise."

They met in Regent's Park every day for two weeks, strolling along the shaded walks and chatting about the years gone by.

"My reception at Oxford wasn't what you'd call pleasant," Burton said in answer to Isabel's question concerning the continentally sophisticated college boy of 1840. "I'd grown a splendid mustache that was the envy of all the boys abroad and the annoyance of all those at home.

The minute I walked in some smooth-faced undergrad laughed at my pride and joy, so I slapped his beardless mug and told him to choose his weapons. That made him and the rest of 'em laugh out of the other side of their mouths. I refused to be shaved till formal orders were issued by the college authorities. Then I threw some strong ideas at 'em on the Shaven Age of England, when her history was at its worst. After that I provoked a few professors with my Italian pronunciation of Latin and my Neo-Hellenic articulation. This lack of appreciation on my part as well as theirs led to the gate in '42. That's when I laid down five hundred pounds for a commission in the Bombay Army."

"I can imagine the frightful despair when you had to leave India just when the Sikh Wars were breaking out."

"Yaas, I seemed to have been a complete wreck—half-blind with ophthalmia, sick at heart and body. One of my Sindi friends said to me: 'What manner of madmen must you English be to leave such a paradise as England and travel without compulsion to such a pandemonium as India? It's written your days are numbered. Take my advice and go home to die.' I did what he said, but unfortunately I didn't die. That made me think I was destined for greater things. I s'pose the only success that came out of my Indian career is I was able to understand monkeys. I collected about forty of 'em, had 'em live and eat under human conditions, and learned their peculiar language. I've compiled a simian dictionary, if you'd care to see it sometime."

"Now you wouldn't try to make a monkey out of me, would you, Dick?"

"*Ha-ha!* Allah forbid! I never monkeyfy any but old maids. The young ones I lionize."

Isabel laughed. "But you know, Dick—come to think of it—if you didn't come back from India when you did we may never have met. That's destiny, they say."

"Destiny indeed! And I may never have met dear Louisa," Burton chortled.

"Oh, you don't mean that fast cousin of mine? How positively revolting! And her mother is just as vulgar—"

"Ah yaas, the 'thing divine'! That tawdry baggage of elephantine proportions! 'Left'nant Burton,' she said to me, 'Left'nant Burton, I think it my dooty to ask what your intentions are with regard to my daughter.' 'Your *dooty*, madam—' I replied, bowing the chin of doubt on the collar of meditation. 'Alas, madam, strictly dishonorable! I regret to say, strictly dishonorable!' I later said to dear Louisa: 'Look here, young lady, if I'm going to talk to you you'll need to arrange that I don't have mama's *dooty* flung in my face any more.' 'The old fool!' said she. 'How like her!'"

"How like them both! But anyway, Dick, it was Louisa who told me you could speak almost every language in the world."

Burton laughed. "How like Louisa! But let's see now. Besides all the European tongues I can rattle off Arabic, Persian, Pushtu, Turkish, Armenian, Hebrew, and all the Hindustani and a few East African dialects."

"Good heavens, Dick, how did you ever get started on such a repertoire?"

"Well, Zoo, that's a long story that started at Oxford. Sick of Greek and Latin, and knowing all the other continental languages, I decided to attack Arabic. But there was no one willing to teach me, so I began to teach myself. And how I began! I wrote the Arabic letters the wrong way—from left to right instead of from right to left. Pascual de Gayangos happened to be visiting Oxford at the time, and I thought I'd impress him with my dilettante orientalism. Well as you may know, the Don is as much an Arabist as he is a historian. He nearly died laughing when he saw me scrawling from left to right, but afterwards he set me straight and showed me how to copy the alphabet."

"But how did you ever manage to learn all those Hindustani dialects so quickly and fluently? Why I should think it would take at least a year for most people to master even one of them!"

"That's because they lack the right kind of coaching. I used to get hold of a native—preferably a woman—and have her talk to me. I followed her speech by ear and eye with the keenest attention, repeating after her every word until I acquired the exact accent and the true meaning of each sentence. I never left her before the lesson was learned—before my own speech was indistinguishable from her own—which meant I sometimes spent a sleepless night listening to and then repeating a lot of unsavory gossip. Y'know, Zoo," he added with a suggestive grin, "the *beebee* or white mem-sahib was a rare bird in those wild and wanton days. The natural result was the triumph of the *booboo* or dark mistress. When I arrived in India I found every British officer in my regiment well-provided with at least one of these Hindu helpmates. So I naturally followed suit and took to my bosom a whole harem of 'em! That's how I had an excellent first-hand opportunity of studying all the pros and cons of the booboo system. You can well imagine the cons. But as for the pros, the walking dictionary is all but indispensable to the student. She not only teaches him Hindustani grammar, but also the syntaxes of native life. It's a sad state of affairs to see this time-honored institution dying a slow death of Grundyitis. Old Clive himself should turn over in his grave!"

Isabel smiled somewhat sheepishly. "Was it when you were dallying with all those Hindu demireps that you became an ascetic Sufi and a wandering dervish?"

Burton cackled. *"Toujours perdrix!* A Sufi or Mystic works out his own salvation without the guidance of a spiritual master. The effect of such independence of spirit is to produce a reprobate of some distinction. This naturally led to my becoming a dervish and making the pilgrimage to Mecca. Ever since my return to Europe, dozens of people have been asking me if I'm the only Occidental who ever found his way to the headquarters of the Muslim faith without being recognized as anything other than an Oriental. My answer is, as far as I know, *yes.* My Eastern origin was never questioned when I entered the penetralia of Islamic life, and my position was never what renegades would call apostate."

"Well tell me, Dick, how would you now compare the two places—you know, Mecca and Harar? What I mean is, which one was the hardest to enter?"

"I'd say the most difficult place for a white man to enter is Harar. Almost any circumcised European can get into Mecca alive, but of course his chances of leaving in that condition are very slim indeed. No known European has ever passed through the gates of Harar and lived to tell about it. I had trouble enough even as an Arab! They gave me the traditional treatment given every outsider. The first white men who went to Abyssinia were kept prisoner till they died. Every white man who tried to penetrate Somaliland was tortured to death before he could reach the capital. The whole country is inhabited by a dangerous race. They're never done mutilating and murdering one another, so there's little hope they'll spare a European's life as long as they remain uncivilized in a state of tribal anarchy. Although I got a paid leave, the Government gave me no protection whatever. Still and all, I blazed a trail in that so-called Dark Continent. Now others can be guided by the light it leaves."

"You may laugh at this, Dick, but I had such horrible dreams about you. When I heard you were desperately wounded I prayed for you night and day, but they said you had cut your way gallantly through the enemy. I was so thankful to God for your safety." Burton flashed a look of surprise. Before he could say anything, Isabel touched his cheek lightly with the tips of her fingers. "Oh, that must have been awful for you. I think I felt it myself when I heard you'd been wounded."

Burton grinned boyishly, and his grin brought her closer to him in spirit. "Y'know, Zoo," he said, "the sensationalists like to picture me yanking out the javelin that transfixed these jaws, when the unromantic truth is that Herne had to extract it with the help of a terrified Somali. I couldn't dislodge it to save my skin! It destroyed my palate and four good back teeth. And as you can see for yourself, it left these two ugly scars on my cheeks."

"But Dick, how in heaven's name did you eat?"

"I didn't. In fact, I couldn't! I was on a liquid diet till I reached Aden, where Doc Steinhaeuser made it pleasant for me to chew again. That's when I decided to make a beeline for the Dardanelles and volunteer for the Crimean campaign. I thought it'd recover my spirits. I'd never been in a pukka battle, so here was my big chance. Anyway, promotions are easier won in war than in peace; and I was due for a boost. The powers that be offered me a staff appointment as captain in Beatson's Bashi-Bazouks, then training in Turkey. I licked 'em into shape and hopped on over to Constantinople with a plan to march my bazouks to the relief of Kars. That's when I broke a lance with our bad-tempered ambassador to the Sublime Porte, Lord Stratford de Redcliffe, who gained his prodigious reputation in Europe chiefly by living out of it. He called me the most impudent and imprudent man in the Indian Army. I got into official disgrace, was told to leave Turkey, and never smelled powder. So Kars fell, just as I predicted. And here I am now with only one impression of a wasted year. The man who makes warfare fatal to all engaged in it will be the greatest benefactor the world has yet known!"

"Well, Dick, I think the hardship of my life is that Mother won't let me set foot inside of it—which is naturally the only thing I long to do. As it is now, I have little better than a terribly dull slow existence. Oh, but I love solitude. I've become conditioned to it by now. I've met with people who daren't pass a moment alone. Many seem to dread being alone with themselves. Every right-minded person must think, and thought comes only in solitude. One must ponder upon what one is, what one has been, and what one may become."

Burton nodded. "Solitude is often the best society. It prepares one for the worst."

Isabel trembled with excitement. "Dick, I worship ambition! It's infamous the way half the men and women in the world live and die and are never missed, leaving nothing behind them but a tombstone. By ambition I mean men and women who have the will and power to change the face of things. Some people are a little hard on me for being the same to the fallen women as to the good ones. But those who are loudest in severity are generally the first to fall when temptation comes. Dick, I want to *live!* I hate the artificial existence of London. I hate the life of a vegetable in the country. I want a wild, roving, vagabond life. I wish I were a man. If I were, I'd be you. But being only a woman, I'd be your wife."

They were sitting on a blanket in a lovers' covert of the Botanical Gardens. Burton grabbed her in his arms. His eyes blazed with a fierce craving for her.

"Oh, Dick—" she breathed.

He kissed her hungrily, then pressed his lips to her cheeks and throat. "I want you, Zoo," he murmured. "I want you like I've wanted no other woman."

Isabel sighed, pressing him to her bosom in a desperate embrace. He could feel her throbbing ardor. "Oh Blessed Mother of God—!" There were tears in her eyes, and her face was flushed with burning emotion. "Oh, Dick—hold me, hold me close! I'm so afraid without you. Oh Mother of God! Life has no meaning—Dick, Dick, without you I cannot feel I'm a woman. Dick, I love you so much it's like a raging fever. Oh Mother of God, I can't help myself! Hold me, Dick! Oh, darling—my darling—hold me a moment more. Tell me you love me."

"I love you," he said. "Goddamnit, I love you like madness! I've carried my life in my hand to Mecca and Harar, and I've held off three hundred savages, and now I'm falling prey to a pair of blue eyes."

"Oh kiss me—kiss me again, Dick!"

"I'll kiss you till we both die!"

"What a curse is a heart! With all to make me happy, still I pine and hanker for you—my other half—to fill this emptiness. I've prayed to God that you might be mine."

"God? Hell! Pray to Satan and you'll still be mine! Love me, Isabel Arundell, and give the devil his due. Richard Burton will love you for the glory of God."

"You're a strange man, not like other men. Whenever I'm with you I'm not myself—spiritually, I mean. You make me see things in your own eyes—like a fever or a momentary madness—and when I'm alone again, I recall my own unbelief and worldly ways of thinking, and am frightened by my weakness and your dangerous manner."

"Dangerous in what way?"

"Dick, my darling, please forgive me; but I have no right to love a man who calls himself a complete materialist—who has studied almost beyond the depth of knowledge—who professes to acknowledge no God, no Law, human or divine. I'm a devout Catholic—you're an atheist—and yet I love you purely, passionately, and devotedly. There's no longer an emptiness in my heart. It's at rest forever with you."

"Then stop listening to hateful, unnatural lies. Stop being morally immoral. Do what your heart tells you. You want to live—then *live!* What are you afraid of? Are you afraid of sinning? What's sin? In the name of heaven and hell, what's sin! When has it become sinful to live, and to love? No man lives but that he loves also. What does your religion teach you but living death and spiritual hate? Listen to what St. Augustine said: 'Love, and do what you will.' He was Father of the Latin Church, and his word is—or should be—law. You say you can't help yourself. What help do you need? Love me if you will! *Live* if you will! Head straight for heaven and leave the rest of the world in hell."

"Oh my darling, my darling! Whatever the world may condemn in you of lawless actions or strong opinions— whatever you are to the world, you're perfect to me. I wouldn't have you otherwise than you are."

"Then could you dream of doing anything so drastic as to give up civilization for the rest of your life, and if I can get the consulate at Damascus, go and live there with me? No, Zoo, don't give me an answer now. It'll mean a very serious step for you—no less than giving up your people and all you're used to, and living the sort of life Lady Stanhope led. I see the capabilities in you, but you must think it over."

"Think it over? Oh Dick, Dick—I don't *want* to think it over! I've been thinking it over for the past five years, ever since I first saw you on the ramparts at Boulogne. I've prayed for you every day, morning and night. I've followed all your career, read every word you ever wrote, and I'd rather have a crust and a tent with *you* than be queen of all the world. And so I say now—yes, yes, *yes!*"

They strained in each other's arms, and their kiss was long and delirious. Gasping and sighing, she chewed his lips and tongue as he pressed to suck her breath away. Burton was tense and boiling with passion. He slipped his hand up her dress, between her smooth white thighs, where he inflamed her to a feverish ecstasy. Isabel clasped and urged him. She quivered and cried, and in a few moments their crisis was complete.

"Forgive me," he said. "I ought not to have asked so much."

"Oh my darling—oh, how can you say that? Blessed Mother of God! It's just as if the moon tumbled down and said, 'I thought you cried for me, so I came.'"

"No, I don't mean that. Your people won't give you to me."

"I know that. But I belong to myself. I give myself away!"

"That's all right then. Be firm, and so shall I."

17 : The unveiling of Isis

How Thought is impotent to divine the secret which the gods defend:
The Why of birth and life and death, that Isis veil no hand may rend.

A week later, in early September, Isabel said to her secret lover: "Mother is violently prejudiced against you. When I told her I'd been seeing you she nearly had a fit. 'He's not an old English Catholic, or even a Catholic,' she said. 'He has neither money nor prospects. What's more, the man is utterly evil and insane. I've heard nothing good of him to warrant your taking such an interest in him. I forbid you to see him!'"

Burton snorted, saying:

> "Fast by the side of Thing Divine,
> By spirit-parson fresh made mine,
> In apparition grim—I saw
> The middle-aged British mother-in-law!"

"Oh, but you mustn't mind Mother. She didn't seem to object when I invited you over as a casual acquaintance. In fact, she seemed rather impressed—as she was at Boulogne. I think you fascinated and amused and pleasantly shocked her all at the same time. And as for Daddy and my brothers and sisters—well, Dick, let me tell you— you completely magnetized them. Just this morning I heard Daddy say to Mother: 'I don't know what it is about that man, but I can't get him out of my head. I dream about him every night.' He says you have the brow of a god and the jaw of a devil."

Burton laughed warmly, then a cold look came over his face. "Zoo, there's something I haven't told you. I'm going back to Africa."

"Oh, darling—no!" Isabel hugged him with alarm. "When—when will you be leaving?"

"Not till sometime early next month, I expect. Hey now," he kissed her forehead, "you're not going to unman me with tears and entreaties, are you? After all, if I can't be a successful soldier I'll just have to keep on being a notorious explorer."

"But darling, why in heaven's name do you want to go back to that awful place?"

"For the unveiling of Isis, goddess of the Nile! My burning desire has been to discover and explore Lake Tanganyika, that fabulous Sea of Ujiji cradled by Ptolemy's Mountains of the Moon. I'd also like to learn the ethnography and study the ethnology of its tribes, and find out the export of the produce of the interior. Thanks to the influence of Lord Clarendon, Secretary of State for Foreign Affairs, the F.O. and the R.G.S. have favored me with a thousand pounds, and the E.I.C. has allowed me two years' leave of absence to command the expedition."

"Oh, thank heavens you're not going alone! I thought for a minute—"

"No, indeed not! I'm going with Jack Speke, a brave and intelligent chap. I've the utmost confidence in him. Y'know, Zoo, he suffered as much as I did at Berbera. That means we both have a score to settle with that so-called Dark Continent."

"But doesn't it make your blood run cold—you know, just the thought of facing all those horrible savages again?"

"*Kuchh dhar nahīn hai!* There's no such thing as fear. But the Hindus have another saying I like even better: 'A scorpion in a corner stings itself to death. A coward blames the gods. They laugh and let it die. A man goes forward.' I never think about being afraid. As for 'all those horrible savages,' fear of man is a feeling unknown to me; and I despise it in others. But as the Turks say, 'Of ten men nine are women!' "

Isabel was entranced. Her heart throbbed frantically, tears sparkled in her eyes, and she quivered with a thrill of mixed emotion.

"I'm in the highest spirits! How can I think of fear? Fear to me is an immediate sensation. It never troubles me otherwise. It's something you learn to live without. Believe me, Zoo, one of the gladdest moments in human life is departing on a distant journey into unknown lands. With a single effort you shake off the fetters of habit, the lead weight of routine, the cloak of care—the very slavery of civilization. In England men are slaves to a grinding despotism of conventionalities. Free of all this, man feels happy once more. His blood flows with the fast circulation of youth. Excitement gives a new vigor to his muscles. A sense of sudden freedom adds an inch to his stature. The dawn of life bursts again. The bright world is beautiful to the eye. The glorious face of Nature gladdens the soul. A journey appeals to Imagination, to Memory, to Hope—the sister Graces of our moral being."

"Oh, Dick, you make the most awful and dangerous things sound so fantastically wonderful and pleasant!"

"What can be more fantastically wonderful and pleasant than the unveiling of Isis? Zoo, I've read with greed all the great geographers and travelers of ancient and modern times—devoured every important book I could lay my hands on that treats of African exploration. From the days of Ptolemy to those of Bruce, poets and adventurers have prayed for the ultimate unveiling of Isis—for the discovery of the sources of the Nile. But for two thousand years every effort has proved fruitless. I strongly believe Lake Tanganyika, or rather the streams that feed it, is the fountainhead of the Nile. I'll wrest from that river its most sacred and jealously guarded secret if it's the last thing I ever do in life, and the glory of discovery will be mine and mine alone."

"But darling, what about Jack Speke? I thought you and he were—"

"Jack disagrees with me. He thinks the northern Nyanza lake is the source of the Nile, but time will soon tell which of us is right. At any rate, if one of us unveils Isis the other will expose Osiris."

"Is Osiris the god of the Nile?"

"Yaas, indeed he is! The ancient Egyptians held that

the surging waters of this sacred river came pouring out of his giant phallus, which Osiris excited with his own hand in a continuous onanism."

Isabel blushed at Burton's plain speaking.

"Tanganyika is situated in the unknown and uncharted center of intertropical Africa. It's never been seen or explored by any European—only Arab traders and the local tribes."

"You mean no white man has ever tried to go into the interior and find this lake you say is the source of the Nile?"

"Only one European ever attempted to penetrate the lake regions of Equatorial Africa, and he was murdered."

Isabel shuddered. "Do you know who the poor man was?"

"Yaas. A French naval officer, Lieutenant Maizan. They say the Wakamba or the Wazaramo caught him, stripped him naked, and abused him sexually among themselves. They then lashed him spread-eagled upside down to a couple of bamboos, and treated him to the slow death of a thousand cuts. It took 'em several hours to carve the poor devil up, ending with a ceremonial excision of his genitalia, when he finally died. So y'see, Zoo, that's why they call Africa the Dark Continent. Deadly jungles, incurable diseases, wild animals, savage natives. Why it's a magnificent hellhole of mystery and barbarity!"

In the warm afternoon of October 3, Richard Burton and Isabel Arundell met for perhaps the last time in Regent's Park.

"When we leave this place," she said, laying her head

on his shoulder, "you will go one way in life and I another; and who knows if we may ever meet again?"

"Have faith in your destiny as I have in mine," he said, touching his lips to her soft golden hair. "Fate alone knows the answer, will it or nill it."

"What pains me so much is that you know I shan't be allowed to receive any letters at all from you—that it's not safe for me to write often, and then say only what others might read. Oh, Dick, why does it have to be this way? Why does it have to be that Mother must never know of our love? It would cause her pain, I know—but why must I be afraid of hurting her?"

"The answer to that lies somewhere within yourself, Zoo, if you'll only try to find it. You're not a child anymore. You're a woman now, with a mind and heart of your own. You must know what you want in life and reach for it, and never stop reaching till you get it or die. So I leave you the task of breaking the news of our engagement to your people—when, where, and how you please —as it'd be impossible for us to get married till after I come back. That'll give you time to think over our affair, decide if it's worth the risk, and prepare your mother for the inevitable shock."

"Richard Burton loves me! What else do I have to think about? Oh, my darling, when you come back to me— Mother or no Mother—I'll marry you at once! It's our destiny. I know it—I feel it. We must fight and suffer for each other, but it's all coming true—just as Hagar Burton said it would!"

"Who's Hagar Burton?"

"Oh, darling, I never told you, did I? It's the most

strange and wonderful thing! As you know, Dick, I've always been enthusiastic about gypsies, Arabs, and everything Eastern and mystic—and especially about a wild and lawless life. Well, I often went into the gypsy camps near our country place and sat with them, listening to their stories and asking questions. I was strictly forbidden to associate with them, but it was my girlish delight. My particular friend was a tall, slender, handsome woman— Hagar Burton. She had lots of influence in her tribe. You know, Burton is a common gypsy name. Well anyway, I spent many a fascinating hour with her. She used to call me 'Daisy.' The last day I saw Hagar Burton in her camp she cast my horoscope and wrote it down for me in Romany."

"What prophetic pearl did she pick for you?"

"She said I'd cross the sea and be in the same town with my Destiny. Every obstacle would rise up against me. My life would be like one swimming against big waves. But she said God would be with me, so I'd always win. She said I'd bear the name of her tribe and be right proud of it. That I'd be as the gypsies are, but far greater than they. My life would be all wandering, change, and adventure. One soul in two bodies in life or death, never long apart." Isabel caught her breath. "But that isn't all she prophesied! She also said I'd have plenty of men to choose from but that I'd wait for years, because I'm destined to you from the beginning. The name of her tribe would cause me many a sorrowful, humiliating hour; but when the rest who sought him in the heyday of his youth and strength faded from his sight, I'd remain bright and pure to him as the morning star which hangs like a diamond drop over the sea. She then bade me be ever-constant—that my destiny would triumph, the name she gave me would be mine, and the day would come when I'd pray for it, long for it, and be proud of it."

"Well! *Māshallāh!*"

"That was back in 1850, just before we went to Boulogne. When she said good-bye, she called me 'Daisy Burton.' That's why, the minute I saw you there on the ramparts, I seemed to know down deep in my heart that someday you would marry me."

Isabel opened her handbag and took out a crucifix and a medal of the Blessed Virgin on a gold chain. She kissed him, then placed it around his neck. "We Catholics call this the Miraculous Medal. Darling, promise me you'll wear it throughout your journey. It will bring you back safely to me if you do."

"I promise," he said, returning her kiss. "In fact, I'll show it to you the minute I get back. But take away the gold chain! They'll cut my throat for it out there. I'll attach 'em to a steel necklace. And here, Zoo—" He reached into his jacket pocket and pulled out a folded slip of paper. "Here's a little something for you to remember me by. It isn't much, and it's rather high-flown, but still and all it's me."

She took it with trembling hands and read:

To Isabel:

Now I see a glorious hand
Beckon me out of dark despair,
Hear a glorious voice command,
   "Up, bravely dare!"
She points me to a grisly land
Where all breathes death—earth, sea, and air.

Her glorious accents then demand:
"Go, meet me there!"

R.F.B. *Oct. 1856*

"Oh, Dick, it *is* you! Darling, it's beautiful. I'll keep it next to my heart with your picture every minute of every day you're gone."

"Well, Zoo," he said after their embrace, "it's getting rather late."

"Yes, I know. And again we must say good-bye till— oh, darling, I almost forgot! We're all going to the theater this evening to see *Pizarro*. Please come with us."

"Yaas, I'll try and make it—if the pressure of work wills it." He seemed uneasy and eager to leave.

"Well, darling," she smiled, clasping his hand, "if I don't see you this evening we'll meet here again tomorrow. Good-bye, my love, and please try to come."

He winked. "Good-bye, Puss."

She blew him a kiss; and he stood and watched her walk out of sight, returning her waves of farewell with a long sad stare.

Early the next morning, soon after breakfast, Isabel ran to her room with a message crumpled up in her hand. A few moments later Blanche looked in and saw her lying across the bed, her face buried in her pillow, sobbing bitterly.

"Zooie—Zooie dear, what's the matter?"

"Richard's gone," she cried. "Oh, God, I knew it—I just knew it! I saw him in a dream."

Blanche picked up the crumpled piece of paper and read:

Isabel,

By the time you receive this I will have gone. Please forgive me. I love you.

Adieu sans adieu, mon minette.

R.F.B.

At 2 A.M. Saturday, October 4, Captain Richard F. Burton and Captain John H. Speke left London for Southampton, where they boarded a steamer bound for Zanzibar. There were no "good-byes," no *"bon voyages,"* no rip-roaring send-off.

But the two men were not alone. Their traveling companion was Destiny.

18 : The fountainhead of the Nile

Essence and substance, sequence, cause, beginning, ending, space and
time:
These be the toys of manhood's mind, at once ridiculous and sublime.

January, 1857.

Burton and Speke were heading into the heart of
Africa. They hired a crew of Swahili boatmen and several long canoes, loaded them with luggage and enough
supplies to last them at least several weeks, and then
raced into the interior.

In their tent at night, by lantern light, Burton filled his
journal with the vivid impressions of day:

> Now, while writing amid the soughing blasts, the rain,
> and the darkened air of a southwestern monsoon, I remem-
> ber with yearning the bright and beautiful spectacle of
> these African rivers whose loveliness, like that of the dead,
> seems enhanced by proximity to decay.

The hippopotamus raised his head from the waters, snorted, gazed upon us, and sank into his native depths. Alligators, terrified by the splash of oars, waddled down with their horrid claws dinting the slimy bank and lay like yellow logs, measuring us with small malignant green eyes deep-set under warty brows. Monkeys rustled the tall jungle trees; and all around reigned the eternal African silence, deep and saddening, broken only by the curlew's scream or by the breeze stirring the treetops, whispering among the matted foliage, and swooning upon the tepid bosom of the tide.

Now, the moon rains molten silver over the dark verdure of the wild palms. The stars are as golden lamps suspended in the limpid air, and Venus glitters diamondlike upon the front of the firmament. The fireflies sparkle simultaneously over the earth; then, as if by concerted impulse, their glow vanishes in the gloom of the ground.

The river is a sable streak. In the jungle, beasts roar fitfully; and the night wind mingles melancholy sounds with the swelling murmur of the stream. At times I hear the splashing of huge animals as they scramble over the shoals, struggling with loud grunts up the miry banks. Then again all is quiet. After a protracted interval of silence the near voice of a man startles me in the deep drear stillness of the night, as though it had been some ghostly sound.

Leaving the coastland creeks, Burton and Speke began their long walk of death through the seething jungles and over the searing plateaus of the Unyamwezi territory of Tanganyika.

Burton gazed with sore and bleary eyes at an eternity of plains baked and cracked like bread crust. The boiling sun sucked steam out of the bush behind him, where razor-sharp spear grass slashed his arms and legs. The jungle air was sticky and stifling. It exuded a rotten and sour aroma of vegetation and bugs, a feverish stench that never oozed above the thick mists wreathing the treetops.

Burton was aroused to emotional violence when the black monsters that were piling up on the horizon came tumbling overhead, lashing him with liquid scourges. Jagged streaks of white-hot fury ripped the canopy of heaven, and the lion-god's deep-echoing roar shook the bowels of the earth. When the drencher fled from the scorcher's glare, raw vapors arose from the soggy ground.

Burton was wrung by this reeking, sepulchral heat. The fire beneath his feet burned through the soles of his shoes like red-hot coals, sending sharp pains shooting up his legs.

From dawn till dusk Burton and Speke were bitten, stung, and harassed by swarms of flies, bees, wasps, hornets, gnats, fleas, and ticks. From dusk till dawn they were attacked by legions of mosquitoes, scorpions, ants, spiders, cockroaches, lizards, snakes, rats, and lice. A torturing thirst made the terrible sleeplessness even more terrible, for both men were racked by recurrent fever.

Night after night they were driven out of their tent by armies of huge black pismires, whose poisonous bites burned like red-hot needles. These driver ants drove the thin-skinned pack mules mad with pain. The two bwanas and their African bearers turned the tide with kettles of boiling water, but it was all they could do to keep from being eaten alive.

Within a month all the mules were dead, half of them killed by the climate and the other half torn to pieces by hungry hyenas. The porters dropped like flies, and dozens of them deserted, so that Burton abandoned all his weary efforts and anxiety about the baggage. Speke didn't seem to care anymore. So why should he? If they reached their destination with only the bare skin on their bodies, that was enough.

Trembling with weakness, Burton staggered over the sun-split earth while Speke lay babbling with fever in a creaking litter. The fiery reflected heat engulfed him in waves of delirium. He fell down fainting almost every half hour, after which one of his servants would lay a wet rag over his face to protect and revive him.

By the lurid light of a blood-red sunset, Burton scrawled feebly in his journal:

> There seems nothing left for me but to lie down and die. Before we set out, Jack told me he was tired of life—said he'd come to Africa to be killed. His wish is about to come true.
>
> We're both perfectly wretched. Every morning dawns with a fresh load of care and trouble, and every evening we know that another miserable day will dawn. But I've never given up the determination to risk everything, myself included, rather than return unsuccessful. I've undertaken this expedition with the resolve either to do or die. I've done my best, and now nothing seems to remain for me but to die as well.

Burton was suddenly forced to lay aside his writing by a weird sensation of nervous irritability. He began to shiver, then sweat, harrowed by alternating cold and hot chills. His burning eyes felt as though they would burst in his throbbing head. Icy flashes shot up his legs, followed by tearing flares of fire. His feet and tongue started to swell, and his palms and soles were aflame with tingling as if pricked by a thousand needle points. Then he saw before him the yawning pit of hell. He thrashed and screamed as three-headed hags came howling out of the steamy depths, their fangs bared to devour him. Monstrous serpents writhing in green slime hissed death to the intruder, and thundering herds of hideous were-animals swarmed to rip and claw him to ribbons. Then he soared away into limitless space, where he heard the hollow tinkling of camel bells and saw the dromedary of death trotting towards him. It was only a skeleton, but its eyes were live coals and it bellowed horrendously.

Burton gasped, lurched forward, and vomited. He fell back in a swoon, floating off on a greenish cloud. He was now partially paralyzed. His limbs seemed to wither and die. He didn't move, he didn't eat, for an entire week. During the day, numbness and extreme lassitude tortured him with anxiety and depression. But the nights were even worse. His listlessness was aggravated by lack of sleep, and a ravenous thirst threw him into fits of desperation. The convulsed mind cast off its burden of suffering in delirious dreams, while alternate feelings of being crushed and of flying away plagued him continually.

Speke, who was prostrated by anemia and remittent malaria, now began to suffer from an inflammation of the eyes that caused almost complete blindness. Drained to mere skin and bones, and nearly deaf as well, this fair-haired athlete saw nothing but through a misty veil. To purge the poison in their systems, both he and his older partner kept dosing themselves with quinine and morphine till they were able to travel again. Neither of them uttered a word of complaint. In fact, they didn't say a single word to each other for over a month.

How delicious was their escape from the reek and fetor of the river valley to the pure sweet highland air! Stagnant jungle and clammy heat gave way to cool dry slopes and fragrant tablelands. The azure was flecked with opalescent fleece, and sunbeams boiled on the quartz-quilted ridges. Burton watched storms of wild birds swirling up from the water holes, while antelopes bounded in ricochets over the plain, terrified at sight of the approaching safari.

Their greatest labor was now before them. Tottering and trembling with ague, their heads swimming and ears stunned by weakness, they gazed in despair at the natural stairway of root and rock up which they had to climb.

Speke was so faint that he needed three servants to support him. Burton, the stronger, managed with one. They struggled up long steps of loose white soil, gnarled roots, and rolling stones—past huge black boulders and wall-like sheets of grim-faced rock. Every now and then they stumbled, dropped to their hands and knees, then lay flat on their stomachs for a few moments, overcome by coughing and thirst and fatigue.

Suddenly, while they were resting, Bantu war cries rang hollow from hill to hill; and Burton looked up to see files of Nyamwezi warriors streaming like lines of black ants over the crests and down the narrow paths.

"What's that?" Speke mumbled, straining to his hands and knees. "What's that? Where's my gun?"

Burton didn't hear him. He grabbed his Colt carbine from one of the bearers and said: "Jack! For God's sake, get down behind that rock! We're being attacked!"

A clattering shower of spears kicked up the loose pebbles and gritty soil around them, while torrents of arrows crackled off the crags and went whirring into several shrieking porters.

Speke crawled to cover. "I can't see them, Dick," he stammered. "Dick, I can't see them! You'll have to hold them off yourself. Dick? *Dick!*"

"Yaas, I hear you. I can hardly see myself, goddamnit!"

Burton leveled his weapon, took a longer aim than usual, and squeezed the trigger. The sharp bark of the carbine rebounded over the neighboring heights. He had drawn a bead on the Wahumba chieftain himself, a stark-naked ebony giant with ostrich-feather headdress and bright-colored shield. The bullet smashed through hippo hide and human flesh, and the sprinting seven-footer leaped into the air and plunged down the ravine. There was a tense hush and standstill as his spiraling form and long-echoing outcry faded into the darkness far below.

Burton now heard a vibrant rumble of terror-shaken voices, and moments later all the natives had disappeared over the mountain.

By resting every few yards and clinging to their servants, they finally reached the summit after six agonizing hours. Exhausted, they fell down among aromatic shrubs to recover strength and breath. Speke was almost in a state of coma, and could hardly talk. Deafness and blindness made him look and sound like a croaking cadaver. Burton glanced behind him. The blurred view aroused a vague but poignant retrospect of severe hardships past and gone.

That evening Speke was seized with a fever fit and raving-mad delirium. He became so violent that Burton had to take away his weapons, and many of the porters deserted in panic. Bwana Speke was afflicted by the evil eye. This was a bad omen, bad medicine. Death appeared stamped upon his features. For two nights he carried on like a rabid lunatic, then came to himself and was able to advance. Burton believed that the attack had left a permanent cerebral effect, for Speke never seemed the same again. He withdrew into his shattered soul, piling up all the pieces and pulling them in after him.

On Saturday, February 13, 1858, the hundred-man safari labored up a steep stony hill bristling with thorny scrub. Speke was half-carried, half-dragged by his grunting and groaning gunbearers. Burton, using a bamboo stick for support, climbed with the added help of his servant Sidi Bombay.

Setting his numb and swollen feet on the summit, Burton glanced up and was blinded by a silvery radiance that blazed through the trees in front of him. He pointed with his stick. "What's that streak of light?"

"It must be the water you're looking for, bwana," said Sidi Bombay.

"It can't be!" Burton rasped, yanking away from his servant. Quavering with anger and anxiety, he staggered forward a few more steps.

Burton glared in dismay. He suddenly felt sick, and the tears welled up in his eyes. An explosion of rage made him a snarling savage. He smashed the stick across his knee and fell against a tree, sobbing and swearing.

"Look at it, Speke! Goddamnit, look at it! Look at what we risked our lives and lost our health for—a goddamned pisshole! Look at that great Sea of Unyamwezi! *Ha-ha!* Burton's Folly! To think I was humbuggered by

Arab exaggeration! Come on, goddammit! Let's get out of here before I kill somebody. We'll head north and explore Lake Nyanza."

"But bwana," Sidi Bombay cried, "ain't you gonna take a look?"

"What's there to look at, you bloody ass?" Burton said viciously. He raised his hand to strike the gaping African.

"No, bwana, no!" Sidi Bombay scrambled off into the trees.

Burton fumbled for his revolver. "Come back here, you dirty bastard! Come back or I'll blow your head off!"

"No, bwana, no! *Ya-a-a-a-ah*, bwana!" All at once Sidi Bombay dropped to his knees, threw up his arms, and slapped his woolly head. "*Yow! yow!* Come see, bwana, come see!" He jumped up and down, hooting and howling like a jolly ape and pointing towards Lake Tanganyika. "*Yallah! yallah!* Quick! quick!"

"What's eating that damned nigger?" Speke muttered. "He sounds like a raving lunatic! What's the matter? Where is he? What's he see?"

"Shit-eating black, I'll kill him!" Burton answered, stumbling off into the trees.

"Look, bwana, look! Behold the big water!"

The dazzling effects of fever, the veil of foliage, the shimmering heat, the garish sunlight illuminating a barely visible but lustrous thread of the water fronting the fishing village of Ujiji—all these deceptions had shrunk Lake Tanganyika's true proportions in Burton's eyes.

The whole scene suddenly burst into view, filling him with wonder and delight. Burton grabbed hold of Sidi Bombay and shook him affectionately. They hugged each other and wept, heaving sighs of relief and joy.

Sidi Bombay grinned broadly. "What a great big piss-hole, bwana!"

Burton cackled loudly. He gazed out as if ensorceled by this long-sought vista.

Lake Tanganyika lay in the lap of the mountains, basking in the brilliant tropical sunshine, as far as the eye could see from north to south. A strip of lush emerald green and a ribbon of glistening yellow sand were fringed with sedges and rushes stirred by the ripples of a vast stretch of scintillating pale-blue water sprinkled with foamy-white crescents. Towering in the background were hard-featured ridges haloed with pearly haze and sharply penciled against the glaring cerulean sky.

The smiling shores of this mighty lake seemed enchantingly beautiful to Burton after the melancholy monotony of the East African seaboard—spectral mangrove creeks, rank jungles, sun-parched plains, and black-mire flats.

Forgetting all the dangers and difficulties of the past, as well as the uncertainty of return, Burton felt willing to endure double what he had endured. He would gladly suffer all over again just for a single glimpse at what he now considered the greatest geographical discovery since that of Columbus. Here, perhaps, lay the secret of centuries—the fabulous mystery that had baffled and fascinated men of science and adventure since the days of Herodotus.

"Jack! Jack!" he said, clutching Speke's shoulder. "Look! Look at the fountainhead of the Nile! Think of it, Jack—here and now are fulfilled the longings of two thousand years! Isis is unveiled! I'm heir of the ages!"

Speke grumbled and gasped. "Look at what? I can't see! It's all mist and glare. How d'you know this is the source of the Nile? It's too small to be the source. The Arabs even said that. You heard them. They said the Nyanza is much larger. I tell you Lake Nyanza is the source of the Nile. Y'hear what I say? Nyanza! *Nyanza!* I'm not wasting any time here. This is *your* lake—this isn't *my* lake. This is *your* source of the Nile; but I'm going to find *my* source, and I'll prove you're wrong. I'm going to discover the *real* fountainhead of the Nile! Stay here if you like, but I'm heading north. I'm going to find and explore the true fountainhead! I don't need you to tell me what to do anymore. What d'you know? You don't know anything! You're never wrong, are you? You're one of those who never *can* be wrong. But I'm going to prove you are! You never admit you're wrong, but I'll fight till you do. I'll make you eat your pride! The world will then know that John Hanning Speke, not Burton, discovered the source of the Nile."

This was an anticlimax to everything. To relieve the shock, Burton laughed in Speke's face. "Go ahead and prove what you will!" His face then became appallingly grotesque, and his eyes were like those of a stalking panther. "But don't ever cross me. If you dare cross me, Speke, I'll kill you."

19 : The knives are sheathed

Never repent because your will with will of Fate be not as one.
Think, if you please, before you do; but never rue the deed when done.

While Richard Burton lay racked with fever, John Speke limped north to discover the enormous Nyanza.

For nearly a month Burton was haunted by a sinister hallucination. He kept seeing himself as two people, each of whom hated and tried to kill the other. Richard Burton clashed with Richard Burton, the one straining to strangle the other. "I hate you!"—"I'll kill you!" "Masquerader!"—"Impostor!" "You're not me!"—"Neither are you!" "*I'm* Richard Burton!"—"No, *I'm* Richard Burton!" "I hate you!"—"I'll kill you!"

These phantom struggles ended abruptly when Speke returned triumphant.

"The Arabs' tale has been proved to the letter!" Speke said with a sneer. "The minute I saw Nyanza I knew it was the *real* source of the Nile, not *your* so-called source. It's a far more extensive lake than the Tanganyika—so broad you can't even see across it, and so long nobody knows its length."

Burton stared at him expressionless. "How strange, how very strange," he drawled, "that such an imaginative inspiration should excite such unimaginative sarcasm. How utterly astounding! So I obtained accurate information from the Arabs, eh? You're damned right I did! I roughly mapped out the position of Nyanza, and you went and found it exactly where I placed it. How famously original! What is now proven is that the Arabs and my charts were correct. What isn't proven is that Nyanza feeds the Nile. Your convictions are strong, but your reasons are weak. They remind me of what Lucetta said when justifying her penchant in favor of Sir Proteus: 'I have no other but a woman's reason. I think him so because I think him so.'"

Speke was hot with fury, but being afraid of Burton he said coolly: "I'll say no more on the subject except that I'm renaming it Lake Victoria in honor of Her Majesty. As of now, my lips are sealed."

"Yaas, and I'll say no more on the subject except that Nyanza's new name is in the tritest tradition—the kind that gets a man his K.C.B."

From that moment on, not a word was uttered between them about either discovery. Late at night Burton penned in his journal:

Jack hates me. This morning he announced to me the startling news that he had discovered the sources of the White Nile. It was an inspiration perhaps.

I shall long remember my last sunrise look at Tanganyika,

enhanced by the reflection that I might never again behold it. Masses of brown-purple clouds covered the sunrise. The mists, luminously fringed with Tyrian purple, were cut by filmy rays; and the internal living fire shot forth broad beams like the spokes of a huge aerial wheel, rolling a flood of gold over the light-blue waters of the lake. And a soft breeze, the breath of morn, awoke the waters into life.

When they arrived in Kazeh—now Tabora, nearly half-way between Lake Tanganyika and the coast—Burton was handed his first packet of letters from home. As she had promised, Isabel sent him plenty of newspaper clippings and scads of domestic scandal.

"How would you like to be out in India again?" Burton said sardonically to Speke. "The bloody show's almost over by now, but it must've been a ripsnorter while it lasted—the entire native population of Bengal in open rebellion, sepoy mutinies and massacres of British officers and officials, wholesale slaughter of European women and children at Delhi and Cawnpore, then an army of retribution to restore the status quo. It's the same old story! I warned 'em a decade ago the devil's breath would soon blow over British India, for which I duly suffered. *Heh-heh* —truth may be blamed, but cannot be shamed! Now justice is served and the devil given his due. The tyrant Hogg has been deposed, all the kings of Leadenhall Street have abdicated, and the *dis*-Honourable John Company is running for his life. But what irony! One of the chief causes of this calamity, Major General *Sir* James Outram, is being hailed as the 'Bayard of India' because he clubbed his way into and out of Lucknow through a rabble rout of wogs, niggers, and pandies."

Opening the last letter, from his sister Maria, Burton learned that their father, the daredevilish Colonel Joseph Netterville Burton of the 36th Foot, had died suddenly over a year ago.

While at Kazeh, the two explorers were lodged in a dreggy cowshed crawling with vermin. The nights were damp, windy, and cold. At dawn on October 10, Speke lurched up screaming. A team of lions, tigers, and leopards harnessed with a network of iron hooks was dragging him like the rush of a whirlwind over the ground. He sat swaying on the edge of his cot, emitting animal moans and forcibly clasping both sides with his hands. "Dick, Dick!" he gasped. "The knives are sheathed!"

Burton had already jumped out of bed. "Sidi Bombay! *Yallah! yallah!* Make him lie down! Hold him still till I get the drugs."

Sidi Bombay was terrified. *"Yā bwānā,"* he wailed, eyes bulging and limbs trembling. *"Kīchyōmāchyōmā!* The fire irons!"

"A-a-ah! a-a-ah!" Speke erupted. "I'm being burned with branding hooks! Get away from me! Get away—I'll kill you!"

Sidi Bombay ran howling out of the shed.

Burton rushed over to hold Speke down. "Take it easy, Jack. The spasms'll be less severe."

Half-stupefied with pain, Speke shrilled: "Don't touch me! Get away! I hate you! I hate you! I'm sick and tired of taking orders from you! Who d'you think you are anyway? I know what you think of me. You think I'm a coward, don't you? You called me a coward at Berbera, didn't you? Didn't you! You think I fell back. You think I was afraid. You think I lost my nerve and ran away. That's why you said, 'Don't step back—keep close together, or they'll think we're running.'"

"Jack, you don't know what you're—"

"Shut up! shut up! I'm sick and tired of listening to you! My diary! Where's my diary? You took it, didn't you? You took my diary! You stuffed it away in the appendix! *First Footsteps in East Africa! Ha!—ha!* Whose footsteps? *Your* footsteps! Not *my* footsteps! No, *your* footsteps! Not *my* diary—*your* diary! You didn't even print it as I wrote it. You rewrote it all yourself. That's why you didn't have to pay for it. You didn't even pay me for my diary! You printed my diary—you used it, you used it— and you didn't pay me for it!"

"What d'you mean? I lost money over the book myself! I offered you something for the journal, but you wouldn't take it. You said it was a 'scientific grant.' Well I edited that thing as carefully as I could. It was full of geographical blunders and informational nonsense. You'd be the laughingstock of the enlightened future if I'd printed the diary the way you wrote it."

"*Ha!—ha!* I asked you to send my collection of specimens to the Calcutta Museum of Natural History."

"Which I did."

"Admit it! admit it! *I* discovered the sources of the Nile! Say it, damn it, say it! Say I found it! Why did you send my collection to Calcutta? I never told you to send my collection to Calcutta! I know why you did it! You wanted all the credit yourself! But it was *I* who found those rare plants! *You* didn't find them—*I* found them! You never consulted me about anything. You went right ahead and did whatever you pleased. You never consult

me! You always do things behind my back! You turned all
the niggers against me. That's why they insult me. They
never do a thing I say! But all your arrangements are
wrong! Everything you do is wrong, but I left all the management to you! *I* never complained! But you can't take
any interest in an exploration unless *you* command it.
Well *I* should have been the leader of this expedition! If
I'd been the leader, we'd have gone straight to Nyanza!
I discovered the fountainhead of the Nile—not you. I
can't take an interest in any exploration if I don't command it. Why should I? What d'you think I am, an idiot!
I never—"

All at once a horde of lion-headed demons and gory
green ogres began wrenching with superhuman force.
They tore out his penis and testicles, ripping off the skin
from his groins and then stripping the muscles and ten-
dons of his legs down to the ankles. With body rigid, eyes
glazed, lips protruding, Speke began to bark with a
spasmodic chopping motion of the mouth and tongue
which so changed his natural appearance that Burton no
longer recognized him.

When the convulsion had ended, he started to whine:
"Oh, mama! mama! I can't breathe! I can't breathe!
Mama, help me! I can't—mama? Mama! Mama, why
aren't you there? Hey! *Hai,* subahdar! Get those men in
line! File firing—ready at the command! Present, fire!
Hāzir, chhōrro! Hāzir, chhōrro! Dick! Dick! The knives are
sheathed!"

That was the crisis. Burton never left him. Day and
night for more than a month, scourged with pleurisy and
pneumonia, Speke was nursed by his malaria-stricken
companion.

"Go away! Leave me alone! I want to die! D'you hear me? I want to die!"

But Burton wouldn't let him. He didn't even dare to let Speke die.

After more than two-and-a-half years, a slip of paper in an envelope postmarked *Zanzibar, 20 April, 1859,* arrived at Montagu Place. The note was undated and unsigned, but it consisted of seven lines in that familiar hand:

To Isabel:

That brow which rose before my sight,
   As on the palmer's holy shrine;
Those eyes—my life was in their light;
   Those lips—my sacramental wine;
That voice whose flow was wont to seem
The music of an exile's dream.

Isabel quivered as she read it again and again, pressing it to her pounding heart. Tearfully she now knew that everything was all right. Her lover was safe, and soon he would return to her.

But at Zanzibar, still weak from insomnia and remittent malaria, Burton penned in his journal the day Speke left for England:

I hear the sounds I used to hear:
The laugh of joy, the groan of pain.
The sounds of childhood sound again.
   Death must be near!

Mine eye reviveth like mine ear.

As painted scenes pass o'er the stage,
I see my life from youth to age.
   Ah, Death is near!

The music of some starry sphere—
A low, melodious strain of song—
Like to the wind-harp sweeps along.
   Yes, Death is near!

A lovely sprite of smiling cheer
Sits by my side in form of light.
Sits on my left a darker sprite.
   Sure, Death is near!

The meed forever deemed so dear,
Repose upon the breast of Fame,
I did but half while lives my name.
   Come then, Death, near!

Where now thy sting? where now thy fear?
Where now, fell power, the victory?
I have the mastery over thee.
   Draw, Death, draw near!

20 : Return of the stranger

But we? Another shift of scene, another pang to rack the heart.
Why meet we on the Bridge of Time to 'change one greeting and to part?

On Sunday afternoon, May 22, Isabel sat daydreaming in the anteroom of her sister's West End home when the jingling doorbell made her jump.

The butler answered. "Mrs. Pigott is out right now, sir, but she'll be back for tea if you'd care to wait."

In that second Isabel heard a sharp, resonant voice that thrilled her to distraction: "Yaas, well I didn't come to see Mrs. Pigott. I came for Miss Arundell. Is she here?"

"Dick! Oh, Dick!" Isabel sprang to her feet.

Burton shoved the butler aside and rushed into her arms.

"Oh, Dick—my darling, my darling—" she sobbed, hugging him desperately.

Burton stroked her soft golden hair, touching his lips

tenderly to her ears and neck. They kissed in passionate hunger.

"Here," he said, pulling out his handkerchief, "let me dry those tears. Now then, give us a great big smile! 'See, the conquering hero comes! Sound the trumpets, beat the drums!' *Ha-ha!*" He jerked his head. "Let's get out of here."

"But Blanche—"

"The devil with Blanche. Come on! I told the jarvey to wait." Burton took her by the arm and led her out the door. Isabel was still in a daze. He helped her into the cab and said: "Drive about!"

"Where?" the cabby blurted from above.

"Anywhere!"

The Cockney shrugged. "Righto, guv'na!"

Burton climbed into the cab and slipped his arm around Isabel's waist.

"Oh, Dick," she sighed, laying her head on his shoulder, "I think my heart's stopped." Isabel was stunned with joy. "Darling, what a wonderful shock you gave me! I didn't even know you were here! I feel like one coming to after a fainting fit or a long dream. Oh, Dick, when did you get back?"

"I landed yesterday. Came straight to London to find you. Look!" He reached into his shirt and showed her the chain around his neck. Still attached were the crucifix, medal, and a silver locket containing her picture. "I wore it all the time I was in Africa," he smiled.

"Oh my love," she said, kissing him, "I told you it was a Miraculous Medal. It brought you back safely to me." She took his hand and pressed it against her bosom.

"Do you feel it, darling? It's the locket where I keep your picture and the poems you wrote for me. I wear it always next to my heart."

"And what a heart! Why it's beating like a drum!"

"Oh, Dick, this is all a fantastic dream! Who has ever been so happy in reality as in imagination? Oh, darling— darling. You were in my every thought and dream. I'm so proud of you, I can't express what makes my heart so wild with love. I prayed night and day that God would help you now and always, and bring you back safe and sound."

"I think that but for you I would've died out there. I want to cry, but I can't."

Isabel gazed at him with moist eyes. Burton's jet-black hair was streaked with gray. She bit her lip, and the tears trickled down her cheeks. The yellowish skin of his cadaverous face was etched with the anguish and anxiety of nearly three years. His shrunken lips and haunting eyes told her of his torment. He was like a living corpse, able to limp but a few moments before his emaciated body collapsed.

"I entered Africa at a fatal season when the wet monsoon makes it a hotbed of malaria, but I was tied by scanty means and a limited leave. It was neck or nothing, and I determined to risk it. So I went into unknown territory without any money, without armed support, without even the bare necessities of life. I led the most disorderly caravan that any man ever gathered together, but I discovered the Tanganyika lake. I brought home enough information to smooth the path of all who choose to follow. I opened the line to Englishmen, and they have but to follow me. What Africa needs is an honest man at the head and plenty of machinery, but she won't get what she wants now."

"But why, darling? What's the matter?"

"What's the matter! This's what's the matter! The F.O. and the R.G.S. gave me the cold shoulder. The Indian Army brought me under the reduction. I'm almost penniless, only a few friends left. Speke's the hero of the hour. Zoo, I swear to God! I think if it weren't for you I'd die— just shoot myself in the head."

"Oh, darling, no! You mustn't think that way. I know you love me—and I can't express how deep and pure my love is for you—but you have so much more to live for than for me. Think of what you've done! Oh, Dick, my dearest—no man has ever done in all his life the things you have done in only a decade. And darling, you know, they say that sometimes when we think our hopes are shattered God is granting us some extraordinary favor. You must believe this, Dick, with all your heart."

He smiled and hugged her tighter, brushing the tears from her cheeks.

Isabel kissed him. "Oh, my darling, I've never felt closer to you—never felt the strength of my love as I do now. No matter what has happened or will happen—had you been ever so unsuccessful, had every man's hand been against you—you're still my earthly god and king, and I could kneel at your feet and worship you. I feel so proud of you, dearest, I like to look at you and think— *You're mine, and there's no man on earth the least like you.*"

Burton stared at her for a few seconds, then he covered his face with his hand and wept. "Zoo, why? Why did I do all these things? What was I trying to prove? That I'm more of a man than other men? That I can do what no other man can do? Why did I leave you, Zoo? I must be mad. I drove Jack insane. I pushed him too far—I know it. He couldn't take it, so he cracked. He just fell apart, all in little pieces. Zoo, I tell you I made him crack. And that's what I'm afraid of. I'm afraid of what I might do to you. I've always been afraid that way—down deep, almost unknowingly. Yaas, I see it all now. I'm a dangerous man. I destroy everything and everybody that comes into my life. That's why I'm more like a wild animal than a human being. I can't be tamed—I *won't* be tamed—and that's why I can't stand civilization. If I have to live with the things I hate they'll have to lock me up in a cage or shoot me once and for all!"

"Oh, Dick, how can you say those awful things? You frighten me when you talk that way. I don't care what you think. You're not a wild beast—you're an extremely sensitive and intelligent human being. And that's the whole trouble. That's why you seem so out-of-place in our so-called civilized society. We're really nothing but brutes in disguise, and you expose us for what we are. You say the very things we never dare to say—the things we're afraid even to think, lest we give ourselves away to one another. You can do things no one else can do. You know, you see, you understand things that are far beyond us all. You're a hundred years ahead of your time. Oh, Dick, can't you visualize yourself as you can the seemingly hostile world that won't accept you for what you are? All these years you've been looking for love, trying to prove yourself a man capable of love. Richard Burton, you have a wondrous capacity for love. Why do you run

from it? Why are you afraid of it? Do you think it will unman you if you dare to express it? Be a stranger to the
world—the world couldn't care any less about you—but
please don't shut me out of your heart. You've been hurt
many times, I know. People have hurt you, but they don't
matter anymore. The only thing that matters now is the
love that binds us together as one—the love that has made
you a spiritual part of me."

"Perhaps you're right. I want to think so, Zoo—goddamnit I do!—but it's hard to drive things out of your
memory. Y'know, when I was in Sind I met a lovely Persian girl. I worshiped her, and she returned my affection.
I would have married her and brought her home with
me, but she died suddenly of cholera. A beautiful bud
plucked and crushed just before the bloom of life. For
some years I couldn't bear to think of it without the
tears coming to my eyes and a swelling of terrible emotion in my throat. For a long time it was like an open
wound irritated by the salt of memories. I suffered fits of
depression. The thought of her preyed on my spirits. I
had to run, and keep on running, if only to forget. When
we dare to be happy—when we dare to love and be
loved—Fate steps in and with one fell swoop snatches us
out of our little dreamland and drops us back into bitter
reality, that terrible loneliness we try to live with."

"Yes, but there's always something that keeps us going—
some hope, some dream, some ambition to help fill the
void. I feel so alone, yet I'm so full of faith! Oh, Dick, if I
could only go through life trusting one faithful heart and
pressing one dear hand. Is there no hope for us—no pity
for so much love? I can laugh, dance, and sing as others
do; but always there's a dull gnawing at my heart that

wearies me. Sometimes we feel a want of love and a want to love with all our strength. There's no man capable of receiving this at the time; so we accept the love of others as a makeshift, an apology, to draw our attention from the painful feeling, and try to fancy it as love. How much in this there is to fear!"

"Fear. *Ha-ha! Kuchh dhar nahīn hai*—There's no such thing as fear! Why do we fear? What are we afraid of? Ourselves, or others, or both? Who knows! Who cares! Why rack our brains with such dangerous nonsense? Let's live—and love!"

For nearly a year Burton and his publisher worked on the manuscript of his monumental two-volume classic, *The Lake Regions of Central Africa*. He and Isabel met in Regent's Park for an hour or so almost every other day, and their conversation drifted off and on from John Speke to marital plans.

"During Jack's delirium he let out all his little grievances of fancied wrongs of which I hadn't even the remotest idea."

"What wrongs are these, darling? I don't understand. What did he say?"

Burton told her, then added: "I can't tell how many more things I'd unconsciously done. And what made things worse, I crowned it all by not accepting his loud assertion that *he* had discovered the sources of the Nile. Y'know, Zoo, I'd have never known he was pondering these things in his heart if he hadn't raved them out in delirium. He's always been secretive and rather sneaky— keeping things to himself now, and then complaining later. Behind all that blond hair and blue eyes there's an immense

fund of self-esteem so carefully concealed that few seem
to suspect it."

"But how could he be so mean? Why if it weren't for
you, he wouldn't even be where he is today. He'd be dead!"

Burton laughed grimly. "Jack told me when we left
Zanzibar that he was tired of life and was going to Africa
to dig his own grave. He'd have succeeded if it had not
been for me! Poor Jack. Having been unaccustomed to
sickness, he could neither endure it himself nor feel for it
in others. He took pleasure in saying unkind, unpleasant
things while both of us lay in pain. I was attacked by
fever twenty-one times. I suffered temporary paralysis,
deafness, and partial blindness. With an ulcerated jaw I
couldn't eat, only drink, for nearly a month. I should've
been dying, but I was keeping Jack alive instead. I didn't
have time to die. Saving his life must've saved mine. But
let me tell you, Zoo—he didn't lift a finger to help me.
Not once! Strange, but in all my fever fits and for hours
afterwards I had a queer feeling of divided identity. I
never ceased to be two persons who thwarted and opposed each other. And I also thought I was able to fly!"

"How ominous! Well, darling, I read those articles of
his in *Blackwood's;* and I was never so angry in all my
life. According to him, *he* was the head of your expedition
at Berbera, *he* gave all the orders, *he* was the first to turn
out when you were attacked, and no one but *he* had the
courage to defend himself."

"It's hardly worth-while contradicting. It's obvious that
expedition could only have been commanded by a man
who knows Arabic and some of the other African languages of which he's perfectly ignorant. But that's like his
great inspiration. He put forth a claim no geographer in his

right mind can admit—a claim so weak and flimsy that no geographer has yet taken the trouble to contradict it."

"He's just jealous, that's all. He'll never be the man you are, and he knows it. Have you heard all those nasty rumors he's been spreading about you—that you're a murderer and a thief, and that you never paid the porters?"

"Yaas, yaas. I've heard 'em all, including a few that don't bear repeating. Those are the ones that originated in India, where they called me the 'white nigger.' As far as our porters were concerned, there wasn't a soul to stand by Jack and me except ourselves. Had anything happened we'd have perished for sure! When we were ill they mutinied and deserted, then came back to cause trouble again. They didn't do a damned thing but steal and lose our goods. Not a one of 'em would work. That's why I had to keep buying and bartering for pack animals at every Arab settlement we reached. When I asked for water, they refused to get it. I had to threaten 'em with my gun if I wanted a drink. When we arrived in Kazeh they all went on a rampage and raped every man, woman, and child they could lay their hands on. They were like a pack of wild dogs. They exposed their genitals and copulated right in the open streets. Then, after all these trials and tribulations, I had the unfortunate honor of encountering our new consul at Zanzibar, Captain Christopher Rigby. Dear Kitty! Y'know who he is? Sir James Outram's fair-haired boy, John Company's protégé *par excellence*. He's one of the rogues who ran me out of India—the greenhorn griff they assigned as chief interpreter in place of me. The very day I arrived in Zanzibar he began badgering me about not paying the porters all the money they expected. And how did he find that out? Why none other than John

Hanning Speke lodged a complaint against me at the consulate in behalf of 'those hateful niggers,' as he loved to call 'em. Well, I told Rigby and Speke they could both go to hell before I'd pay a penny more to that mob of dissipated drones. Then, adding insult to injury, either Rigby himself or someone connected with the consulate deliberately mislaid the manuscript of my book on Zanzibar because it contained some unsavory criticisms of white supremacy there."

"Oh, Dick, how can men be so cruel?"

"It's the law of the jungle, my dear—kill or be killed. Being too weak to move, I couldn't leave with Jack. But he went with the first steamer out of Zanzibar. I said when we parted: 'I'll hurry up, Jack, as soon as I can.' Still we were to all appearances friends. And the last words he ever said to me were: 'Good-bye, old fellow. You may be quite sure I shan't go up to the R.G.S. till you come to the fore and we appear together. Make your mind quite easy about that.' On May 9—the very day after he returned home—Jack called on Sir Roderick Murchison, told him he'd discovered the sources of the White Nile, and set afoot the scheme of a new exploration. When I reached London on the twenty-first I found the ground completely cut from under my feet. In less than a week Jack had lectured before the R.G.S., had become the toast of the town and the lion of London society, and had been given the sum of two thousand five hundred pounds—fifteen hundred more than I got—to go to Africa at the head of a new expedition. I was given the cut direct."

"But why, darling? It was as much your expedition as it was his. Besides, it was your project and you did three times more than he did."

"You ask me why? Old Murchison hates me, that's why. He has done me the honor of not honoring me. My own long-cherished plan of entering Africa through Somaliland, landing at the Arab town of Mombasa, was dismissed as unworthy of notice. Jack in those *Blackwood* articles assumed the whole credit to himself, saying he did all the astronomical work and taught me the geography of the country, which makes me laugh."

"You weren't even invited to take part in the new expedition, were you?"

"No, *'lhhamdulillāh!* Jack chose to advantage Captain James 'Dryasdust' Grant, that old young man who won a V.C. at Lucknow. He's a perfect foil for Speke."

"What do you think of him now that all this has happened? I remember you used to speak very highly of Speke."

"*Ha-ha,* yaas, I did. Jack's one of the bravest fellows in the world. If he has a fault it's overweening vanity, and being so easily flattered. In good feminine hands he'd be the best of men. Let him alone. He'll be very sorry some day, though that won't mend my case." Burton drew a slip of paper out of his jacket pocket and handed it to Isabel. "These are the sentiments of a lone traveler."

She read:

I have built me a monument stronger than brass
    And higher than the Pyramids' regal site;
Nor the bitterness shown nor the impotent wind,
    Nor the years' long line nor the ages' flight,
        Shall e'en lay low.

Not all shall I perish; much of me
    Shall vanquish the grave and be living still

When Lord Macaulay's Zealanders view
  The ivied ruin on Tower Hill,
    And men shall know

That when Isis hung in the youth of Time
  Her veil mysterious over the land,
And defied mankind and men's puny will,
  All that lay in the shadow my daring hand
    Was first to show.

"There's only one man in all the world who could be master of such a spirit as mine," Isabel said when they discussed marriage. "People may love a thousand times, but the real sacred fire only burns once in one's life. Perhaps some feel more than others, but it seems to me this love I bear for you is the grandest thing in the world and worth all the rest put together."

"Then what are we waiting for? We love—now let's live!"

"They say it's time I married. Perhaps it is. But it's never time to marry any man one doesn't love. I know I love you—and yet do I? How certain can I be? You may be a delusion of my brain. But how dull is reality! What a curse is a heart! With everything else to make me happy I can't help longing for you, my other half, to fill this void. I feel as though I'm not complete without you. Is it wrong to want someone to love more than one's family and friends? What will my life be alone? They point out all the matches I might make if I took the trouble, but the trouble I will not take. I have no desire to be a nun. I don't consider myself good enough to offer to God. God created me with strong passions. God has given me food for hunger, drink for thirst, but no companion for my loneliness of heart—till I met you. I can't bear to separate myself from all thought of you. Neither do I expect God to work a miracle to make me happy."

"What d'you mean? Are you the one who's now afraid? If so, why?"

"Darling, try to understand. Mother is ill—you know that. Being the first child, I've always been her favorite. She's frightfully possessive, I know, but she can't help herself. Dick, she idolizes me. She always did. I'm her 'perfect daughter,' her 'darling Zooie.' She's grown worse in the past few years, but it's her illness. She's deathly afraid of losing me. How can I go against her, knowing these things? It would kill her, I know."

"How d'you know? How can you be sure she's what you say she is—'ill'?"

"Dick, she's my own mother! I, if anyone, ought to know whether or not she's—"

"Yaas, yaas. And what did she say?"

"She said you're the *only* man she'd never consent to my marrying. 'I'll forbid it to my dying day,' she said. 'I'd rather see you in your coffin than be the wife of that blackguard Burton.'"

He howled with laughter. "God bless 'er, she's a woman half-after my own heart—stubborn as a mule!"

"Sometimes I think I'm not half grateful enough to my parents—that I don't do half enough for them, considering what they are to me. Although we're not wealthy, what do I lack? What kindness do I not receive? Yet I seem in such a hurry to leave them. Oh I know I'm not a child anymore. I'm twenty-eight years old, practically an old maid. But what can I do? I'm destined to you by an everlasting love, and yet I'm also duty-bound to Mother. There's almost nothing I wouldn't do to add to her comfort, and it would grieve me to the heart to forsake her, and yet if I knew for certain I'd never have my wish of being wedded to you I'd rather be dead right now than go on suffering any longer. So how can I reconcile all these things in my mind? I'm miserable, afraid to hope, and yet I dare not despair when I look at you, my darling, and when I know the enraptured state of my heart."

"What can I say, Zoo? It's all in your hands now. Either you marry me or you marry someone else."

"Oh, Dick, my dearest—believe me when I say I so love and care for you I'd never have the courage or desire to take upon myself the duties of married life with any man but you. I've seen so much of married life—husbands so unjust, so selfish and provoking—and I've always felt I could never receive an injury from any man but you without everlasting resentment."

"Perhaps you should never marry. And the more I think of it, perhaps I shouldn't either. It might never succeed. That would only mean greater misery. No, Zoo, consider it for the common good if marriage isn't in the stars for us. And if it isn't—if we never marry—I'll then know Fate brought us together to decide that for each other."

"Dick, my sweet love, believe me—if you and I never marry, God will cause us to meet in the next world. We cannot be parted. We belong to each other. Despite all I've seen of false, foolish, weak attachments—of unholy unions—still I believe in the one true love that binds a woman's heart faithful to one man in this life and, God grant it, in the next. How worthless I'd be to any other man but you! I could never love anyone who wasn't daring and spirited. I always feel inclined to treat the generality of men just like my own sex. I believe I've now as much excitement and change as most unmarried women, and yet I find everything so frightfully slow. I long to rush around the world. I feel as though I'll go mad if I remain at home much longer. What others dare I can dare. And why shouldn't I? I feel that we women simply are born, marry, and die. Who misses us? Why shouldn't we have some useful, active life? Why—with spirit, brains, and energy—why are women to exist upon worsted work and household accounts? It makes me sick, and I will not do it!"

21 : The city of the saints

Ah me! my race of threescore years is short, but long enough to pall
My sense with joyless joys as these: with love and houris, wine and all.

In the spring of 1860, when Richard Burton's unique *Lake Regions of Central Africa* was published, he and Isabel were still debating the problem of marriage.

"Daddy doesn't object in the least. In fact, he's awfully fascinated with you. You know how much he likes you. He's always having those dreams about you."

Burton chortled. "Yaas, but what about your poor mother—the nightmares she must have!"

"She still refuses to hear anything good about you. She says the Arundells are staunch old English Catholics while the Burtons have no religion at all, and she says everything you speak and write shows you to be an agnostic. 'Richard Burton is not a Christian and has no money.' That's all I ever hear. She's always repeating those horrible stories they tell about you—that you've killed men in cold blood, that you're terribly vicious and immoral— but I know all these things are lies, and I tell her so, and anyone else who repeats them—I don't care who they are."

"I hope you haven't been fighting with your mother over me!"

"Well, we've had a few bitter words between us. But since she believes herself to be fair and logical in every way, and since she's only interested in my present welfare and future happiness, I forgive her and say as little as possible."

"And what little is that, may I ask?"

"I told her I was fighting for my whole future life and my natural destiny—that I'd waited for nearly ten years, and that I'd sooner die than lose the one who makes my life worth living."

"Well then, we'll just have to take the law into our own hands. Since we can't get your mother's consent, we'd better marry without it."

"No—no, that won't do. I can't bear the thought of going against Mother. I'm afraid it might kill her."

"Yaas, well you and your mother certainly have one characteristic in common. You're both as obstinate as mules."

There was painful silence for a long while after that.

A tap at the door one warm April morning brought Isabel an ominous envelope. With a deep-drawn breath she opened it, took out the note with trembling hands, and read till the tears streamed down her cheeks:

Isabel,

I'm off to Salt Lake City, and shall be back in December. Think well over our affair, and if your mind is then made up we will marry. Choose between me and your mother, to marry me if you will. If you haven't the courage to risk it, I'll go back to India and you'll never see me again.

Think about it. *Adieu sans adieu.*

R.F.B.

Isabel ran to her room and cried herself sick.

Standing on a promontory overlooking a vast desert valley, Burton pointed to the Great Salt Lake glimmering in the fiery sunlight and said gravely: "Water, water, everywhere!" He then pointed to the City of the Saints, baking in the dry crisp heat: "But not a drop to drink!"

Brigham Young, who loved a joke on the Mormons as much as he loved his two-dozen wives, chortled with equal gravity.

It was August, 1860.

Burton was decked out in buckskins tucked into U.S. Army boots, an old English shooting jacket, and a shabby black slouch hat. A bowie knife stuck in the belt that held his two Colt six-shooters, and he puffed and chewed away on a long slender Havana.

"Mr. Young, just look at me—a poor unmarried man. I've come all the way to Salt Lake City looking for a wife, but now I find there are no wives to be had—all the ladies having been snapped up by the Saints."

Brigham Young smiled leeringly. The governor of Utah territory and chief prophet of the Church of Jesus Christ of Latter-Day Saints was a big, cold-blooded son of the soil dressed in black frock coat, black trousers, and a black stovepipe hat. "Haven't you gotten at least one proposal?" he said, stone-faced. "Why I thought I sent a—"

"Ah, indeed you did, Mr. Young! A lovely child, but not quite to my taste. On being refused, it seems she spread the rumor it was the other way around—like a certain Miss Baxter, who refused a man before he axed 'er!"

The middle-aged spiritual leader of Mormondom chuckled dispassionately.

"Y'know," Burton drawled, gnawing his cigar, "I've traveled several thousand miles just to see a community that's sensible enough to permit polygamy. Mormonism is the only Western religious and social order that practices a plurality of wives. I'm quite familiar with the custom in the East, but I know next to nothing about your particular system. Perhaps you'd be good enough to make me a convert, so I can study your society."

Young eyed him in his usual unaffected manner. "You mean to say you'd like to join our colony and become a convert to our faith?"

Burton nodded, a sharp glint in his eyes.

Young smiled and shook his head. "No, captain. I think you've done that sort of thing once before."

Before leaving the Land of the Saints, Burton dashed off a letter to his old friend Dr. Norton Shaw, secretary of the R.G.S.:

Salt Lake City
Deseret
Utah Territory
Sept. 7

My dear Shaw,

I reached this place about a week ago and am living in the odor of sanctity—a pretty strong one it is too—apostles, prophets, *et hoc genus omne.* In about another week I expect to start for Carson Valley and San Francisco. The road is full of Indians and other scoundrels, but I've had my hair cropped so short that my scalp is not worth having.

Can you put my whereabouts in some paper or other, and thus save me the bother of writing to all my friends? Mind, I'm traveling for my health, which has suffered in Africa, enjoying the pure air of the prairies, and expecting to return in a state of renovation and perfectly ready to leave a card on Muata Yanoo or any other tyrant of that kind.

Meanwhile, ever yours,
R. F. Burton

22 : The marriage of Haji 'Abdullah

Another boasts he would divorce old barren Reason from his bed
And wed the Vinemaid in her stead. Fools who believe a word he said!

Richard Burton arrived in London after Christmas. He sent word to Isabel that he wished to see her at once. They met at the usual spot in Regent's Park.

"I've waited five years for you," he said to her after they had kissed and embraced. "The first three were inevitable on account of my journey to Africa, but the last two were not. Our lives are being spoiled by the unjust prejudices of your mother, and it's for you to consider whether you haven't already done your duty in sacrificing two of the best years of your life out of respect to her. If once you really let me go—mind, Zoo—I'll never come back. Why? Because I'll then know you haven't got the strength of character that *my* wife must have. Now, you must make up your mind to choose between your mother and me. If you choose me, I'll stay and we'll marry. If not, I'll go back to India and then on to other explorations; and you'll never see me again. Is your answer ready?"

"Quite," she said sharply. "I'll marry you three weeks from today, let who will say nay."

Burton gave a shout of delight—"*Māshallāh! Ha-ha!*" —and grabbed her into his arms. Isabel nearly fainted when he sucked her breath away with a savage kiss.

She caressed him and said: "Mother is still obstinate as a mule, but I've worked all my mulishness out of me. I'm almost thirty years old, and can no longer be treated as a child."

"Good girl!"

"I went straight to Mother and Daddy the minute I got your message, and you know what I said?"

"No," he replied with a wink and a kiss on the forehead. "What did you say?"

"I said, 'Richard Burton and I are engaged to be married!' "

"Indeed! And what did your father say?"

"He said, 'I consent with all my heart if your mother consents.' "

"And your mother said—?"

" 'Never!' "

Burton let out a howl of laughter. "And what did you say to that?"

"I said, 'Very well then, Mother! I can't sacrifice our two lives to a mere whim of yours, and you ought not to expect it, so I'm going to marry him whether you like it or not. No one turns away from real happiness, unless they're out of their mind. My heart and affections are my own to give. I rob no one. I was born for love. Even if you had cast me out of the house, if all society had tabooed me, if I'd been forbidden to go to Court—it wouldn't have kept me from him. He is my destiny. I'd rather have a crust and a tent with him than exchange places with the Queen. I love him, I need him, I want him. I'm going to marry him—will it or not—so don't torture yourself a moment more. You cannot fly in the face of God, nor can I.'"

Burton cackled. "You and your mother are both gifted with the noble firmness of the—"

"I know! Don't say it." She pecked his lips with her own. "You know, darling, I asked all my brothers and sisters; and they said they'd receive you with delight. Mother then offered me a marriage with Daddy and my brothers present, and she and my sisters not. I felt that would be a slight on you, a slight on your family and a slur on me—which I don't deserve, nor do you—so I refused it. Last night I went to Cardinal Wiseman and told him the whole story as it now stands. He asked me if my mind was absolutely made up, and I said 'Absolutely!' Then he said, 'Leave the matter to me.'"

"Yaas, he asked me to call on him this evening. Wiseman's an old friend of mine, y'know. Before I went to Africa he gave me a special passport recommending me to all the Catholic missions in wild places throughout the world."

"Oh, Dick, wasn't that wonderful of him! When he told me about it I nearly collapsed with joy. I never knew that you and he were such good friends. He's a wonderful man, isn't he? He's been my confessor all my life. Oh, darling, it'll make things so much easier for us—your being old friends and all."

"Yaas, I know. That's what I call Fate. It gives you a little more than you least expect."

"More than your greatest expectations! My only regret is that I'm bringing you no money."

"That's not a disadvantage as far as I'm concerned! Heiresses always expect to lord it over their lords, and I couldn't stand two husbands in the house."

"Oh, Dick, my dearest love—I'm so excited it makes me shiver all over. Let's make plans immediately."

"Well, for one thing we'll have no show. As far as I'm concerned, a grand marriage ceremony is a barbarous and indelicate exhibition."

"I couldn't agree more! Darling, we'll have a quiet little wedding all to ourselves and only our closest friends. If you wonder why I've set the date for three weeks hence, it's because I want to be married on Wednesday the twenty-third of January. It's the Espousal of Our Lady and St. Joseph."

"No, that'll never do. Wednesday, the twenty-third, is one of my unlucky days."

"Then let it be on the Vigil, Tuesday the twenty-second."

"The twenty-second it'll be! Now let me make one stipulation. Zoo, I want you to give me your solemn promise that if I should die before you, no Roman Catholic priest shall be secretly or otherwise introduced into my death chamber."

"But why—?"

"Never mind why. D'you understand? No Catholic priest at my deathbed, either surreptitiously or otherwise."

"Yes, I understand."

"Now promise."

She crossed herself. "I promise."

That evening Burton called on Cardinal Nicholas Wiseman in his quarters at the Warwick Street Bavarian Catholic Church.

"Richard," he said, "I want you to give me three promises in writing. *One,* that Isabel shall be allowed the free practice of her religion. *Two,* that if you and she have any children they shall be brought up as Catholics. And *three,* that you and she shall be married in the Catholic Church."

"Practice her religion indeed!" Burton snapped, signing the pledge without a second's delay. "I should rather think she shall! A man without a religion may be excused, but a woman without a religion is not the woman for me."

It was a sunny but raw Tuesday morning, January 22, 1861, when Captain Richard Francis Burton stood kicking his heels on the front steps of the Warwick Street Church. Clad in a shaggy shooting jacket and white trousers, with both hands thrust in his pockets, he puffed heatedly on a long black cheroot and darted occasional glances in both directions.

Burton was shivering a little, as much from nervousness as from the cold. For an anxious second he wanted to make himself scarce. He wavered, teased by conflicting tensions. Then it was too late to leave. Fate decided the issue in a flash.

At approximately half past nine, just as Burton was about to take that first step of escape, a cab came rumbling down the street and pulled up short in front of the church.

Dr. George Bird jumped out. "Morning, Dick!" he waved, helping Isabel Arundell and then his sister Alice out of the cab.

Burton snatched the cigar from between his teeth and tossed it away. He gazed at Isabel as she walked towards him wearing a fawn-colored dress, black-laced cloak, and snow-white bonnet. They smiled briskly at each other. Burton winked, while Isabel was afraid to utter a sound for fear some magic spell might be broken.

Saying nothing in their excitement, they went arm in arm into the church. Burton waited patiently as Isabel did her genuflections, took holy water, and crossed herself several times in succession, tearfully mumbling little prayers all the while. Then he himself took holy water, made a very large sign of the cross with a loud "In the name of the Father, and of the Son, and of the Holy Ghost," then led her down the aisle with an arrogant swagger and a twisted smile on his lips.

"Another moment and I'd have been a dead man, but I was too quick for my assailant. I swung around with my sword and sliced him up like a lemon."

Isabel and Alice shuddered laughingly.

Bird cracked a clever smile, emptying the bowl of his pipe in the palm of his hand. "Now, Burton, tell me—how d'you feel when you've killed a man?"

Burton blew out a cloud of smoke. "Oh, quite jolly, doctor! How do you?"

When the wedding breakfast was over and the newlyweds were about to leave, Dr. Bird laid his hand on Captain Burton's shoulder and said: "Y'know, it's hard to believe; but after all these years it's happened at last. It surprises me to think you two are finally spliced."

"I'm even more surprised than you!" Burton said, slipping an arm around his wife's waist and kissing her on the cheek. "Isabel's a strong-willed woman. She was determined to have her way, and she's had it!"

The newlyweds walked arm in arm from the Bird residence on Welbeck Street to Burton's bachelor quarters on Bury Street, where Isabel's luggage had been sent. As soon as they arrived, Burton sat down at his desk, grabbed paper and pen, and dashed off in a fine running hand the following note to Mr. Henry R. Arundell of Montagu Place:

'Abdullāh   Bury Street
El-Hhājj   St. James
                                              Jan. 23, '61

My dear Father,

   I've committed a highway robbery by marrying your daughter Isabel at Warwick St. Church, and before the registrar. The details she is writing to her mother.

   It only remains for me to say that I have no ties or liaisons of any sort, that the marriage is perfectly legal and "respectable." I want no money with Isabel. I can work, and it will be my care that time shall bring you nothing to regret.

                              I am
                                  Yours sincerely,
                                     Richard F. Burton

"Darling, why did you date it the twenty-third—tomorrow?" Isabel said, looking over his shoulder.

"Because I plan to post it first thing in the morning. As for the rest of today and all of tonight—" he eyed her with a sensuously suggestive grin, *"inshallāh!* we're *incommunicado* to the outside world."

"But what if friends come to call and congratulate us?"

"We won't answer. We'll make 'em think we're out. And that reminds me, Zoo. There's one thing I can't do, and that's face congratulations. So if you're agreeable, we'll pretend we've been married ever since I got back from America—or no, better yet—nine months ago, before I left."

"I'm agreeable, love," she smiled, kissing his forehead. "Now, let me get unpacked and clean up all this mess. Good heavens, darling, I don't know how you could stand living with yourself! Why the whole place is a rummage of books, manuscripts, weapons, Oriental bric-a-brac—and dust, and cobwebs, and—oh, Dick, what a disgrace! If this is how bachelors live, I thank God you're no longer a bachelor! Well, talking about it won't get it cleaned up."

"Oh no you don't," he said, pulling her down into his lap. "There's plenty of time for that." He pressed her lips with his own—tenderly, then with avid emotion. "Now you're mine. At last you're mine."

"Oh, Dick—my darling—" she murmured, "shall I get undressed?"

"D'you want to get undressed?" he teased.

"I want to do whatever pleases you, my husband."

"Aren't you afraid to get undressed in front of me?"

"I'm not afraid of anything anymore, now that I'm your wife—*Richard Burton's wife.*"

"*Ha-ha!* Would you believe I'm a little shy? I'm no hot amorist, y'know."

"I don't care what you are—you're perfect to me. Oh Blessed Mother of God, forgive me! Dick, I'm yours—heart, body, and soul! Take me, beloved—oh, take me! I've waited ten long years for this. Do it—oh, do it! Oh, Dick, how madly I love you. You're my earthly god and king. I worship you—I give myself to you. Do whatever you will with me—I'm only a sinful slave of passion. I can't help myself! I need it, I want it! Oh Blessed Mary, Mother of God—oh, oh—!"

"Does it hurt, Puss?"

"No—no, not really."

"I'll stop if it hurts."

"No, don't stop! Oh, Dick, it feels so strange—like you're a part of me all over. Oh, no—don't move! Please don't move. Hold it there. Oh, my darling, it's as if I want to swallow you up. It makes me thrill all over! Kiss me, Dick. Say you love me. Oh, Dick, I think I want to faint. Oh, Dick—Dick—I can't stand it anymore! Dick, it's so strong! Oh, what a feeling—so wild and deep—it's almost painful."

"By Allah, I'll tickle us both to death!"

"Oh, God forgive us—what a way to die!"

"How does it feel now, my sweet Pussy?"

"Oh, darling, let's not talk anymore. It's too good to spoil with words. Oh, hold me, Dick—hold me close. Let me dream. It's so warm, so awfully soothing and wonderful. Oh, darling, let me hold you—squeeze you. Keep it—oh, keep it there. Don't move. I want to dream—dream—dream forever and ever."

23 : The foreign office grave

That eve so gay, so bright, so glad; this morn so dim, and sad, and gray.
Strange that life's registrar should write this day a day, that day a day!

One muggy midsummer day, just before the publication of her husband's *The City of the Saints*, Isabel came bursting into their apartment brimful of joy.

"Darling, look—we've done it at last! All our applications and exertions haven't been in vain. Look, darling—it's right here in the *London Gazette*. The Foreign Secretary, Lord Russell, has been pleased to appoint you—Captain Richard F. Burton—to the consulship of Fernando Po, with a salary of seven hundred pounds a year."

"What!" Burton jumped out of his seat, snatching the paper from her hands. "Fernando Po! That whiteman's grave? Seven hundred pounds—chicken feed! In other words, I've been civilly shelved in a godforsaken hole where all my valuable energies will be needed just to

keep myself alive. What devilry! They want me to die.
But I intend to live, just to spite the devils!"

"Oh but Dick, how can you talk that way? I think it was
so wonderful of Lord Russell to—"

"Wonderful! *Māshallāh,* I like what you call 'wonderful'! Nanny Poo—the Foreign Office Grave. Official banishment, I call it! Excommunication to a West African
pesthole! The acceptance of this miserable post has now
given 'em an excuse to strike my name off the Indian
Army List. My past life has now become like a blank
sheet of paper, a *tabula rasa.* Now I must open a new
account in the F.O. Morgue. Tell me what Indian officer
accepting a political appointment hasn't been retained in
the army on half pay? You can't name a one! Outram,
Rigby—they've all kept their rank. All of 'em but me. But
then I'm not one of the office rats of Bombay. My enemies
may be congratulated on their mingled malice and meanness. They've swept out my whole nineteen years' service
as if it had never been—and without a vestige of pay,
thanks, or pension. At the age of forty I find myself with
nothing but a plague spot to call my reward for services
rendered to Queen and country."

"But darling, you have me—we have each other. What
more do we need?"

"We need to eat and live decently. They're treating me
like a man who's been idling away his time and shirking
duty. Well I can show—no, I can prove—that every hour
has been employed for my country's benefit in study,
writings, languages, explorations. Are my wounds and
fevers, and perpetual risk of health and life—not to speak
of personal losses—are all these things to go for nothing?
Ever since Elphinstone's death, the Bombay Government

hasn't taken into consideration one iota of my service—but casts the whole into oblivion. I consider the Bombay Government to be unjustly prejudiced against me on account of the private piques of a certain half-dozen individuals—Outram for one, the biggest office rat of 'em all."

"But why, darling? Why don't they like you?"

"For reasons it's better you never know."

"Dick, I don't understand. If it's only jealousy, we can fight back tooth and nail. We don't have to let them do this to you just because they're jealous."

"They hate me, d'you understand? They hate me for what I am, and I hate 'em for what *they* are. And they know I hate 'em as much as they hate me. They're afraid of me, Zoo. They're afraid of what I might do to 'em if ever I got the chance. To them I'm a dangerous man. As for fighting back, why bat your head against a brick wall? They all sit in the same nest. They rule the roost. It's a hopeless state of affairs."

"But *why*—why is it hopeless? They're just jealous, that's all!"

"No, that *isn't* all! They want me to die, I tell you. But by god I intend to live just to spite the devils!"

It was Saturday morning, August 24. The howling wind whipped her wringing-wet dress as Isabel stood huddled against her husband on the Liverpool dock. They were being lashed by a torrential rain, but neither seemed to mind. There was no thought for the weather, only for the agony of parting.

"Well, Puss," he said, squeezing her to him, "the *Blackbird* is waiting. Ominous name, eh? Too bad the climate's fit only for beast and Burton, or I'd be taking you with me."

"But I'm a Burton now," she said, kissing him.

"Yaas. But unhappily I'm not one of those independents who can say, *Ce n'est que le premier pas qui coûte.* For me, from first to last, each step is a hard one to take."

"Oh, Dick—Dick—" she hugged him, "I'm going to miss you so."

"Oh, Puss, for goodness' sake—please don't cry and unman me. Come on, now—be an independent. *Ce n'est que le premier pas qui coûte*—It's only the first step that's hard to take."

Soaked to the skin, Isabel watched and waved till the steamer became a faintly blinking dot in the thick gray mist.

A heartwrench, Burton thought, *and all is over. Unhappily, I'm not one of those independents.* He sighed and went below.

Captain Richard F. Burton, Her Britannic Majesty's consul at Fernando Po, arrived in Santa Isabel, capital of that pestilential island off the West African coast, on the sweltering afternoon of September 26.

At 3 P.M., while Burton and his Krooboys were unpacking and putting things in order, the biggest black dandy in town came swaggering into the consulate, slapped him on the back in a familiar fashion, then said with a loud guffaw: "Shake hands, consul! How-de-do?"

Burton turned slowly, his eyes ablaze like a wild beast. There was a sinister look on his face as he glared for a few seconds at the smirking African and his insistently open hand. Then he said: "Hey, boys, throw this goddamned nigger out the window!"

The Krooboys, flashing their ivories with sadistic delight, rushed over and grabbed the wide-eyed open-mouthed Negro by his arms and legs. With three swings they pitched him screaming out of the broad window and into the courtyard twenty feet below, where he leaped up and limped away yelping like a wounded animal.

One of the Krooboys remarked with a broad grin: "Now de niggers ob Nanny Poo do mo'e 'Salaam' dan 'How-de-do' to Massa Consul, Sir!"

A startled group of Spanish merchants, who stood by the doorway calmly awaiting the British consul's word of recognition, suddenly started an excited murmuring among themselves.

Burton shut them up with a resonant roar as he slammed his fist down on his desk. "These people can be respectful until spoiled by Europeans, after which they're insufferable! Those goddamned sentimental humanitarians make me sick. That affecting appeal, 'Am I not a man and a brother?', accompanies on the seal of the Anti-Slavery Society a kneeling Negro who should've been shown on all fours." Burton glowered at the gaping Spaniards. "Wait till you've lived with blacks as long as I've lived with 'em! You so-called philanthropic Negrophiles always have to give in. Whenever someone speaks of the Negro's place in Nature, I comment on the progress he's made from the original ape and how he might eventually hope to rise into a white man."

"But *señor—!*" one of the merchants gestured.

"The African race is a spoiled race, and neither education nor anything else can raise it to the level of responsibility! The pure Negro is always eight years old. His mind never develops. It needs miscegenation to provide and improve any intellect. Cowper says that 'skins may differ, but affection dwells in white and black the same'—which I deny. Affection, like love, is the fruit of animalism refined by sentiment. In this respect the pure black is little more than a brute. He breaks everything he can lay his hands on, then laughs like a spoiled brat. And what idiotic curiosity! I saw three of 'em blow out their feeble brains by trying to turn a loaded musket into a pipe."

"But *señor—!*"

"I always make a fine distinction between Negroes and niggers. That black buck we tossed out the window is what I'd call a 'nigger.' The rare few who show themselves fully equal in intellect to the white races of Europe and America afford incontestable proof that the pure-blooded Negro can be civilized."

"But *señor—!*" the merchant insisted.

Burton scowled fiercely. "What the hell d'you want, goddamnit?"

A small beady-eyed man scuttled forward, bowing. "We've come to welcome you to our humble island, *señor* consul," he whined in broken English, "and pray that your stay here will—"

"Is that all?"

"Oh no, *señor!* We wish to make a complaint."

"Very well then, make it!" Burton lit a cigar. "What's on your mind?"

"If it please your excellency—the ship captains are in the habit of unloading their cargoes in such a big hurry and steaming off again without losing a moment for more money that this causes us great inconvenience and loss, since we have not time to read and answer all our correspondence; so we humbly apply ourselves to you for—"

"Yaas, yaas. I understand," Burton snapped, waving him away. "Consider the matter settled. First chance I get, I'll see your worries are over."

"Oh, *muchos gracias, señor* consul!" they all repeated, bowing obsequiously, and left.

Burton called after them: "But don't think it's money that makes 'em clear out o' here so goddamned fast. This island is a haven of whores, and it's also a hellhole of venereal disease and every other ailment known to man!"

About an hour later an American merchant-marine captain came clumping into the consulate and said matter-of-factly: "Okay, consul, quick with my papers! I wanna be off."

Burton flashed a slight frown. Without once looking up from his desk, he answered indifferently: "I haven't finished my letters."

"*Aa*, damn your letters! I can't wait for *them!*"

"Just hold your water," Burton drawled, unfolding a long sheet of paper. "Let's refer to your contract. *Hmmm.*" He read silently for a few seconds. "According to this, you have to stay here eighteen hours' daylight in order to give the merchants an opportunity of attending to their correspondence."

"Yeah, I know," growled the skipper, mopping his brow. "But that rule's never been enforced."

"Are you going to stay?"

"No, damn it all! Why should I?"

"Very well," Burton said dryly, rising from his seat. He stared him straight in the eyes. "Now listen carefully. I'm heading over to the governor's, where I'm going to range two twelve-pounders. If you leave one minute before the prescribed time expires, I'll send the first shot right across your bows and the second slap into you. Mark me, I'm a man of my word. Good day."

Burton walked out. The American, not knowing what to make of it all, stood dumb-struck. He stayed the requisite eighteen hours.

Burton spent many a long and lonely night at his desk —gazing at the fireflies flickering in the orange trees outside his window, listening to the snarls of wild dogs and jackals in the courtyard, and smelling the aroma of rotting refuse in the harbor.

He yawned, dipped his pen, and resumed writing to Isabel:

> Fernando Po is an island in which man finds it hard to live and very easy to die. Strangers flee the place like a pestilence, and the natives crawl about like vermin. Can it be that by some inexplicable law, where Nature has done her best for the happiness of mankind, Man, doomed to misery, must work out his own unhappiness?

Burton dropped his pen with a sharp sigh. He rubbed his eyes, then rested head in hands to gather his thoughts. A half-empty bottle of brandy and a box of cigars served as paperweights. Burton clutched the bottle, gulped the brandy down, then grabbed a cigar. Dipping his handkerchief into a bowl of water, he slapped it over his face and neck.

Isabel's latest letter again caught his eye. He picked it up and read what was already a matter of memory:

To a Beloved Husband During a Long Absence:
Oh when wilt thou return, my love?
  For as the moments glide,
They leave me wishing still for thee,
  My husband, by my side.
And ever at the evening hour
My hopes more fondly burn,
And still they linger on that word:
  Oh when wilt thou return?

He glanced over the ten-page letter, his weary eyes catching certain passages:

Whenever anyone asks, Daddy still says: "She's married to Dick Burton, and thank God for it!". . .

I think Mother is now reconciled to it, even though she still says: "Dick Burton is no relation of mine!" . . .

Mother never thought I'd have the courage to oppose her; and now that I have, I think she's secretly proud of me and blesses the both of us. . . .

People sometimes say such impertinent things, which they know to be untrue, like: "You know, Mrs. Burton, your husband is keeping a harem out at Nanny Poo." . . .

With my husband in a place where I'm not allowed to go, and I living with my mother and father like a girl, I'm neither maid nor wife nor widow.

24 : The city of the dead

Coming to the feast unbid, I found the gorgeous table spread
With the fair-seeming Sodom fruit, with stones that bear the shape of
bread.

In November, 1863, Richard Burton received a communiqué from Lord John Russell, Secretary of Foreign Affairs, appointing him Her Britannic Majesty's Commissioner to the Court of Dahomey. His instructions were to proceed to Abomey, the forbidden capital of this equally forbidden West African kingdom, and present a petition from Queen Victoria to King Akhosu Gelele.

The British Government wanted Burton to induce the black despot to cease the so-called Dahoman Customs, an annual inquisition involving human sacrifice and cannibalism, and desist from his management of the million-dollar slave trade.

Burton said to himself: *Is that what they really want, or do they want to get rid of me once and for all?* He grinned sardonically. *They want me to die, but I'll outlive every last one of 'em!*

> My heart aches to accompany you on your dangerous mission. Just think, my love, that with a magic lantern and some slides representing New Testament scenes I could convert Gelele and his court from fetishism to Catholicism.

Burton laughed when he read this characteristic sentiment in Isabel's latest letter, thinking how both of them would be put to death for practicing Christian witchcraft.

At 11 A.M. on Saturday, January 2, 1864, Captain Burton entered Abomey and stalked up the ruddy shale-blanketed street towards the Kumasi Palace. Death drums throbbed in the sepulchral stillness, echoing the macabre message that the new-year customs were now being observed.

There was no visible sign of human life as Burton walked along the dusty road, through the smoldering heat. The muffled crying of babies was barely heard above the monotonous pulsation of the drums of doom.

Burton shuddered with uncertainty. He gazed anxiously at the dilapidated adobes, a webwork of clay the color of dry blood. Then he looked at other things.

Dozens of dying goats, their mouths dripping blood, dangled from the skeletal trees that lined the road to the palace. Burton could see they had been impaled, and many of them wriggled in the throes of death. Others, their throats slit, were lashed to a row of stakes driven in the red-spotted ground along the roadside. Headless chickens—more than Burton cared to count—decorated the gnarled limbs of every tree.

Black wooden images of Legba, the Negro Priapus and

West African god of lust, glared at the white intruder almost every step of the way. Each squatting Legba clutched in his hands an enormous circumcised phallus longer than himself and proportionately thick. Burton noticed that the glans was daubed with bright red paint to represent hymenal blood, while the shaft of each phallus was smeared with palm oil symbolizing the god's seminal libation.

As Burton approached the palace, he passed a line of poles topped with human skulls. The stench of stagnant gore cloyed his nostrils, its sickening sweetness making his head swim. A long open shed lay on the left-hand side of the road, its slanted roof stained with sacrificial blood. Burton stopped for a few seconds to stare at the curious spectacle that caught his eyes.

Nearly two dozen naked Negroes half-stood, half-sagged in a continuous row, their arms strapped behind them over a wooden rail. Nude Negresses sat on stools beside each human sacrifice or "goat without horns." One girl fanned away the flies, while another rubbed and manipulated a victim's erect penis with moist hot hands. All of them were moaning and wailing in a delirium of lust. Burton understood this ritual masturbation as an appeasement of Legba, a habitual masturbator who traditionally created the Ewe tribes with his first ejaculation.

In another shed, Burton saw the flesh-and-blood oblation ceremonies of circumcision being performed by old men and women armed with rusty razors. Pubescent boys stood to have their prepuces sliced off, while little girls sat with splayed legs to have their clitorises cut out.

In yet another shed, Burton beheld several pregnant females undergoing a crude operation. Having been caught in the act of adultery, they now suffered the unripe fruit of their swollen wombs to be removed prematurely and impaled on a lance. Tied to the tables, they were then left to die a lingering death with their bellies ripped open.

Burton moved on. Startled by the harsh squawking of turkey buzzards, he glanced over to the right of the road. A dozen dead bodies were hanging by their heels from the trees. Buzzards, perched on the lower limbs, were pecking away at them. Burton watched with a certain fascination as one of the birds plucked out a string of entrails, shook it in his beak, then gobbled it up in a few seconds.

A long row of nude victims dangled head downwards on rough scaffolding. Burton could plainly see that they had been castrated and then clubbed to death. Their legs were lashed wide apart to reveal gaping wounds where the genital organs had been lopped off, and their heads were bruised and bloodied.

Burton understood that these men had been sexually mutilated in honor of Legba and of the royal harem. Since the penis and testicles were considered the seat of strength in a man, there was no doubt in Burton's mind that these revered parts had been cooked and eaten by the king and his caboceers. In this he recognized an ancient African custom whereby warriors cut off and devour the generative apparatus of their captive enemies in order to enhance their own physical force.

At the open gateway of the Kumasi Palace sat six decapitated corpses, stripped naked and also castrated. Turkey buzzards were picking away at them, unmindful of the white intruder.

Burton glared at six more cadavers on the other side of the gate. These victims, apparently all in one piece, were propped up on Gold Coast stools. Burton surmised they'd been strangled to death. Each was attired in a striped convict's shirt and nightcap. Their legs were spread and their hands arranged clasping their exposed genitalia. Burton shut his eyes for a minute, composed his unsettled mind, then strode directly through the gateway.

The courtyard was clustered with carrion birds, feeding on decapitated corpses bound to a series of stakes or supported by poles having been passed up their rectums.

A dozen heads greeted him inside the gate. They lay on the ground in V-shaped double lines of three, their faces downward. The cleanly severed necks attracted Burton's close attention. He imagined they must have been removed with a single expert stroke of a razor-edged chopper.

Heaps of white ashes and splashes of gore were additional traces of cannibalism and human sacrifice. Outside the entrance of the ramshackle red-clay palace stood a huge pyramid of skulls, and atop the box-shaped building the flag of Dahomey flapped in the blood-warm breeze. Burton would always remember it—a decapitated black head, a crimson butcher knife, and a torn heart bleeding on a white background.

Two blue-swathed eunuchs invited Burton by gesticulation to be seated under a tamarind tree and await the presence of his majesty. Burton nodded compliance and sat down on a stool, contemplating the stenchy horrors that surrounded him.

A moment later the king appeared, ushered into the

courtyard by the drubbing of drums and the blaring of bugles. He was attended by a platoon of fierce-looking stark-naked amazons armed with scimitars and blunderbusses. Burton had never seen anything like them in all his life. Six-foot tall, robust, big-bosomed and broad-bottomed, these royal leopard women were the hell-roaring terrors of the Slave Coast.

Akhosu Gelele, followed by his court officials and caboceers, strutted under a black-fringed scarlet parasol. On his right was a slave boy holding a silver spittoon, on his left a slave girl fanning him with peacock feathers. Burton stood up to admire the imposing sight. Tall, handsome, and powerfully built, Gelele was garbed in a violet silk toga and blood-red satin skullcap. Attached to a crimson shoulder sash, a European rapier swung at his side; and a jeweled necklace of human phalanges lay upon his broad chest. Gelele's upper arms and lower legs were ornamented with silver bracelets, and his feet were encased in ruddy leather sandals.

An ear-splitting salute of blunderbusses honored the English commissioner. Screwing up his red-rimmed eyes, Gelele grinned and held out his hand. Burton stared for a second at red-daubed talons three to four inches long and sharpened to a point, the kind of claws a king uses to gouge out the eyes of his enemies. Burton smiled, shook hands, and snapped fingers with the black tyrant.

"Mawnin'—mawnin', Mashna Burton!" Gelele boomed.

"Good morning yourself, Akhosu Gelele!" Burton responded, tipping his forage cap and twisting his mustachios.

The king eyed the commissioner's regimental sword.

With an acknowledging smirk, Burton detached it from his belt and handed it to him. "Here—have a look," he said.

Gelele leered, then handed it back. "Okay, Mashna Burton," he rumbled, hawking loudly and spitting in the silver pot. "We palaver 'bout dis'n anodder time. Now, Mashna Burton—"

"*Wē*, Akhosu Gelele!"

"Why you no bring me white woman? Last *māshnā* come here, him promise me white woman."

Burton laughed. "What d'you want a white woman for? White women are sparrow meat compared to a mighty cock like you! Look what I've got for you—presents from the English Queen. Hey, Krooboys, break open the boxes! Just feast your sights on these. A crimson silk-damask bell tent, a richly embossed silver pipe with amber mouthpiece, two richly embossed silver belts with lions and cranes in high relief, two richly engraved silver trays, and an elegant chain-mail jacket and gauntlets."

Gelele made a cursory examination of the gifts. "Tent jim-dandy, but too small—too small sittin' unner in heat. Silver pipe good, but ole red-clay wood-stem pipe better. Silver tray okay, but too small—too small usin' fer shield. Nebber wear belt. Hand no fit in glove. Coat good fer target, nuttin' else. Spear stick clean through 'er. Okay, Mashna Burton—tell English Queen Akhosu Gelele want carriage, horse, white woman. Really want white woman! *Ummm,* white woman got jim-dandy cunt!"

Burton laughed again. "Who ever told you that? Just as your hand won't fit in that glove, your tool will never fit in a white woman's sheath."

"Why? Okay, why Mashna Burton say Akhosu Gelele

no fit in white woman crack? Akhosu Gelele fit in eb'ry black woman crack! Why Akhosu Gelele no fit in—"

"Because white women are much smaller than black women in the size of their slits, just as white men are much smaller than black men in the size of their joy sticks."

"Okay, how big white woman slit?"

"Only three inches deep and very narrow."

"*Hē! hē!* You take measure Akhosu Gelele. Akhosu Gelele big—ver-r-ry big! Akhosu Gelele two handful hard."

"Eight inches? *Wallāh,* what a giant! You'd impale a white woman."

"*Ummm,* white meat good fer impale. Impale white woman to death! All Dahomey man slave, all Dahomey woman wife Akhosu Gelele. Akhosu Gelele get eb'ry Dahomey girl afore husband. Akhosu Gelele like Legba. Akhosu Gelele got strong, strong prick. Akhosu Gelele—"

Burton interrupted: "Why don't we both sit down and I'll tell you why I came."

"No sit—*dance!* Mashna Burton dance!"

Burton scowled, clapping a hand on the hilt of his sword. The first and erenow last time a man had ordered him to "dance" was in a Carson City saloon. "D'you plan on joining me if I do?" Burton had asked, sizing up the gunslinger. "Not so long as I got this pointed at yer feet I don't!" was the answer. So Burton had made one of his split-second moves and shot the man dead.

Akhosu Gelele flashed his ivories. "*Hē! hē!* Mashna Burton dance!"

Burton eyed him narrowly. "D'you plan on joining me if I do?"

"Sure! sure! Akhosu Gelele like dance! Mashna Burton, do *he* like dance?"

"*Wē! wē!* Yassuh! yassuh!" Burton replied, appreciating the fact that Gelele expected the British commissioner *not* to refuse cavorting with him.

Taking Burton by the wrist, the king of Dahomey led him into the open center of the courtyard amid the tempestuous applause of the encircling onlookers. Facing one another, each performed his native stomp. While Burton had the honor of enacting the Hindustani jig of a whirling dervish, Gelele executed the traditional Dahoman decapitation *danse macabre*, to the accompaniment of a violent storm of clapping and chanting and cacophonous music.

"Okay, Mashna Burton," the profusely sweating Gelele wheezed, ending his dance of death. "Now drink health de ghost Akhosu Gelele pappy!"

The king called for rum, and it came in two human skulls boiled white and clean.

Burton seized one of the skulls from the slave boy, held it high in his hand, and said lustily: "To the health of your father's ghost!" He then tossed it off with his usual zest.

Having guzzled his rum and pitched the skull over on the pile, Gelele snapped his fingers at an old eunuch, who pranced up to Burton holding something wrapped in a blood-soaked towel.

"You brave man, Mashna Burton," the king said. "You ver-r-ry brave man. Akhosu Gelele gib Mashna Burton jim-dandy present!" He nodded to the eunuch, who unwrapped the gift and handed it to Burton. It was the bloody head of a Negro, with penis and testes stuffed in its mouth. "Noggin Abeokuta king! You like, Mashna Bur-

ton? Okay, you eat Abeokuta meat. Be mo'e brave man!"
He laughed deeply, again snapping his fingers. The old
eunuch returned with a second bloodstained towel. *"Ho!
ho! ho!* Head de son Abeokuta king! You like, Mashna
Burton? See fat meat stick out mouth? Make Mashna Burton ver-r-ry *ver-r-ry* brave man. Make white man hab big
prick too! *Ho! ho! ho!"*

Burton held the two dripping heads amid a thunder of
applause. Then he tossed them back to the eunuch, snarling: "Put 'em in the juju house!"

Gelele frowned. "Mashna Burton no like present?"

"No," he said, eyeing the king sharply. "No more than
you liked yours. I think we've wasted enough time, don't
you? I didn't come here to be made a fool of. At least six
or seven hundred human beings are slaughtered every
year to appease Legba. Goddamnit, this is cold-blooded
murder!"

The king shook his head. "No murder! Akhosu Gelele
kill only criminal, kill only war prisoner. Criminal kill,
Akhosu Gelele kill criminal. White God say 'Eye fer eye,
tooth fer tooth!' Legba say 'Head fer head, meat fer
meat!' Akhosu Gelele kill war prisoner. If Akhosu Gelele
war prisoner, him die too. No save Akhosu Gelele, so
Akhosu Gelele no save dem!"

"I don't give a goddamn *what* your excuses are. I want
you to put an immediate end to these outrageous Customs. Those are my orders."

The king shrugged. "Hand Akhosu Gelele tied. If
Akhosu Gelele stop Custom, Dahomey people kill Akhosu
Gelele. Custom ver-r-ry *ver-r-ry* old. Stop Custom, Legba
ver-r-ry angry. Legba make people kill Akhosu Gelele."

"Yaas, well what d'you have to say for the slave trade?

Will Dahomey people kill Akhosu Gelele if he stops the slave trade? Y'know," Burton leered, "the English Queen is resolved to stop the traffic in human flesh, and the United States of America will no longer allow her vessels to carry live cargo. Why? Because she's now fighting a *ver-r-ry* bloody war—a tribal feud, you might call it—all over this rotten business of slavery."

The king gestured heatedly. "Abe Lincoln, him free blackman slave. Bad, *ba-a-ad* thing! No mo'e slave, no mo'e business. All you white man, you start big slave business. Make Dahomey rich, make Legba happy—make people happy! Akhosu Gelele sell white man what white man want. White man pay Akhosu Gelele big, *big* money. Akhosu Gelele rich. No mo'e slave, Akhosu Gelele poor. Dahomey poor, Dahomey people unhappy. People unhappy, people kill Akhosu Gelele. Tell English Queen, Akhosu Gelele stop slave business if English Queen pay Akhosu Gelele two hunnerd thousand dollar a year. Den Akhosu Gelele, him do widout slave business!"

Burton laughed aloud.

The king joined him. "*Ho! ho! ho!* Mashna Burton, you ver-r-ry brave man! Akhosu Gelele make Mashna Burton brigadier gen'ral Dahomey leopard-woman army." The king snapped his fingers at a naked slave girl, who wiggle-waggled over carrying a small ebony-and-ivory box. Gelele flipped open the lid and pulled out a long string of big green beads, the Dahoman Order of the Garter—*Honi soit qui mal y pense.* He slipped it over the commissioner's head. "Now Mashna Burton brigadier gen'ral Dahomey army! *Ho! ho! ho!* Okay, okay! Here present fer Mashna Burton favorite squaw." He pulled out a necklace of human bones, slipping it around the commissioner's neck. Then the king presented him with a silver crucifix on a silver chain, saying: "Here juju. Make good voodoo, Mashna Burton. Jim-dandy juju, keep 'way evil spirit!"

Burton was surprised to see a bronze chameleon instead of a representation of Christ attached to the cross. He suddenly realized that the Catholic missionary from whom Gelele got the "juju" must have previously removed the human image and replaced it with a reptile for fear his highness might be inspired to crucify a few convicts in the priest's honor.

"Okay, Mashna Burton. Next time come, you bring white woman." The king grinned broadly. "Akhosu Gelele want white woman. *Ummm,* white woman hab jim-dandy cunt!"

Having been made the butt of Dahoman humor, and considering his mission a miserable failure, Burton had no intention of ever returning. Without acknowledging the king's facetious request, he merely scowled and shook hands.

As Burton was about to leave Abomey, grinning Gelele again offered his hand and snapped fingers with the British commissioner. "Mashna Burton, you ver-r-ry good man." He then rolled his head with a frown. "You good man, but too angry."

When Burton left the bloody kingdom of Dahomey he wrote to Isabel:

It is evident that to abolish human sacrifice there is to abolish Dahomey. As for cannibalism, the fact is that they can't afford to reject any kind of provisions. Concerning the slave trade, Lincoln's Emancipation Proclamation is the writing on the Dahomey wall.

There is apparently in this people a physical delight in cruelty to beasts as well as to men. The sight of suffering seems to bring them enjoyment, without which the world is tame. Probably the wholesale murderers and torturers of history, from Nero downwards, took an animal and sensual pleasure—all the passions are sisters—in the sight of blood and in the inspection of mortal agonies. I can see no other explanation of the phenomena which meet my eye in Africa.

I've seen enough horrid sights to turn a man's brain. I had to be perfectly calm and dignified while seeing these things, or they would have had a curlike contempt for me. No humane Englishman would dare sell his dog to a Dahoman Negro. When I think of all the bloody scenes I've witnessed in West Africa—at Abomey especially—that phrase "God's image in ebony" lashes me to fury.

On his return to Fernando Po, Captain Burton received no official acknowledgment of his services from the Foreign Office. Instead, Lord Russell sent Isabel the following telegram:

TELL CAPTAIN BURTON THAT HE HAS PERFORMED HIS MISSION TO MY UTMOST AND ENTIRE SATISFACTION.

Enraged at this, Isabel wrote a scathing reply to the Foreign Secretary, who answered her by letter:

My dear Mrs. Burton,

I know the climate in which your husband is working so zealously and so well is an unhealthy one, but it is not true to say that he is the smallest of consuls in the worst part of the world. Many have inferior salaries, and some are in more unhealthy places.

However, if I find a vacancy of a post with an equal salary and a better position, I will not forget his services. I do not imagine he would wish for a less active spot.

He has performed his mission to Dahomey very creditably, to my entire satisfaction.

I remain, Madam,

Your most humble and obedient servant,
Russell

25 : The meeting at Bath

The light of morn has grown to noon, has paled with eve, and now fare-
well!
Go, vanish from my life as dies the tinkling of the camel's bell.

September, 1864. Richard Burton was back in London, on leave from the consular service.

"You know, darling," Isabel said one evening as they lay in bed, "they say Speke and Grant have explored the western and northern shores of the Victoria Nyanza, and followed for some ways the river shooting northwards from it. This is what they claim to be the main stream of the Nile, while Nyanza is the source."

Burton stirred irritably. "That's what Jack always claimed, but I still hold that Tanganyika and its affluents bear the honor of being the headwaters of Father Nilus. In any event," he added with a note of sarcasm, "the whole thing'll soon be thrashed out at Bath when Jack and I hold our public debate on this the great issue of our times."

"Oh, that reminds me! You know what that trouble-maker Laurence Oliphant said to me the other day?"

"No, what?"

"He said Speke told him, 'If Burton appears on the platform at Bath I'll kick him!' "

"Well that settles it! By god, he'll kick me then!"

Isabel grinned. "Bath is Speke's native town, you know."

"Yaas, I know. But nothing short of my dropping dead will keep me from that meeting. I'm anxious to hear all the details about Jack's so-called discovery. He performed a magnificent feat, and has now risen to the first rank among the explorers of our day."

Burton's sarcasm made Isabel say: "After all this time, darling, why should there be such bitterness between you?"

Burton snorted. "Suffice it to say, Zoo, it's no longer a 'Dear Dick'—'Dear Jack' relationship. Every time he gets a chance to blow off steam in front of an interested audience, he pats himself on the back and sticks a knife in mine."

"He says such awful things about you, Dick, it makes me ill to think of them."

"What, that I'm sexually perverse? That I tried to seduce him into unnatural acts while in Africa? That I practiced sodomy and pederasty with Arabs and Negroes? That I fornicated with Negresses and was castrated in Harar? '*Steghfrullāh!* What more could that chronic masturbator have to say about me?"

There was tense, painful silence. Then Isabel murmured: "Do you still love Jack?"

"I don't want to talk about it," he answered sharply. "It's all over and done with now, and I don't want to talk about it."

Isabel was hesitant and cautious. "I never told you, darling, but I went to see Jack last week. He seemed in a very bad way, so nervous and—yes, frightened. Well anyway, he said to me: 'I'm so sorry, Mrs. Burton. I don't know how it all came about. Dick was so kind to me— nursed me like a woman, taught me such a lot—and I used to be so fond of him. But it would be too difficult for me to go back now.'"

Burton sat up in bed. "Goddamnit, Zoo, why the hell did you have to go to him and beg?"

"Oh, Dick, I didn't beg! I only tried to bring about a reconciliation between you and—"

"Thank you, thank you—but I want no reconciliation, nor do I need any reconciliation. I'm telling you once and for all, I don't wish to have any further private or indirect communication with Speke. As far as I'm concerned, the man is dead. Only an image remains for the moment of truth, and this disputation at Bath promises to be a hot one to end all hot ones."

:

The British Association for the Advancement of Science was holding its annual meeting at Bath on the week of September 12-16, 1864.

On the morning of the fifteenth, Burton met the celebrated African geographer James M'Queen outside the lecture hall marked *Section E: Geography and Ethnography.*

"Well, Dick, all set to fight?"

"Fight what?"

"The Nile Duel! Why they expect quite a crowd tomorrow to see the big show. Some conference this, eh what? Must be several hundred scientists and geographers here. Even Livingstone's expected for the grand finale. Y'know, Dick, he hasn't any time for Speke—says the poor bugger turned his back on the real sources of the Nile."

"Yaas, well—what more can one say at a time when the English-speaking world is bowing down before its latest idol, a plaster saint named John Hanning Speke?"

"Well our little tin god is in for a big surprise. For the past year he's been singing 'The Nile is settled.' Watch him change his tune when Dick Burton, Doc Livingstone, and Jim M'Queen take the stand! What the devil did Speke do? He took a quick look at a large sheet of water when he was with you in '58. He took a little longer look at that same large sheet of water when he was with Grant in '62. Now he tells us the Nile is settled!"

"*Ha-ha!* Y'know, Jim, Speke has invested the Nile Basin with an amount of fable unknown to the days of Ptolemy. I daresay the old Greco-Egyptian would turn over in his grave if he knew that after two thousand years of scientific achievement, civilization should still find the rest of the world living in such an extreme looseness of geography."

"Talk about 'extreme looseness'! Have you heard what they're saying about Speke's morality?"

"*Ha-ha!* No, what? Can it be any worse than what they say about my own behavior?"

"Ah, but that's just it! Speke's been singing all those hymns of hate about *your* sexual conduct. Now he'll have to change his tune. Jack Petherick got all the inside information from some of Speke's porters. Y'know, Dick, he used to be consul at Khartoum till Speke accused him of being mixed up in the slave trade."

"Yaas, I know. Petherick wouldn't kiss Speke's ass, so Speke had him recalled. Nearly ruined the poor man. They tell me his wife's still a nervous wreck."

"Well, in a sense Petherick's got his revenge. He's got the dog running around with his tail between his legs."

"Why? What's the dirt?"

"Speke did the same things he accused you of doing. He said you measured the private parts of Somali men and examined the circumcised secrets of Somali women. Well what an engineering job he did on the King of Karagwe's fat wife! Speke got her to strip naked, had her sidle and wriggle all around the hut for him, then began to measure her—bosom, buttocks, thighs, everything. After infinite exertions on both sides, he finally got her laid upon the floor. Watching all the while was the queen's sixteen-year-old daughter, as stark-naked as her mother. Speke promised to take off all his clothes when he measured her. Being a virgin, she wouldn't let him lay her out; so Speke had to be satisfied with the girl's handiwork and an exhaustive amount of frenching. He then measured the king's equipment, and the king returned the compliment by handling Speke very well indeed. Now when Speke complained of being lonely at the King of Buganda's palace, the truth is he was constantly accepting presents of black harem girls and rejecting all but the prettiest. They kept him so damned busy he didn't even have time to explore *his* source of the Nile. In fact, the porters say Bwana Speke was all the time amused and employed in drinking native booze, courting the king's youthful mother, being buggered by the king—to whom he paid like compliment—shooting cows, and restoring order among his rebellious female intimates. One of the reasons why the king presented Speke with black mistresses was to find out whether the offspring would turn out black or white. Speke got six of them pregnant, but he never returned to his Garden of Eden on the Nile to see how Nature fashioned his children with a touch of the tarbrush."

"What scandalous nonsense! I don't believe a word of it, and neither do you."

"Well, Dick, whether or not Speke did what comes naturally—or unnaturally—under the circumstances, the truth is he measured the King of Karagwe's fat females and accepted girls from the King of Buganda. I can't say the same for Grant! At least he remained a modest gentleman. Nobody ever caught *him* drinking pombe, fingering and flirting with Negresses, and collecting black harems."

"I should think not! Not 'Dryasdust' Grant, that old young man. I hear they made him baron in Uganda. Why the poor devil was already made barren in England!"

"*Hey-hey!* A good one for the gallery. But how do you

like old Murchison awarding Speke the R.G.S. Founders' Medal?"

"As I told my wife, old Murchison hates me. He has honored me by not honoring me."

"Y'know, Dick, Rigby's got an extended leave from Zanzibar. They say he's leading the opposition tomorrow."

"Yaas, so I've heard. He's been haunting the R.G.S. for more than a year now, earning such an estimable reputation as the Rat of Saville Row. Rigby hates my guts. He'll do anything to see me laughed out of Bath. But the truth's on my side. Though it may be blamed, it can't be shamed! As Speke suffered with me in purse and person at Berbera, I thought it only fair to offer him the opportunity of renewing an attempt to penetrate Africa. I couldn't expect much from his assistance. He wasn't a linguist, nor a man of science, nor even an accurate observer. The Court of Directors of the E.I.C. officially refused him leave of absence. I obtained it for him by an application to the local authorities at Bombay. During the exploration he acted in a subordinate capacity. As may well be imagined, among a party of Africans whose languages he ignored, he was unfit for any other *but* a subordinate capacity! Before leaving Aden he made a spontaneous promise not to appear before the R.G.S. till after my return, when we'd go up together. Reaching London, he lost no time in securing for himself the exclusive right of working the field which I had opened. And from that day on he's placed himself in evidence as the prime mover of an expedition in which he signed himself 'Surveyor.'"

At that moment Captain John Speke entered the building. It was the first time Burton had seen him face to face in nearly five and a half years. Their eyes met for a few seconds, and Burton noticed the torment festering in Speke's taut expression. The man looked ill—very ill. Burton wanted to say something, wanted to catch hold of his arm, but it was too late. Speke passed him by without pausing, without saying a word.

Jim M'Queen broke the poignant spell. "Well, well," he said, laying a hand on his friend's shoulder, "who should be coming but Mrs. Dick Burton. By Jupiter, what a queenly woman! The most beautiful woman in the whole damned place! You should be right proud of her."

"I am," Burton muttered, pulling out his pocket watch. "Let's go inside."

Burton and Isabel sat on the platform close to Speke. Almost every minute he glanced at them, and they at him. His face was pained. Isabel smiled faintly. Burton evinced a burning stare—searching, pondering.

Colonel Christopher Rigby stood at the lectern, lecturing on Zanzibar. All of a sudden Burton lurched out of his seat and said: "Damn your eyes, Rigby! None but a jackass would say there are no Abyssinians in Zanzibar!"

Rigby swung around. "Who are you calling a jackass? When I say there are no Abyssinians in Zanzibar, I speak with authority! But perhaps Captain Burton conveniently forgets that I'm still Her Britannic Majesty's Consul at Zanzibar," he added, sneering.

"I don't give a goddamn what you are!" Burton replied, stalking over to the lectern and snatching up the map pointer. "But perhaps Colonel Rigby conveniently forgets all about the two Abyssinian sluts I saw massaging him on his verandah back in '59. Now does Colonel Rigby still say there are no Abyssinians—not even *half-blooded* Abyssinians—in Zanzibar?"

The audience, which had been paralyzed in a tense and expectant hush, now rustled with laughter. Rigby turned red with embarrassment and rage. Isabel blushed, snickering into her handkerchief.

Swinging the pointer like a saber, Burton paced from one side of the platform to the other—and so close to the edge that the people in the front row felt as though a tiger were about to pounce upon them.

While Burton was loudly proving his effective retort with blazing eyes and incontestable counter-evidence, the audience was further amused by the enthusiasm of Mr. Arundell, who was attending the convention with all his sons and daughters. "Tell him, Dick, tell him!" he said, half-laughing and half-snarling. His children had to hold him down, otherwise he would have dashed onto the platform and attacked Rigby with his cane. "That's my son-in-law, and thank God for it! The greatest man England ever produced!"

At approximately half past one, Speke stopped his persistent fidgeting and muttered: "Oh, I can't stand this any longer!"

As he got up from his chair, M'Queen said tauntingly: "Will you be wanting your seat again, sir?"

"I hope not!" Speke answered, and left the hall.

Burton watched his departure out of the corner of his eye. Finishing his harangue, he bowed in mockery to Colonel Rigby and handed the man his calling card. The flustered consul read what his F.O. colleague had written on the back:

Two loves the Row of Saville haunt,
  Who both by nature big be.
The fool is Captain (Barren) Grant;
  The rogue is Colonel Rigby.

On Friday morning, September 16, Sir Roderick Murchison, Dr. Norton Shaw, Captain James Grant, Colonel Christopher Rigby, Dr. David Livingstone, Mr. James M'Queen, and Captain and Mrs. Richard Burton filed onto the platform and took their seats in the huge lecture hall of *Section E*. The ninth chair stood vacant.

Burton scowled at the assembling crowd of several hundred spectators—men of science and the arts, newspaper reporters, and distinguished people from all walks of professional and nonprofessional life. When the hall was jam-packed, the rear doors were opened to accommodate an outside audience.

Burton didn't appear outwardly nervous, but he clutched his notes with sweaty hands.

Isabel sat demurely, with a faint smile on her lips. She was elegantly arrayed in a black satin dress trimmed with white lace, and her majestic beauty attracted the immediate attention of one and all. Isabel was also nervous, and a little frightened.

M'Queen nudged Burton. "What d'you bet he won't show up? He knows when he's licked. Just look at Grant and Rigby. They're worried to death, but daren't show it."

Burton made no reply. He kept eyeing the door—anxious for Speke's arrival, anxious to get it all over and done with.

Ten, fifteen, twenty-five minutes. The ninth chair still

remained empty. The audience stirred and murmured impatiently, in growing suspicion. Where was Jack Speke? Was he backing out of the great debate?

A few moments later the president of the British Association for the Advancement of Science entered the hall, and a note was handed around in silence. When Burton received it he read:

> Captain Speke lost his life yesterday at 4 P.M. whilst hunting on his cousin's estate. He was missed in the field and his kinsman found him lying upon the ground, shot through the body close to the heart. He lived only a few minutes and his last words were a request not to be moved.

"Oh my god, he's killed himself!" Burton uttered, passing the note to Isabel. She clutched his arm, watching the terrible emotion at work in his tight-set expression.

When they entered their London apartment late that evening, Burton wept long and bitterly. "Jack! Jack!" he sobbed. "What have I done—what have I done?"

For nearly two weeks Burton shut himself in, sick to the very soul with guilt-ridden grief. Isabel, her nerves shattered, was unable to sleep. All night long she smoked one cigarette after another; and during the day she did everything in her power to comfort and encourage him, and explain away the tragedy as a merciful act of God.

When the trial of self-torture was ended, Burton emerged in fairly good spirits. When asked by reporters what he thought of the "unfortunate accident," Burton invariably replied: "Nothing will be known of Speke's death. I saw him at one-thirty, and at four o'clock he was dead. The charitable say he shot himself, the uncharitable that I shot him."

To his wife and trusted friends he said: "The verdict of the coroner's inquest was 'Accidental death by gunshot wound.' I beg to differ with 'em. Speke committed suicide to avoid the exposure of his misstatements concerning the Nile sources. Can you tell me how such an experienced sportsman could have been so careless as to attempt to climb over a wall while holding his double-barreled shotgun by the barrels—that gun being loaded, cocked, and without a safety catch? Don't make me laugh! Speke killed himself lest my contention, proven to be correct, should disprove his own. I always said his one fatal fault was overweening vanity. 'Pride goeth before destruction, and a haughty spirit before a fall.' "

Burton penned in his journal:

Now see yon twain from Britain's foggy shore
    Set forth to span dark Afric's jungle plain;
Thy furthest fount, O Nilus, they explore.
    And where the goddess springs to seek the main,
The Veil of Isis hides thy land no more,
    Whose secrets open to the world are lain.
They deem, vain fools, to win fair Honor's prize.
This exiled lives, and that untimely dies.

26 : To talk of many things

There is no Heaven; there is no Hell. These be the dreams of baby minds,
Tools of the wily fetisheer to fright the fools his cunning blinds.

While on leave, Richard Burton spent many a weekend
with his wife at the Yorkshire mansion of his old and influential friend Richard Monckton Milnes, Lord Houghton. There the Burtons were joined by such artistic personalities as Algernon Charles Swinburne, Thomas Carlyle, J. A. Froude, Edward FitzGerald, Charles Kingsley,
John Ruskin, James A.M. Whistler, Dante Gabriel Rossetti, and Ouida.

"Wild animals never kill for sport," Froude said one
evening when the conversation drifted into the horrors of
Dahomey. While the ladies were left chatting in the
drawing room, the gentlemen held their bull sessions in
the study. "Man is the only one to whom the torture and
death of his fellow creatures is amusing in itself."

"Yaas," Burton responded. "Man is by nature an animal of prey, educated by the complicated relations of society but readily relapsing into his old habits."

"Well, now tell me, Burton," Froude asked. "You say the King of Dahomey is so benevolent and enlightened. If so, why didn't he abolish the Customs?"

"Abolish the Customs!" Burton looked utterly amazed. "Would you have the Archbishop of Canterbury abolish the Liturgy?"

Milnes interjected: "I think Dick means by 'benevolent' that Gelele didn't customize him, and 'enlightened' in that he can't be converted by Christian missionaries—eh, Dick?"

Burton laughed. "Yaas, despite all his butchery he's quite a phoenix!"

"*And* a coward," Froude added. "Fear is the parent of cruelty."

"*Kuchh dhar nahīn hai!*" Burton snapped. "There's no such thing as fear." He then lit a cheroot. "Y'know, gentlemen, Buddha refused to recognize the existence of God on account of the mystery of the 'cruelty of things.' The apparent brutality of wild beasts is a strong weapon in the hand of an agnostic who holds that the world is God and governed by its own laws, as opposed to the religionist believing in a personal deity whom he styles the Compassionate and Merciful. Papists opine that cruelty came into the world with that most sinful superstition, 'original sin.' But how do they account for the hideous waste of life and the fearful destructiveness of the denizens of the sea, who certainly never learned anything from Adam and Eve? The mystery of the cruelty of things can be explained only by a law without a law-giver."

"Well I don't pretend to understand the universe," Carlyle said. "It's a great deal bigger than I am. People ought to be more modest."

"All is vanity," Burton replied.

"What's there to argue about?" Kingsley shrugged. "Life is short."

Burton dragged on his cigar. "I find life very long."

All of a sudden Ruskin said: "Burton, they tell me you're an atheist."

Burton flashed, "My religious opinions are of no importance to anybody but myself. *No one* knows what my religious views are. I object to confessions, and I *will not* confess. My standpoint is and ever will be the Truth, the whole Truth, and nothing but the Truth as far as it is in me. I do things because they are *right*—not for heaven or hell, nor for religion, but because they are right as far as I'm concerned. This is what I call a natural law of human intelligence."

After a pause, Burton broke the tense silence: "I can remember when I was a boy in Italy all the little sluts used to ask me, 'Are you a Christian or a Protestant?' Ever since that time I've agreed with Diderot that the world will never be quiet till the last tyrant is strangled with the guts of the last priest."

"I pay divine honors to poetry—the poetry of a man and woman in bed—and nothing else," said Swinburne, half-cocked on brandy, adding:

"When the devil's riddle is mastered
 And the gallows creaks with a Pope,

We'll see Mrs. Grundy the bastard
Kick heels with her throat in a rope."

Burton cackled. "I follow the religion of nature: 'Love thy friends and hate thy foes.'"

"Nature is usually wrong," said Whistler.

"But it admits no lie," said Carlyle.

Burton scowled and said: "Nations are poor judges of one another. Each looks upon itself as an example to the world. Each vents its fanatic philanthropy by forcing its allegedly superior customs and ideas on its neighbors. I'm sick and tired of wandering over the world and finding every petty race wedded to its own petty opinions, claiming the monopoly of Truth, holding all others to be in error, and raising disputes whose violence, viciousness, and virulence are in reverse ratio to the importance of the disputed matter. Y'know, gentlemen, history may one day acknowledge four great protestants. Paul, who protested against Peter's Judaism. Muhammed, who protested against the perversions of Christianity. Luther, who protested against the tyranny of the Pope. And Burton, who protests against the whole damned business."

The room was filled with laughter.

Burton continued: "By Allah, I'd like to know what the clergy of the Church of England does for the three-and-a-half million a year wasted on 'em! As for Judaism, it hasn't changed since the day Jesus ran Shylock out of the temple. It's still the sacred purse strings of the world."

Carlyle said: "If Jesus Christ were to come today, people wouldn't even crucify him. They'd ask him to dinner, hear what he had to say, then make fun of it."

Burton said: "Yaas, well Muslims—like modern agnostics—hold that Jesus of Nazareth would be greatly scandalized by the claims to godship advanced for him by his followers. And there's nothing more enigmatical to the Muslim mind than Christian Trinitarianism. All other objections they can get over, but not this one. And to add to the enigma, the idolatrous association of the Virgin Mary and St. Joseph with the Trinity makes many Muslims conclude that Christians believe not in three but in five persons! This mystical amalgamation they call the 'Riddle God.' Here's what one Arab intellectual said to me: 'They not only say that three equals one and that one equals three. They profess to explain how that curious arithmetical combination was brought about. The indivisible was divided, and yet it wasn't divided. It was divisible, and yet it was indivisible. Black was white and white was black, and yet there weren't two colors but one color, and whoever didn't believe it would be damned.' "

"Well I'll be damned!" said Swinburne, holding up his glass. "Fiddle, we know, is diddle; and diddle, we take it, is dee."

"Oh, fiddledeedee!" said FitzGerald. "What is Truth?"

Burton chortled. "Confucius say, 'Truth hath not an unchanging name.' Burton say:

"Truth is the shattered mirror strown
  In myriad bits, while each believes
His little bit the whole to own."

Kingsley said: "Truth, for its own sake, has never been a virtue with the Roman clergy."

"And what is Virtue?" said FitzGerald.

"Or Vice, for that matter!" said Burton. "I assert there

is no Good and no Evil in the absolute sense as man has made 'em. I hold that man is born in the middle of the road; while the Christian, tormented by 'things divine,' clings to the comforting doctrine of innate sinfulness. Hence the refined egotism that says, 'Do good and get compound interest in a future state.' "

" 'While we, the clergy, get it here and now!' " Milnes added.

Burton continued: "The absolute concept of Good and Bad is one of the whims of mortal will. Whatever seems pleasant to us, we say it's good. Whatever seems unpleasant, we say it's bad. Good and Evil:

"They change with place, they shift with race;
    And in the veriest span of Time
Each Vice has worn a Virtue's crown,
    All Good was banned as Sin or Crime.

"It seems to me that mankind is born to be equally happy and miserable. This leads into the question whether life is worth living, whether man should elect to be born. Well, I think that life, whatever may be its consequence, is built upon a basis of sorrow. All existence is a state of sadness. It's our job to make it sufferable."

Rossetti said: "Eat thou and drink; tomorrow thou shalt die."

"Was never deep in anything but—Wine," FitzGerald answered.

Carlyle said: "Man's unhappiness, as I construe, comes of his greatness. It's because there's an infinite in him which with all his cunning he can't quite bury under the finite."

"Yaas, that's what the Sufi believes," Burton replied. "He says: 'I'm an individual, a circle touching and intersecting my neighbors at certain points—but nowhere corresponding, nowhere blending. Physically I'm not identical in all respects with other men. Morally I differ from 'em. In nothing do the approaches of knowledge, my five organs of sense with their interpenetration, exactly resemble those of any other being. The effect of the world, of life, of natural objects, won't in my case be the same as with the beings most resembling me. Thus I claim the right of creating or modifying for my own and private use the system which most imports me. And if reasonable leave be refused to me, I take it without leave.' My own sentiments are a universal augmentation of the Sufi's. I believe man to be a co-ordinate term of Nature's great progression, a result of the interaction of organism and environment working through cosmic sections of time."

"Do you believe in a life beyond the grave?" said Ruskin.

Burton smiled, fingering his mustachios. "The present life is all-sufficient for an intellectual—not a sentimental —being. Hence there's no want of a Heaven or a Hell. But of course, I'm too unprepossessed to affirm or deny the existence of another world. We may believe what we're taught, but we can know nothing. So I have to regret the excessive importance attached to a possible future state, a so-called spiritual utopia. I look upon this as a psychical stimulant, a kind of daydream whose revulsion and reaction disorder waking life. The sanctimoniously selfish aren't satisfied with the life they have. They must be immortal, such is their astronomical importance in the minute scheme of things. *Measure the world, with*

'*Me*' *immense!* These are the pious frauds who make hell out of everyone else's heaven in order to save their own dirty souls."

FitzGerald recited:

"Ah, love! could you and I with Fate conspire
To grasp this sorry Scheme of Things entire,
    Would not we shatter it to bits—and then
Remold it nearer to the heart's desire?"

Burton said: "The agnostic Greeks would have specimen'd modern man's assumed omniscience in Attic salt. It seems we've all but forgotten Socrates and the wisdom of the gods, *Gnōthi seautón*—Know thyself."

"The folly of that impossible precept!" Carlyle said. "Till it be translated into this partially possible one, 'Know what thou canst work at.'"

"*Inshallāh!*" Burton retorted. "But must we labor in the slavery of darkness? The rule of law emancipates man, and its exceptions are the gaps left by his own ignorance. That natural law is self-awareness, cosmic consciousness, universal empathy. The Arabs have a saying: 'Men are four. He who knows not, and knows not he knows not, he's a fool—shun him. He who knows not, and knows he knows not, he is simple—teach him. He who knows, and knows not he knows, he's asleep—wake him. And he who knows, and knows he knows, he is wise—follow him.'"

"Well, surely of all the so-called rights of man," Carlyle responded, "this right of the ignorant man to be guided by the wiser—to be gently or forcibly held in the true course by him—surely this right is the indisputablest."

"Yaas, yaas—but with great qualification. Wise in what way? I think you'll agree that the inhuman horrors blithely perpetrated by egocentric idealists and sophistical authoritarians—all of 'em very clever men indeed —I think you'll agree they constitute the most telling tragedies of history."

"Yes, but what is all knowledge but recorded experience and a product of history—of which therefore reasoning and belief, no less than action and passion, are essential materials?"

"*Inshallāh!* But what kind of knowledge produced the recorded experience of this product of history, Torquemada, who shed floods of honest tears while causing his victims to be burnt alive? What kind of reasoning and belief produced a bloodthirsty fanatic who in ten years executed over fifteen thousand Jews, and another who beheaded converted heretics lest they lose their immortal souls by lapse from divine grace? And what kind of action and passion produced the innocence—or rather ignorance—of St. Francis, who seeing a man and a maid in a dark corner, raised his hands to heaven and thanked the Lord there was still in the sinful world so much of Christian Charity?"

Carlyle laughed and shrugged. "Happy the people whose annals are blank in history books!"

Burton grinned, quoting an Arab philosopher: "Had you known what I was saying you would've excused me, and had you known what you said I should've blamed you. But you didn't understand me, so you blamed me; and I knew that you were ignorant, so I pardoned you." He then recited:

"Theories for truths, fable for fact,
   System for science vex the thought.
Life's one great lesson we despise,
   To know that all we know is nought."

FitzGerald yawned and drawled:

"One thing at least is certain—this life flies.
One thing is certain and the rest is lies.
The flower that once has blown forever dies."

Burton said: "Ouida tells me the idea of absolute Fate makes her feel as if the world were a jail."

"And so it is!" said FitzGerald. "A monstrous penal colony supervised by some unknown fiendish power.

" 'Tis all a checkerboard of nights and days
Where Destiny with men for pieces plays:
Hither and thither moves, and mates and slays,
And one by one back in the closet lays.

"The Moving Finger writes and, having writ,
Moves on—nor all your piety nor wit
   Shall lure it back to cancel half a line,
Nor all your tears wash out a word of it.

"And that inverted bowl we call The Sky,
Whereunder crawling coop'd we live and die,
   Lift not your hands to *It* for help—for It
Rolls impotently on as you and I."

"*Aiwallāh! aiwallāh!*" Burton said, stroking his beard. "That's why I've never in any way accepted the idea of a personal god. When some idiot asks me if I believe in God, I confound him with a counterquestion: 'What is God?' As much as to say, 'What is Truth?' But *Gawd, Gawd, Gawd*—that's all they blather about, and not a damned one of 'em knows what the hell he's saying. Confucius denied a personal deity for the same reason I do. I hold that idolatry begins with a personal deity. And by idolatry I mean egotism, pride, hypocrisy. But we might as well talk of black-whiteness and of white-blackness. A hundred generations of divines have never been able to unravel the riddle. A million will fail in the future. But this dilemma of God or no-God disappears when we convert the Person into Law, or a settled order of events. As it is now,

> "This world is run by two great schools:
> Enlightened rogues and religious fools."

Carlyle laughed. "Brothers, I'm sorry I've got no Morrison's Pill for curing the maladies of society."

"Listen to Lao-tze," Froude said. " 'Who can clear muddy water? If we leave it alone, it clears of its own accord.' "

"The solution is simple," said Rossetti. "*Love*. Love explains everything. 'He that loveth not knoweth not God, for God is love.' "

"Which proves the 'illusion of truth' is purely personal, a matter of individual taste and temperament," Burton replied dryly. "As Kabir says, '*Māyā marē nā man marē marmar gāyā sarīr*—Illusion dies; dies not the spirit, though dead and gone the flesh.' "

"Ah, the flesh!" said Swinburne, pouring himself another drink.

"She hath a thing well furnished of flesh,
Perfect in beauty and pleasant to thresh;
But underneath, so strait and taut,
A trap where one poor rat was caught.

"One anonymous inkslinger threatened me with castration if I dared to publish such 'garbage of the brothel.' When I least expected it he'd waylay me, slip a bag over my head, then remove the obnoxious organs. He'd seen his gamekeeper do it with cats! I beg to add that my offensive flesh is as yet no worse off than it was before receipt of the *verbum sapienti*."

Burton cackled. "In Egypt, the so-called weaker sex have an imaginative way of murdering men—especially errant husbands and unfaithful sweethearts."

"What do they do?"

"Why they tie 'em down and tear out their testicles! Measures less extreme came to my attention at Alexandria and Cairo, where Haji 'Abdullah practiced medicine back in '53. A host of swollen scrotums revealed how jealous hellcats eunuchize their prey by beating and bruising or twisting and squeezing the testicles. The Fellahin are exceedingly clever in inventing methods of manslaughter. For some years bodies were found that bore no outer mark of violence. Frankish inquisitiveness finally discovered that the barrel of a pistol had been passed up the anus and the weapon discharged internally."

"I say, Dick," Milnes asked, "who was it started that cock-and-bull story that you were caught in a harem and castrated?"

"The same joker who passed the word around that I

robbed a post office in Cairo and murdered two men who penetrated my disguise."

"Well who the damn-hell—?"

"The rogue and rat of Saville Row."

"Not Rigby?"

"Yaas, Rigby! A favorite Persian punishment for strangers caught in the harem is to strip 'em naked and throw 'em to the Negro slaves and eunuchs, whose sodomitical embraces are followed by castration. Rigby was discovered *in flagrante delicto* at Karachi. Six lusty blacks took turns buggering and masturbating him, with the infuriated head of the violated household supervising his abuse. Rigby escaped castration only by the good fortune of his being a British officer, but they circumcised him instead. His anus was so damned sore he couldn't sit his horse for over a week! On leave from India, he lost all his loot in a Cairene panel house. That led to his robbing a post office and heading for home. Knowing I knew all this, he exercised an immediate reform by informing everyone that Dick Burton was a thorough scoundrel. After my pilgrimage to Mecca, Rigby and Palgrave started the silly scandal that I killed a couple Arabs who caught me pissing in a standing position—an indiscretion among pious Muslims. Then Speke took it from there, swearing I was a ball-less anus-beating blackguard. The only *real* Burtonian peccadillo I can put my finger on at this moment is one that was perpetrated in Goa during the fire and folly of youth. I tried to carry off a lovely little Portuguese nun, but her mother superior didn't appreciate my gallantry."

With Milnes and Swinburne asking the questions and egging him on, Burton launched the conversation into

the never-never land of Eastern sexuality. His answers
were the forbidden delight of one and all:

"After much wandering, I'm almost tempted to believe
that morality is a matter of geography—that nations and
races have, like individuals, a pet vice—and that by restrain-
ing one you only exasperate another. . . .

"In 1845, after Charley Napier had conquered and an-
nexed Sind, he began to consider his conquest with a curious
eye. I reported to him that Karachi, then a townlet of some
two thousand souls, supported no less than three whorehouses in which not women, mind you, but boys and eunuchs lay for hire. Being then the only British officer who
could speak Sindi, the old veteran asked me in private to
make inquiries and to report upon the subject.

"The reason for Napier's concern is that Karachi was distant not more than a mile from camp, meaning our sepoys
would soon be lured into sodomy and possible desertion.
I undertook the task on express condition that my report
should not be forwarded to the Bombay Government, from
whom supporters of the conqueror's policy could expect
scant favor, mercy, or justice.

"So, gentlemen, dressed as a merchant and accompanied
by my munshi friend Mirza Muhammed Husayn of Shiraz,
Mirza 'Abdullah of Bushire passed many an evening in the
town, visited all the brothels, and obtained the fullest
details. The most interesting of these is that the boys demanded nearly a double price. The detail especially excited
old Charley's curiosity. The reason proved to be that the
penis and scrotum of the unmutilated boy could be used
as a kind of bridle for directing the movements of the animal. That's why the eunuchs were so meanly paid. None
of 'em had either testicles *or* penis. One Sindi told me that

sodomizing a *sandalī* or complete castrato was like eating
a leg of lamb without the bone.

"Well, to make a long story short, the devil's brother—
Napier, y'know——was recalled in '48. His office was then
filled by none other than our greatest enemy, who immediately began fishing in the old files, looking for something
scandalous to send to Government House. His search was
a success. My long-forgotten report on pederasty in Karachi
was dispatched posthaste to Bombay, where it produced the
expected result. A friend in the Secretariat informed me
that my summary dismissal from the service had been for-
mally proposed by Sir Charles Napier's successor, the late-
*un*lamented Bayard of India, Sir James Outram. The general
consensus of official opinion was that a man who studies vice
must be vicious, and therefore unfit for military command.
But this excess of outraged modesty wasn't allowed, thanks
to Lord Elphinstone, who was no lover of office rats and
Outramists. . . .

"Among savages and barbarians, the comparatively un-
restrained intercourse between the sexes relieves the brain
through the body. The mind and memory have scant reason,
physical *or* mental, to dwell fondly upon visions amatory and
venereal—to live, as it were, in a rustle of imaginary copulation. The utterly artificial life of civilization, which de-
bauches even the monkeys in the zoo, makes a forbidden
luxury of carnal intercourse. It torments the unmarried with
no bodily want save one, damned difficult to come by.
Hence the prodigious amount of mental excitement and
material pruriency found wherever civilization extends. . . .

"Europeans are contemptuously compared with village
cocks by Hindu women who can't be satisfied with less than
twenty minutes of continuous coition. That's why thousands
of Europeans have cohabited for years and had families by

native women without ever being loved by 'em. Muslims and Hindus study—and study intelligently—the art and mystery of physically satisfying the female. That's why it's said abroad that the English have the finest women in Europe and least know how to use 'em. . . .

"Muslims believe in making peace with their wives by knowing 'em carnally. Reminds me of the story of the Irishman who brought over to the Holy Catholic Church three several Protestant wives, but failed with the fourth on account of the decline of his 'converter.' . . .

"The Arabs aver that women prefer an additional inch of penis to anything else this world or the next can offer. No honest Hindi Muslim will take his womenfolk to Zanzibar on account of the huge attractions and enormous temptations offered to 'em there. Debauched females prefer Negroes for the size of their parts. I measured men in Somaliland who numbered six inches when quiescent. But these imposing implements don't increase proportionally during erection. Eight inches is the extreme limit, between six and seven and a half the average. This is a characteristic of the African race—long, thick, and flabby. The pure Arab is below the six-inch average of Europe. His member is extremely small—three inches in quiescence, five in tumescence.

"Being of phlegmatic temperament, the Negro takes a much longer time to ejaculate than the highly nervous Arab. This prolongation is naturally desired by Muslim women. And I may add the same cause has commended these 'skunks of the human race' to debauched females in Europe. But Nature, human and otherwise, commands the union of contrasts—fair and foul, dark and light, tall and short—otherwise mankind would be like the canines, a race of extremes. . . .

"In the Muslim babe the clitoris protrudes beyond the outer labia. Snipping off its head is female circumcision.

I examined the Somali prostitutes who practice at Aden. All of 'em had the inner labia and glans clitoris excised. The moral effect of female circumcision is peculiar. While it diminishes the heat of physical passion it increases mental licentiousness, breeding a debauchery of the brain far worse than bodily lust. It's the sexlessness of a spayed bitch imitated by the suggestive mind of humanity. . . .

"The Muslim harem is a hotbed of sapphism and tribadism. The *sehhīqeh* or 'she who rubs' is known by her large projecting clitoris. Masturbation is so rampant among Arab girls that in many harems such penislike articles as tallow candles are vainly forbidden by the jealous master. Bananas, a great favorite, are always skinned and cut into four so as to be useless. Artificial phalli are now at a premium! . . .

"There's a feminine peculiarity highly prized by the Arabs. It's the use of the vaginal constrictor muscles. Abyssinian women are famous for their control of the vulvar sphincter, which they tighten and loosen at will. The *qebbādzeh* or 'she who clasps' can sit astraddle a man and provoke the venereal orgasm not by wriggling and moving, mind you, but by wrenching and squeezing the virile member with the muscles of her privities—milking it, as it were. Needless to say, these nut-cracker women cost treble the money of other concubines. . . .

"Almost all the black eunuchs of Mecca and El-Medina have wives with whom they practice mutual masturbation, fellatio and cunnilingus, and other diversions till they induce the venereal orgasm. A eunuch's wife once told me she prefered her husband to a whole man because he couldn't impregnate her and because his performance was pleasurably prolonged. There are many ways of making the castrato, but in all cases the animal passion remains. That's because in man, unlike other animals, the *mons veneris* is the brain. . . .

"I once asked a Shirazi how penetration was possible if

his victim resisted with all the force of the anal sphincter. He smiled and said: 'Ah, but we Persians know a trick to get over that. We apply a sharpened tent peg and knock till he opens!' Many a man has been raped by these facetious blackguards. Y'know, gentlemen, none other than William Gifford Palgrave was subjected to this gross insult by none other than the Agha Khan, Hasan 'Ali Shah, whom he infuriated by his Jesuit conversion mania. He often alludes to it by mentioning his 'dishonored person,' but Englishmen never comprehend the full significance of the confession.

"Anglo-Egyptians are still chuckling over the tale of Khedive Muhammed Sa'id Pasha and M'sieu de Ruyssenaer, the high-dried and highly respectable consul general for the Netherlands. Sa'id solemnly advised him to make the experiment, both active and passive, before offering his opinion open the subject. . . .

"*Dzerrāt*—fartermost, or *abū dzirt*—father of farts, is a common nickname among the bean-eating Egyptians. I was once sitting in the Greek quarter of Cairo when arose a prodigious hubbub of boys surrounding a couple Fellahin. These men had been working in the fields about a mile east of town. While returning home, one said to the other: 'If you carry the hoes I'll break wind once for every step we take.' He was as good as his word! And when they were about to part he cried, 'And now for your bakhshish,' which consisted of a volley of fifty—to the great delight of the boys. . . .

"The Arabs assured me that 'nothing pokes and strokes more strenuously than the *qird*,' the hideous Abyssinian ape. This appears to be the popular belief in Egypt, where the men claim their women commit bestiality with baboons. Whether they do or not, the exaggerations I heard must be based on common ignorance. Although it erects stiffly, the penis of the ape isn't long and thick enough to produce that friction essential to a woman's pleasure. Nonetheless, the beast seems to have a natural lust for women.

"When I was at Cairo in '53, a huge dog-faced baboon broke away from his trainer and jumped on a little girl in the street. He was ready to rape her when a soldier drew his bayonet and killed the brute. The event was looked upon as an evil omen by the older men, who shook their heads and said these were bad times when apes attempted to ravish the daughters of Muslims. During my four years' service in West Africa, I heard and saw enough to satisfy me that these powerful beasts often kill men and rape women. But I couldn't convince myself they ever kept the women as concubines!

"The she-monkey shows a distinct lust for man by fondling him and displaying her private parts as if to entice him. There's no doubt that carnal connection has taken place. My Persian munshi assured me he'd witnessed a case with his own eyes. One evening he and another Muslim went out to the jungle to take a leak. When his friend suddenly disappeared in the trees and kept him waiting an unconscionable time, my munshi went to investigate. He found the man sexually united to a she-monkey. Indignant as any good Muslim should be, my munshi reproved him for his bestiality. Then he asked him how it had come to pass. His friend answered that the she-monkey came regularly to look at him when he made water, that he was in the habit of throwing her something to eat, and that her gratitude displayed such sexuality he was tempted and fell.

"In the motherlands of these apes, women have the liveliest fear of 'em. The same is true in Europe. As a lad I once led a party of vacationing English girls to a zoo near Florence. Every last one of 'em fled screaming in fright when they saw the erections and violent masturbation of the big hooting baboons. . . .

"Modern science, out of the depths of its self-consciousness, has settled so many disputed questions. Its latest decision is that none of the anthropoids can bear issue to man. But where's the proof? As far as I'm concerned, whether there'd be issue and whether such issue would be viable are still disputed points. When man shall become a knowing as well as a thinking animal, he'll cast off the puerile prejudices of our age and ascertain by actual experiment if human being and monkey can breed together.

"I laugh to think how the produce would add another difficulty to that pseudo science called psychology. Such a mule would have only half a soul, and issue by a congener would have a quarter-soul. Paul du Chaillu once proposed breeding pithecoid men who might be useful as agricultural workers. His idea was to unite the highest order of apes with the lowest of humanity. I never heard what became of his breeding stables."

"I've just domesticated and tamed the Bird a little," Isabel said on the following evening, "and it wouldn't do to give him an excuse for becoming a wandering vagabond again."

All the guests were gathered for a séance in Lord Houghton's library.

"People kept saying, 'It won't last. She'll never be able to hold him.' Well here he is, and here *I* am, and you don't see any leash around the Bird's neck!"

"Well, Isabel, how *does* it work?" said Marie Louise de la Ramée, the glamorous "Ouida."

"Oh, it works very well indeed!"

"Can you manage him?"

Isabel smiled. "I shouldn't call it 'manage.' Let's say I

advise him. Dick's the only man in the world who could manage me."

"Does he ever come home at night?"

"Oh yes, he always comes home with the milk in the morning."

"We're on the verge of a new science!" Burton said, stemming the tides of conversation. "I call it E.S.P.—extrasensuous perception. And here at Fryston Manor we students of the mystic arts may speak out what we honestly believe to be the truth—without fear of the religionist and the pseudo scientist, and without threat from the Red and Black Terrors."

"Well I daresay, Dick," Milnes exclaimed, "we're all ears! Come, tell us about this—er—E.S.P. Is that what you call it?"

"Yaas. Extrasensuous perception. Let me speak of it regarding the mesmeric state. The experience of twenty years has convinced me that perception is possible without the ordinary channels of the senses. Why shouldn't the brain, or the nervous system, or whatever controls the sensuous processes of man, when artificially excited as by mesmerism or somnambulism, be able to see, hear, and feel for itself? In other words, why should it not be capable of clairvoyance and clairaudience? I assert that it is."

"But how do you go about proving it?" Carlyle said.

"The theory of extrasensuous perception of things sensuous is to be proved or disproved not by hard words, not by mere logic, but by experience. I'm not bound to answer *how*. I affirm that man can do it, that he has done it, and that he still does it. I simply state my conviction that the senses, which after the study of over twenty centuries are as little known to us as the so-called laws of nature, still conceal many secrets. But be that as it may, the senses sometimes are—and often can be made—independent of their organs."

"You say 'made.' Does that mean you believe in spirit phenomena?"

"I know nothing of what is absurdly called spiritualism. I consider myself a spiritualist without the spirits."

There was a rustle of laughter in the room.

"Perhaps you'd care to explain that," FitzGerald said, lighting his pipe.

"*Inshallāh!* As I said before, twenty years of experience has convinced me that perception is possible without the ordinary channels of the senses. It has also convinced me that I've been in the presence of some force or power which I cannot understand. But I don't believe that any so-called spirits are subject to our calls and caprices, or that the dead can be communicated with at all. The superhuman is the superlative of human. We know what our senses and their interpenetration teach us. But no man—positively, absolutely no man—neither deity nor devil, angel nor spirit, ghost nor goblin—has ever wandered beyond the narrow limits of this world, has ever brought us a single idea or notion belonging to another and different world, or has ever eluded the simple cognizance of man's five wits."

"But what of Captain Burton's Sixth Sense?" Ouida said facetiously.

Isabel lit a cigarette. "Dick got his mysticism from the Arabs, his superstition from the gypsies. God knows, I'm superstitious enough; but he's far more so."

Burton cackled. "Not superstitious, my dear, but extrasensuously perceptive. Leave superstition to the religionist. The man of science calls it E.S.P."

"Semantics, semantics," Swinburne drawled, emptying his glass of brandy.

"Yaas, *semantics*. I can't but take exception to such terms as 'psychology.' Why? Because I hold the psyche to be the ego of man, the vital principle that differentiates him from all other men. The soul, like the mind, isn't a thing but a state or condition of things. How can one pretend to scientize the psyche?"

"Then you're not a spiritualist," Ruskin said.

"I defend materialism, if that's what you mean. I can't see with Guizot that the pursuit of psychology is as elevating as that of materialism is degrading. What right has anyone to limit the power of the Supreme Soul of the Universe? Is not the highest honor His who from the worst can draw the best? That thunder is in the air is a fact; and the presence of a cat may be known even though one cannot see, hear, taste, smell, or feel it. I call this force—this sixth sense, if you will—zooelectricity."

"But how do you distinguish between insight and imagination?" Whistler said.

"You don't! What you perceive you perceive, whether any other living soul perceives it or not. Our so-called visions, optical illusions, and hallucinations are a stark reality to those who experience 'em. We see what we see. That's why psychology is a pseudo science. Psychologists cannot systematize the soul, cannot explain away in general terms of delusion and mental disorder the inexplicable extrasensorial perception of each and every individual. Many of the so-called supernaturalisms and preternaturalisms familiar to the Hindus are manifestations of zooelectricity, not imagination. I witnessed in Sind the terrible training and ascetic tortures whereby sadhus and sannyasis either lose their senses or attain the highest powers of magic—of commanding nature by mastering the zooelectrical force, or whatever it may be, that conquers and controls every modification of matter."

"Now don't suppose Dick is a materialist, nor is he a spiritualist in the vulgar sense of the word," Isabel said. "As I am a Catholic, Catholicism is the highest order of spiritualism. It's my belief the theory of zooelectricity suits both spiritualists and nonspiritualists. Since it offers no offense, I think the Holy Catholic Church would accept it as Dick conceived it."

FitzGerald said to Burton: "How would you interpret a relationship between opium or hashish and your E.S.P.?"

"Drugs are an artificial means of inducing *samādhīyōga* or superconsciousness. A notable effect of hashish is wildly to excite the imagination, a kind of ecstatic delirium or phantasmagoria. I used to experiment with it, but now I lean towards more natural methods—yoga, autohypnotism, self-suggestion. It's encouraging to find that medical treatment by mesmerism and hypnotics, so violently denounced and derided a decade ago, is now gradually becoming a part of the regular professional practice. But strange and unpleasant truths progress slowly in England, especially when the opposition is organized self-interest. My old friend Dr. James Esdaile finally succeeded in breaking the ice. He proved the superior effectiveness of animal magnetism over artificial anesthesia by going out to India and performing over three hundred successful, painless, major operations on Bengali patients in mesmeric trance. Quite an experiment and quite an achievement!"

"Well now, Dick," said Ouida, "I hear you're a great mesmerizer in your own right."

"*Ha-ha!* Yaas, yaas—you might say I am. It all started in Sind, over twenty years ago, where I developed an interest in snake charming. Found the game too dangerous and soon gave it up. That's when I took to riding crocodiles. I'd tie a rope around the beast's neck, stand on his back, then off I'd go. One time I won a bet by jumping across a croc-infested canal, using the muggers as logs."

"But tell us about your snake charming."

"I'm afraid there's not much to tell! I took lessons from an old Sindi Muslim. The trick is to attract and distract the snake's attention with one hand while you catch him by the throat with the other. One split-second slip spells certain death when fascinating a cobra, the most delicate ordeal in all the world."

Ouida then said: "Well now, Zoo, does Dick ever snake-charm you?"

"Oh yes, he does it all the time! He always prefers women—especially of the blue-eyed, yellow-haired type. He began with me as soon as we were married. I didn't like it at first, but I soon got used to it."

"Yaas, it's the only way to get a woman to tell the truth!"

"Oh heavens, I tell him everything I know—all my secrets. I sometimes tell him things I'd much rather keep to myself."

Burton cackled. "The greatest of all explorers and dis-coverers will be he who finds a woman confessing in-ability to keep a secret."

"Have you ever had any practical success with your mesmeric talents?" Froude said.

"Yaas, yaas," Burton replied, stroking his beard. "I once cured a dozen Abyssinian slave girls of the perni-cious and price-lowering habit of snoring."

For the rest of the evening Burton hypnotized all the ladies, beginning with Ouida. Isabel was asked to go first, but she begged off. "If you don't mind, folks, I think I'll retire now. I've a splitting headache, and you know I must be up in time for early Mass."

Long after midnight, Richard Burton stomped up the winding stairs carrying a dead-drunk Algernon Swin-burne under his right arm. This was the usual procedure. Having pulled off his clothes and put the poet to bed, Burton retired yawning to his own room.

Several minutes later, while passing by the door, Mil-nes was brought to a standstill by the muffled sound of two angry voices. All of a sudden, just as he started to move on down the hall, Lord Houghton heard a sharp outburst:

"Goddamnit, if any man ever mesmerizes you I'll kill the man and you too!"

27 : Exiled again

My eyes, my brain, my heart are sad. Sad is the very core of me.
All wearies, changes, passes, ends. Alas, the birthday's injury!

The winter of 1865 found Captain and Mrs. Richard Burton in a pestilential Brazilian seaport. F.O. Secretary Lord Edward Stanley had appointed Burton Her Britannic Majesty's Consul at Santos, the Fernando Po of South America.

While Burton was supervising the unloading of luggage, Isabel was first to enter the ratty and ramshackle consulate. A moment later the new consul heard his wife screaming bloody murder. He raced through the bungalow, burst into the master bedroom, and saw a horror-stricken Isabel standing on a chair in the middle of the floor.

Burton cocked an eye, his arms folded across his chest. "Well, well, well," he drawled. "A fine sort of traveling companion *you're* going to make! I s'pose you think you look very pretty and interesting standing on that chair howling at those innocent creatures."

"Oh, but Dick," she gave way to tears, "the place is crawling with cockroaches! Look—some of them are three inches long! Oh, Dick, look at those holes in the wall—bristling with bugs—and all the yellow satin curtains in the drawing room are sprinkled with these crawling things! *Ugh*, it makes my blood run cold! I have a perfect horror of anything black and crawling."

"Yaas, well don't say I didn't warn you! But you wouldn't listen, would you? Oh no, you couldn't wait to rough it! Why the hell d'you think I kept you out of West Africa? Nanny Poo's the pesthole of the Eastern world —alive with bugs, swarming with snakes, stinking with disease. Well here's the asshole of the Western Hemisphere! This's what you wanted, isn't it? Here's your crust and your tent! They sent us here to die. You know that, don't you? Well, I don't give a goddamn what you do, but they're not going to kill me! I'll live to piss on the graves of every last one of 'em!"

Burton stalked out of the room, swearing into his beard.

He had hurt her so much that Isabel dried her cheeks with the back of her hand, sniffed defiantly, and got down from the chair determined to attack all the vermin in Santos.

"I'll show him!" she muttered. Fetching a basin of boiling water and a slipper, in quick order Isabel knocked ninety-seven cockroaches into it. She then called for her husband. "Look, darling, I'm cured!"

Burton howled with laughter. "By Allah, you are!" He

hugged and kissed her. "Please forgive me, Puss. Sometimes I'm not myself."

"Nor am I, dearest one." She pressed her lips to his, then squeezed him close. "I'm awfully sorry, Dick. Please forgive me. I shouldn't have acted so silly. It's enough to make any man furious. But no matter how rough she may become, it's almost impossible for an Englishwoman to view dirt with calm and indifference."

"All right now, you and Kier can get busy cleaning up this rotten place—"

A scream echoed in the next room. It was Kier, Isabel's Irish maid.

"There! You see I'm not the *only* woman who doesn't like cockroaches."

Isabel was to find a lot more to dislike during those three long years of "exile" in Brazil. She penned in her diary:

I do hate Santos. After Providence made the world, it being Saturday night, all the rubbish was thrown down here and forgotten. The climate is beastly, the people fluffy and immoral. The stinks, the vermin, the food, the niggers are all of a piece. If you go one way, you sink knee-deep in mangrove swamps; another you are covered with sand-flies. I'm still covered with boils; and I can't sit or stand, walk or lie down, without a moan. I am irritated and depressed beyond words.

Poet and Arabist Wilfrid Scawen Blunt was then press attaché at the British legation in Buenos Aires. He visited Burton on many occasions, and the two men talked far into the night on Islam and the erotic East.

Burton seldom went to bed sober. He swilled cognac

like water, ranting and raving about religion and politics. Blunt was ensorceled. He had never seen or heard such a sinister human being in all his days.

Burton's aspect was satanic—dark, cruel, and treacherous. The terrifying gleam in those wildcat eyes gave him an almost unearthly appearance. In a soiled unbuttoned shirt, his sleeves rolled up to reveal ropy arms, Burton grew dangerous in his cups. That's when Blunt decided to say "good night." Revolver in hand, Burton would stagger to the privy and then to bed. Isabel undressed him without saying a word. When neither of them could stand it any longer, they left for home.

It was July, 1868. Burton wrote in his journal:

Resigned Santos. I'm tired of it. It's out of the world and leads to nothing.

28 : Home again

How short this life, how long withal; how false its weal, how true its
*   woes:*
This fever fit with paroxysms to mark its opening and its close.

"Tell me, captain, why did you leave the Santos post?"

Richard Burton scowled at Henry M. Stanley, foreign correspondent of the *New York Herald.* "Because
the salary was too inadequate for my position. I was
obliged to use my own capital to supplement—you know,"
he winked, "paying for consular wine."

Stanley chuckled, dashing it all down in shorthand.
"But how did your predecessor manage?"

"By living in one room over a tobacco shop and wash-
ing his own socks three times a week."

"What's your most vivid memory of South America?"

"My most vivid memory of South America, my dear
Mr. Stanley, is that of a Roman Catholic priest trying to
rape a poor peasant girl."

Stanley gaped with surprise.

Burton grinned sadistically. "What's the matter, Mr. Stanley? Didn't you ever read Boccaccio's 'Putting the Devil in Hell'? It's the tale of a young monk who seduces an innocent girl in his cell. And how does he engineer such an enormity? By convincing the child his penis is the devil and her cunnus hell. What more need I say, sir?"

Stanley grunted. Before he could change the ticklish subject, Burton blurted: "Y'know, this isn't blood in my veins. It's Bourbon! I'm descended from Louis XIV."

Stanley anticipated another Burtonism, so he answered: "Well, captain, it's surprising that any man who has such good Scotch-Irish blood in his veins should be proud of a descent from the wrong side of a royal blanket."

"Why, Mr. Stanley, I'd rather be the bastard of a king than the son of an honest man."

"Indeed!"

"Yaas. The only people to be pitied in this world are the mentally and physically weak, whatever their parentage. One of the curses of the nineteenth century is the increased skill of the physician who's now able to preserve worthless lives and burden civilized society with semi-abortions whose only effect upon the breed is increased degeneracy. I want to see every man and woman in England physically healthy and strong. I consider it abominable, *criminal*, that infant monstrosities should be allowed to live."

"But captain—"

"It's regrettable, Mr. Stanley, that so trenchant a state paper as your American Declaration of Independence should begin with so gross and palpable a fallacy—that all men are created equal. Men are *not* born equal, nor do they become equal before their deaths except by artificial leveling. In republics and limited monarchies, where all are politically equal, the greatest social inequalities ever prevail. The Arabs say that people are equal, but in different degrees. And Jerrold neatly expressed the truth when he said we all row in the same boat but not with the same sculls."

"How well did you read that 'trenchant state paper,' as you call it, captain? It clearly states that all men are created equal because they're endowed by their Creator with certain inalienable rights—life, liberty, and the pursuit of happiness."

"A self-evident truth! But let's be realistic, my dear Mr. Stanley. We're none of us living in a utopia. This theory of spiritual equality is materialistically impractical as far as human nature is concerned. The brute fact is that in England and the United States men and women live under an incubus, a perfect system of social despotism intended to make amends for an unnatural political equality among classes born radically unequal as far as their intellects are concerned. Regarding your 'inalienable rights,' few men and no woman can resist the temptation of absolute command. That means no matter what the political system, every damned one of us must fight to preserve his own individuality. In all my thirty years of experience, I've found that under no form of government is man socially freer than under the Islamic system of *laissez faire* tempered by *lex talionis*. It contrasts strangely with the grinding social tyranny that characterizes every mode of democracy."

"Well, Captain Burton, now that I have your political opinions, perhaps—"

"Yaas, yaas. You now want my religious views, eh? Very well, Mr. Stanley. You can tell Mr. James Gordon Bennett and the people of America that the coming great struggle of the twentieth century will be the war between religion and science. It'll be a war to the death. For if science wins—which I'm sure it will—it'll do away with the personal god of the Jews, the Christians, and the Muslims. It'll eliminate the childish doctrine or dogma of future rewards and punishments, and everything connected with the supernatural. It will be shown that law reigns supreme. The police, representing law and order, will be of more importance than the clergy. Even now we might do away with the devil-dodgers. Let everybody become his own priest—a great economy!"

"Is it true that you're an advocate of Islam?"

"'Lhhamdulillāh! My dear Mr. Stanley, every religion is—without exception—the abortion of fear, ignorance, and superstition. But if choose I must, the only *real* organized religion in the world is that of Muhammed. But let me be fair, Mr. Stanley, lest I offend to excess any of your self-righteous readers. Religions, like vices, are geographical and climatic. The Protestant faith suits England, the Catholic Italy, the Muslim Arabia."

"And the Jewish faith?"

"What Jewish faith? I never knew the Jews to have any religion. Why the whole bloody history of Jewry is a denial of Jehovah!"

"What are your views on Roman Catholicism?"

"I object to the Church of Rome because it has added a fourth person to the Trinity. And another thing. Muslims, like Catholics, pray for the dead. But since they do the praying themselves instead of paying a priest to do it, their prayers of course are of no avail."

"But isn't Mrs. Burton—?"

"Mrs. Burton is an old English Catholic. What has that got to do with Captain Burton? A man without religion may be excused, but a woman without religion is un-thinkable."

"Do you believe in a hereafter?"

Burton threw back his head and laughed aloud. "A hereafter! Hallelujah! I shouldn't care to go to hell. I'd meet all my relations there. Nor to heaven. I'd have to avoid so many friends. My dear Mr. Stanley, none of us knows what happens to us after death. All we can do is hope for the best."

"How would you define your religion, captain?"

"My religion is the religion of universal law."

At that moment Isabel approached. "Oh, am I inter-rupting something, gentlemen?"

"Not at all, Mrs. Burton," Stanley said, smiling. "I'm merely conducting an informal interview with your highly opinionated husband."

"Oh, how fascinating! May I join you?"

"Please do, Mrs. Burton. Perhaps you'd care to com-ment on Captain Burton's extraordinary views, you being his wife and closest confidante."

Burton scowled, shifting his position in the chair. He knew what was coming, and he suddenly hated Stanley for it. Why did he have to get her started against him? It wasn't unwitting, he thought. It was downright de-liberate.

Isabel gave a quick glance at her husband and said:

"Well, Mr. Stanley, what am I to say? I don't know what Richard told you, but I protest vehemently his religious and moral sentiments. I point the finger of indignation particularly at what misrepresents our Holy Roman Catholic Church and at what upholds that unnatural and repulsive law he always preaches."

"What law is that, Mrs. Burton?"

"Polygamy!"

Stanley swallowed the laugh that welled up in his throat.

Burton grumbled: "Englishmen, who are restricted to one wife, can't be too careful."

Isabel was about to speak, but Burton growled:

"Legalized monogamy is tyranny, the tyranny of church-controlled law over the privacy of the individual. Love—spiritual unity—is stronger to bind man and woman than any medieval marriage ceremony. And honor is stronger to compel faith than any religious superstitions. Besides, the only true and lasting bond of love the world knows is sexual intercourse. No scrap of paper or ecclesiastical hocus-pocus can sanctify sexual intercourse. Only love and honor can, have, and always will sanctify sexual intercourse. Otherwise it's merely authorized breeding in the selfish interest of church and state."

By now, Burton had attracted a sizable audience in the smoke-filled drawing room of No. 10 Downing Street, where cigar-savoring dignitaries were celebrating Disraeli's defeat by Gladstone.

Stanley ended the interview on the impulse that it was a good time to get a breath of fresh air. As he was leaving, Burton called after him: "Remember, Mr. Stanley

—priests, politicians, and publishers will find the gate of heaven extremely narrow."

"Willy, I hope you're not going to leave the destinies of the British Empire to prigs and pedants," said Benjamin Disraeli, stroking his tufted chin.

The austere-looking William Gladstone snorted.

Burton grinned. "*Riddle:* Why are the Egyptian donkey boys so favorable to the English? *Solution:* Because we hire more asses than any other nation."

Gladstone walked away.

Disraeli chortled. "There goes a sophistical rhetorician inebriated with the exuberance of his own verbosity." The lean and lynx-eyed Lord Beaconsfield turned to the new Secretary of State for Foreign Affairs, Lord Clarendon. "George, I want you to give Burton Damascus. I shall never forgive it if you don't. Man is only truly great when he acts from the passions. Burton is a passionate man. He's a great man. His Christianity is muscular."

George Villiers smiled. "Dizzy, you always drive a nail to the head, don't you?"

"Yes, always—in every block of wood."

Lord Clarendon walked away.

"I say, Burton," Dizzy asked sportively, "is man an ape or an angel? Now I'm on the side of the angels."

Burton cackled. "Well I'm not so sure about man, m'lord, but there's no difference except civilization between an old woman and an ape."

"*Ha!* From the lips of one who used to monkey with the sex. Youth is a blunder, manhood a struggle, old age a regret. But why must we take it out on our poor wives? 'Tis better to ape the French. Every woman should marry —and no man."

"Women, all the world over, are what men make 'em. I always say we English have the finest in Europe and least know how to use 'em."

"And how would you use 'em, pray tell?"

"Practically throughout the civilized world there are only two ways of treating women. Muslims keep 'em close, defend 'em from all kinds of temptations, and if they go astray kill 'em. Christians place 'em upon a pedestal, expose 'em to every temptation, and if they fall accuse and abuse 'em instead of themselves. Women can be thoroughly guarded only by two things—their hearts and the chastity girdle."

Disraeli laughed. "Gird up your loins, O ye women of the world!"

"I'm reminded, m'lord, that Somali women are far superior to their men in muscular strength and physical endurance. On first entering the nuptial hut the bridegroom wields his horsewhip and flogs the living hell out of his bride, with the view of taming any lurking propensity to shrewishness. The wearisome and expensive proceedings attendant upon divorces here in England are unknown in Africa. There you just kick your wife out of the hut, or vice versa, and the deed is done. I'm surprised at the combined folly and brutality of civilized husbands and wives who poison, stab, or otherwise polish off their better halves. The job can be as neatly and quietly, safely and respectably done by a few months of African air at Zanzibar."

At that moment Lady Disraeli approached. "Captain Burton, please come here. I've something extraordinary to show you."

Burton followed the elderly dame over to a mirror.

"Look, Captain Burton," she said, pointing at her own reflection with affected annoyance, "there must be an ape in the glass. Don't you see it?"

Fingering his mustachios, Burton stared for a few seconds. "Yaas, yaas, madam. Quite plainly. I see myself."

Later, Disraeli said to him: "Don't mind my wife. She's an excellent creature; but she never can remember which came first, the Greeks or the Romans."

"Yaas, but what difference does *that* make as long as she's on the side of the angels!"

At dinner, Burton was seated next to the lanky vegetarian archbishop of Westminster, Henry E. Manning.

"Your excellency," said Isabel, who was seated on the other side of the Roman Catholic prelate, "have you heard the wonderful news of Richard's appointment to the consulate of Damascus?"

"Why no, my dear. But I thought you were in Brazil?"

"We were," Burton replied dryly. "Now we're not. Please eat, m'lord. You make me nervous by not eating."

"Oh, your excellency," Isabel said with sustained excitement, "did you hear that Richard has just presented to the Zoological Gardens a curious South American fish that can live out of water and takes but little nourishment?"

"Ah, you must mean Captain Burton's Odd Fish—the one that's causing such a commotion and become the talk of the town. Please tell me about it, Richard."

Burton frowned. "I'm afraid there's nothing much to tell aside from what my wife has already said. Please eat, m'lord. The food's delicious. Yaas, I've often presented rare creatures to the London zoo. But nobody ever bothers to thank me. This peculiar specimen of Pisces, as

Isabel said, can live without water and on little food. A kind of amphibious pinchgut, I daresay. But enough of the Odd Fish! You're not eating, m'lord. Come—dig in, drink up—mortify yourself."

"Richard must take you to the zoo and show you his famous fish," Isabel said.

"Well I'll certainly go!" Manning replied. "I'm really curious to see it."

Burton said dryly: "Then, m'lord archbishop, there will be a pair of Odd Fish. Y'know, you neither eat nor drink; and that's the peculiarity of the other odd fish."

"Well, Captain Burton," Manning retorted playfully, "at least I'll be at home with some of your ancestors the apes."

Burton pulled his mustachios and drawled: "Well, m'lord, I at least have made a little progress. But what about your lordship, who's descended from the angels?"

When the laughter died down, Burton added: "Darwin's theory of evolution has revolutionized my thinking. Now, every time I see a monkey in the zoo I ask him: 'What crime did you commit in some other world, Jocko, that you're caged for now?' I keep asking myself, *I wonder what he did? I wonder what he did?* Then I tell him to mind his manners, or he'll turn out to be the predecessor of some archbishop or prime minister!"

October, 1869. Burton dashed in his journal:

I'm off to Damascus with my books and two bull terriers. Zoo will pay, pack, and follow in December with her entire fortune—a modest £300 in gold—and everything we own, for a life that promises to be all perfume.

From my dull and commonplace and "respectable" sur-

roundings, let the jinn bear me back to the lands of my predilection! Back once more, there to die in peace.

29 : The Emperor and Empress of Damascus

As palace mirror'd in the stream, as vapor mingled with the skies,
So weaves the brain of mortal man the tangled web of truth and lies.

"Darling, we're at the zenith of our career!" Isabel said,
as she and her husband rode out into the Syrian Desert.
"Remember what you said that wonderful day you proposed to me in Regent's Park? You said that someday
we'd have the consulate at Damascus."

"Yaas," Burton replied, bursting with joy, "and you
said you'd rather have a crust and a tent with me than be
queen of all the world. Well I dub thee Queen Isabel of
Damascus! *Ha-ha!*"

"Oh, Dick, it's all come true! Everything Hagar the
gypsy predicted has come true! Oh, Dick—my darling—
now we can both be truly happy."

"Yaas, *inshallāh!* Think of it, Zoo. The jinn have brought me back to the land of my predilection, a region so familiar to my mind that even at first sight it seems a reminiscence of some bygone metempsychic life in the distant past. Again I ride under glorious skies, whose every breath raises men's spirits like sparkling wine. Once more I see the evening star glittering like a diamond on the black-satin canopy of the Eastern firmament. The afterglow magically transforms the desert into a fairyland lit with a light that never shines on other soils. Then the black tents —ah, the Bedawin! The campfires, the bleating of flocks, the tinkling of camel bells, the wild weird song of lads and lasses—*'Lbedwīy'l-bedwīyeh!* O Allah, the rave of the jackal! the ranting hyena! And the most musical of music, the murmuring palm trees answering the whispers of the night breeze with the softest tones of rippling water. Zoo, I know—I feel—what Fate is! Here lie all the secrets of everlasting life. The mysteries of creation and destruction. The alpha and omega, the first and the last, the beginning and the end of time. Here in the desert, man knows and feels the infinite force that determines the destinies of the universe."

"Yes—yes, my love—I feel it too. It's a strange and awesome sensation of being closer to God—so close, so frightfully close, we dare not deny His eternal and divine existence."

"Well pray, Zoo. Pray to God that this is the journey's end, that this is the final resting place. I can't bear to think that this is all a mirage, a fleeting fancy of Fate. D'you hear the camel bells? D'you know what they're ringing?

"One moment in Annihilation's Waste,
  One moment of the Well of Life to taste.
    The stars are setting, and the caravan
  Starts for the Dawn of Nothing—Oh, make haste!"

Entering an Arab village, the Burtons dismounted to join a small crowd of wide-eyed children surrounding a wandering dervish.

Burton grinned knowingly. "*Heh-heh-heh.* Just keep your eye on this, Zoo. It's your first lesson in Arab psychology."

Isabel watched intently as the old dervish lowered his stick and drew a large circle in the dirt. "*Ed-dunyeh,*" he rasped. "The world!" He then opened his sack and placed a scorpion inside the circle. "*En-nās.* Mankind!"

The scorpion, thinking it had achieved freedom, began to run around the circle—but never attempted to go outside. After the scorpion had raced several times around the inside edge, the dervish lowered his stick and divided the circle in half. The scorpion stopped for a few seconds, then started to run around inside its half of the circle. The scorpion ran faster and faster, apparently looking for a way out but never finding it.

"Darling, how strange!" Isabel said. "The scorpion doesn't dare cross over the line. Why? Why is that?"

Burton snickered ominously. "Odylic force, my dear. The poor devil's self-hypnotized. Keep watching."

After a few minutes the dervish divided the half circle. The scorpion became frantic. Soon the dervish made a space no bigger than the scorpion's body. "*Deqīqet-hheqīqeh,*" he grated. "The moment of truth!"

The scorpion, dazed and bewildered, found itself unable to move one way or another. Raising its venomous tail, the scorpion turned rapidly round and round in a farcical frenzy. Whirling, whirling, whirling till all its spirit and energy were spent. In utter hopelessness the scorpion stopped, lowered the poisonous point of its tail, and stung itself to death. Its torment was ended.

"Oh, Dick, how awful and cruel! What is it supposed to prove?"

"That a scorpion in a corner stings itself to death. A coward blames Allah. Allah laughs and lets it die. A man goes forward."

"Well now, *yā sittī*," Burton said one evening after his return from an exploratory excursion into the desert, "what has my Queen of the East been up to these past three days?"

"Oh, I've been attending weddings, circumcisions, funerals—anything that's going on."

"Have you been in any harems yet? Y'know, I asked 'Abdel-Qadir if you could tour his—"

"Oh, I already did! In fact, darling, I visited several of the harems here in Damascus. But I was especially excited about seeing that of 'Abdel-Qadir. He has five wives, you know. One of them is very pretty."

"Yaas, well how did you like talking to 'em in Arabic?"

"I found them all very pleasant, only at first they used to ask me such a lot of inconvenient questions that I became quite confused."

"*Ha-ha!* What kind of inconvenient questions did they ask?"

"Oh, they were awfully curious how many times a week I had intimate relations with my husband. And they were always puzzled because we have no children."

"Yaas, yaas. Go on."

"Well, I then asked them how they could bear to live together and pet each other's children. I told them that in England if a woman thought her husband had another wife or mistress, she'd be ready to kill her. They all laughed heartily at me, and seemed to think it a great joke."

"Yaas—you have a lot to learn about the Arab mind."

"Oh, and I also went to another circumcision at 'Abdel-Qadir's house—the fourth I've been invited to so far."

"What did you think of it the very first time?"

"Oh, it was something awful! There was a loud crash of cymbals to drown the poor little victim's cries, and with one stroke of a knife the operation was finished in a second. The part cut off was then handed around on a silver platter as if to force all present to attest that the rite had been performed. I felt quite sick the very first time, and I couldn't look. But after that I accepted a compliment paid to the highest rank. I held a boy in my arms while the ceremony was being performed."

"*Māshallāh!* You're learning fast! Have you seen much of the city?"

"Oh yes, indeed I have! I started at dawn this morning and rode all over Damascus. Oh, Dick, what shocking contrasts! The Muslim quarter is clean, the Christian quarter dirty, and the Jewish simply filthy."

"Yaas, I know. It's like that in almost every city. An indication as to the true character of the respective races."

"I had to gallop through the ghetto holding my hand-

kerchief to my face. Such a horrible smell, it was sometimes choking! Everywhere the streets are piled with
heaps of garbage, and dead dogs are lying about. Oh,
Dick, how can people be so squalid?"

"Because they're 'civilized,' that's how. They're sweating and stinking under the incubus of modern civilization,
which is raping hell out of 'em. And there's not a goddamned thing I can do about it."

"Oh, and guess who I saw parading through the streets
in his gold-trimmed victoria?"

"It's easy to imagine. None other than the wicked and
wily Wali himself."

"Yes. He saluted me with a sickly smile. Reminded me
of an old tomcat, indolent and fat."

"Yaas, a well-fed cat—with long claws."

"You know him, Dick?"

"Know him! I nearly killed him with my bare hands!
Must've been twenty years ago, in Paris. Rashid Pasha,
the Turkish Bluebeard. The second and latest time I saw
him was in '53, when Mirza 'Abdullah left England for
Arabia. The minute I stepped aboard the steamer, who
should I run into but my old enemy? I think he recognized me, but was too damned scared to say anything.
Well, he's come a long way in all these years. A spoiled
child of fortune. The rawboned Egyptian army officer,
now the fat-assed governor general of Syria. What wonders Allah wills! There you have it, Zoo. Fate. Fate again
—then, now, and forever. I knew it, could feel it then as
strongly as I do now. I tell you, Zoo, seventeen years ago
I sensed in all certainty that Rashid Pasha and Richard
Burton would meet again someday to settle the score once
and for all. Now that day is drawing near. *Ha-ha!* Be-

ware, Rashid Pasha—beware. Richard Burton is waiting for you to make your move."

"Oh, darling, never mind him." Isabel hugged and kissed her husband. "Sometimes you frighten me, Dick. Why do you take notice of such little things?"

"I'm like an elephant's trunk. I can pick up a needle and root up a tree."

"Oh, you silly one! Did you enjoy your jaunt?"

"Immensely! I thought when I came here that Syria and Palestine would be so worn out my occupation as an explorer was clean gone. But what a pukka surprise! This is virgin land, and all previous travelers have kept to the beaten tracks. Ah that Brigham Young were here, to plant a million! The sky would then no longer be brass, nor the face of the country a quarry. There was hardly a mile I rode over that I didn't come across some kind of ruin— broken pillars, altars, inscribed slabs, monoliths, tombs. Why the whole place's teeming with archeological interest! Y'know, Zoo, study of the Holy Land has the force of a fifth Gospel—not only because it completes and harmonizes, but also because it makes the other four intelligible. That's the most important thing of all!"

Isabel smiled. "Why darling, if I'm not mistaken I think you've contracted that strange disease you call 'Holy Land on the Brain.' Thank God, things are looking up! It's a good omen, Dick—your renewed interest in the Bible."

Burton laughed. "Happy, Puss?"

"Deliriously!"

"Then let's go to bed. We shouldn't want 'Abdel-Qadir's women to tell him the new English consul never makes love to his one and only wife, should we?"

"Indeed not! But don't worry, dear. I told them we did it almost every night."

"*Bismillāh!* That kind of wishful thinking is worthy of any Arab woman. I fancy you've finally penetrated the Muslim mind. Congratulations—and now to bed, where dreams become a reality!"

Early the next morning, Burton swaggered into the consulate to find it swarming with merchants and money-lenders.

"My god, what a lot of Jews!" he said to the vice-consul. "Why the whole of Noah's Ark is turned out here!" Burton took off his tarboosh, catapulted it to the kavass on the end of his stick, then slammed the iron down hard on the top of his desk. "All right, gentlemen! If you'll please approach me one by one, I'll be more than happy to hear your problems and give you each a helping hand."

A short, stocky, well-dressed man stepped forward. He was bearded and bespectacled, and his head was bald except for a black skullcap. He extended his hand. "Let me introduce myself, your excellency. My name is Solomon Donemberg." He spoke with a thick accent.

Burton shook hands, sat down, and motioned for Mr. Donemberg to be seated. "What can I do for you?"

"If you please, your excellency—what can we do for each other!"

Burton eyed him narrowly.

Donemberg laid his left hand on the desk. Under it was an envelope. He smiled smugly. "I represent these gentlemen you see behind me. We welcome your excellency to Damascus. We trust your consulship here will be a long and fruitful one."

Burton scowled, nodding impatiently. He flicked his hand. "Enough amenities, I thank you. Now, Mr. Donemberg, what's on your mind?"

"This, your excellency. As you doubtless have been informed, the previous occupant of this very important post was—shall we say—an extremely foolish man. He had absolutely no understanding of the inestimable value of mutual co-operation. He—"

"Excuse my interruption, sir, but it's my knowledge that the man who occupied this office before me was recalled on charges of offering and accepting bribes. Am I correct?"

"Yes, but—"

Burton grinned. "Not only an extremely foolish man, Mr. Donemberg, but I daresay a very indiscreet one for getting caught at it!"

"Exactly—exactly, your excellency! I said the exact same thing myself. A very indiscreet man indeed."

"Yaas." Burton still evinced a wry grin, his eyes riveted on the envelope under Donemberg's hand. "Tell me, Mr. Donemberg, is that by any chance—?" He paused, leering at the man.

"Oh, but your excellency, I should never call it that!"

"Call it what?"

"Well, you know—"

"No, I *don't* know, Mr. Donemberg. Tell me what it is."

Donemberg smirked, his hand pressing the envelope. "Consider it a gift for services rendered."

"What services?"

"The services of supporting and preserving the interests of British-protected subjects."

"Interests in what regard?"

"In regard to collecting rent and rates of premium, and in settling debts and arrears with Turkish-protected subjects. Do I make myself clear, your excellency?"

"Perfectly, Mr. Donemberg. *Perfectly.* You want me to aid and abet the interests of the Jews, who are British-protected subjects, against those of the Arabs, who are under Turkish protection. Correct?"

Donemberg chortled. "You are not a man who—how do you say—minces? You put things in plain words!"

"Yaas, Mr. Donemberg, I call a spade a spade. It's one of my notorious eccentricities. By the way, Mr. Donemberg, d'you know who I am?"

"Why no—that is, I do not know you by name."

Burton's grin became startlingly grotesque. He ran his fingers through his beard, glaring at Donemberg like a black panther. "Tell me, Mr. Donemberg. How much money is under your hand?"

Donemberg, distracted by Burton's ensorceling stare, suddenly gave a start. "Oh, this!" He lifted his hand. "It contains two checks in the amount of five thousand pounds each. All you need do is write your name on the—"

Burton stood up, leaned forward with both hands flat on the desk, and said coldly: "If you were a gentleman of my own standing, and an Englishman, I'd just pitch you out the window. But as you're not, you may pick up your ten thousand pounds and walk down the stairs."

Donemberg twitched, squinted, then smiled nervously. "But we only want—" he gestured with a shrug.

"Yaas, I know what you want. You want me to exact delinquent rent with the kurbash, and strangle usurious interest out of all your victims. Well, I think, sir, you'd better hire and pay a consul for yourself alone. That could easily be arranged. Just send a prayer to your God Almighty, Baron Rothschild. He owns Whitehall, y'know, and he's always obliging in cases like yours. As for myself, I wasn't sent here as a bailiff to tap the peasant on the shoulder in your behalf."

Donemberg lurched out of his seat and snatched up the envelope. He shook a finger at Burton. "I shall report you to the British consul general at Beirut. I shall charge you with dereliction of duty and insulting a subject of the Crown."

"It's by far the best thing you can do, Mr. Donemberg," Burton said dryly. "I have no power to alter a plain line of duty."

"You shall regret it—mark my words," Donemberg replied, waving the envelope in Burton's face. He flashed a sardonic smile. "Remember what happened to your predecessor. He was a greedy fool. You are an unrealistic idealist. That is even worse. All you idealists are one and the same. You fail to see that all your dreams are lies."

"Are you through, Mr. Donemberg?"

Donemberg sneered. "For now, *yes*. But just you wait —" He wagged a finger at Burton, winking and nodding to his friends and associates.

Burton exploded. He grabbed his stick and slammed the top of the desk. "Get out of here, you goddamned Jew! D'you think I'm going to be bumbailiff to a bunch of bloodsuckers!" Burton's teeth were bared, his eyes ablaze. He stalked around the desk, brandishing his stick at the retreating merchants and moneylenders. "I'll not have the British consulate turned into a debt-collecting agency for a lot of bloodsucking leeches! Get out of here before I rap you one!"

Darting through the doorway, he roared down the hollow stairway after them: "You goddamned pack of Hebrew hyenas, if you ever come back here again I'll kill you! There isn't enough money in the world to buy me!"

On the night of August 26, 1870, Captain Burton pitched his tent in the Syrian Desert. While he was seated by the campfire chatting with his Arab servants, a mounted messenger suddenly appeared and handed him an urgent letter from the chief dragoman of the British consulate at Damascus. Burton opened it and read:

Dear Sir,

The Christians in Damascus are in great alarm. Most of them have left, and others are about to leave. Their alarm was occasioned by the following facts:

Signs of crosses were made in the streets in the same way which preceded the massacre of 1860. On the 23rd instant a certain Muhammed Reshid, a government inspector, being in disguise, caught a young Jew, twelve years old, in the service of Solomon Donemberg, a British-protected subject, making signs of crosses in a cabinet of a mosque at Suq el-Jedid. Yesterday another young Jew, in the service of Jacob Marco, a French Jew, was caught also. These two boys were taken to the Turkish Government. Being underage, they were at once released. It is believed by Christians that the Muslims are the authors of these signs, either directly or indirectly.

Nasif Meshaqeh

Burton ordered his horse saddled and his revolver cleaned. At 6 A.M. the next morning he strode into the *mejlis* or council chamber at Damascus, where the Turkish tribunal was still in emergency session.

His voice thundered in the hollow hall: *"Bismillāh! Which of you is to be hanged if this massacre isn't prevented? It'll cost you Syria! Unless you take measures at once, I'll telegraph to Istanbul and have the whole damned lot of you thrown out on your fat asses!"*

"What would you have us do, effendi?" said the *mufettish* or city inspector.

"I want you to post a guard of soldiers in every street. Order a patrol all night. I'll go the rounds with the police commissioner. Let the soldiers be harangued in the barracks. Tell 'em that on the slightest sign of mutiny the offenders will be banished to the Danube. Issue an order that no Jew or Christian shall leave the house till all is quiet."

All these measures were taken by ten o'clock and continued for three days. Not a drop of blood was shed. The frightened Christians who had fled into the mountains now began to come back. Damascus was like the calm after a storm. Burton had averted a bloody massacre. He penned in his journal:

> In the East, men respect manly measures and ironfisted action—not the hysterically philanthropic pseudo humanitarianism of the West. The Eastern mind is always in extremes, and must be dealt with accordingly. I would never hang an Oriental without publicly burning his corpse in a pigskin and then throwing the ashes into a common cesspool.

"They're calling us the Emperor and Empress of Damascus," Isabel said angrily.

Burton snorted. "The Rothschilds consider me a dangerous man. I'm deeply flattered." He slapped down the newspaper. "Burton the Jew-Baiter. *Ha!* The charge of religious intolerance is a novelty to me. The world has generally given me credit for something too much the reverse!" He lit a cigar. "Had I a choice of race, there's none to which I'd more willingly belong than the Jewish. Then I'd do what Jesus of Nazareth did. I'd chastise those who made me feel ashamed of my origin. Here the Jewry serve as a synonym for all devilry. I'd give the devil his due."

Burton stood up and walked over to the window. "Y'know, Zoo, even during the worst days of Jewish persecutions their moneybags were heavy enough to lighten the greater part if not all of their suffering." Hands clasped behind him, he paced the floor. "They're mostly a body of respectable men—hard-working, inoffensive, of commercial integrity—with a fair sprinkling of pious, charitable, innocent people. I tell you, Zoo, I'm ready to defend their lives, liberty, and property. But I *will not* assist 'em in ruining villages and in imprisoning destitute debtors on trumped-up charges. I'd willingly deserve the praise of every section of the Jewish community of Damascus, but in certain cases it's incompatible with my sense of justice and my conscience."

"You don't deserve *that* kind of praise, Dick. You're Richard Burton, not a wretched jackal."

He puffed furiously on his cigar. "I've found villages in ruins, homes empty because the masters were thrown in jail, children starving and women in tears at my feet. I

found these things being done in the name of England.
My predecessor accepted bribes and kept his mouth shut,
but I'll do neither." Burton picked up several sheets of
paper from the *secrétaire* and handed them to Isabel.
"Here's my report to the F.O. It should wipe out once
and for all any silly sneers at my alleged Jew-baiting and
so-called anti-Semitism—a misnomer that makes me
laugh."

Isabel read:

> In June, 1870, I prepared a dispatch for our ambassador
> at Constantinople on the system of defrauding the poor and
> of "running" villages by the Damascus Jewish moneylenders.
> I will now try to explain how these matters stood and still
> stand.
>
> In former days, when not a few Europeans were open to
> certain arrangements which made them take the highest
> interest in the business transactions of their clients, a radi-
> cally bad system was introduced into Syria. The European
> subject or *protégé*, instead of engaging in honest commerce,
> was thus encouraged to seek inordinate and usurious profits
> by sales of the government and by loans to the villagers.
> In such cases he, of course, relied entirely upon the protec-
> tion of a foreign power, on account of the sums to be
> expended in feeing native functionaries before repayment
> could be expected. Thus the consuls became, as it were,
> bumbailiffs whose principal duties were to collect the bad
> debts of those who had foreign passports.
>
> Today, Damascus contains a total of forty-eight adult
> males protected by H.B.M.'s Consulate; and of these there
> is a triumvirate of Shylocks. Most of them are Jews who
> were admitted to, or whose fathers acquired, a foreign
> nationality given with the benevolent object of saving them
> from Muslim cruelty and oppression in days gone by. These

protégés have extended what was granted for the preservation of their lives, liberties, and property to transactions which rest entirely for success upon British protection.

The case of No. 1 (Solomon Donemberg), whom we will call Judas, is a fair example. He has few dealings in the city, the licit field of action. Since the death of his highly respectable father in 1854, he has been allowing bills signed by the ignorant peasantry of the province to accumulate at simple and compound interest, till the liabilities of the villagers have become greater than the value of the whole village. A, for instance, on the eastern skirt of Mount Hermon, owes him 106,000 piasters which were originally 42,000. He claims 5,000 purses from the B tribe, upon a total debt of 242,000½ piasters in 1857. I have not yet passed through a single settlement where his debtors did not complain loudly of his proceedings. Some villages have been partly depopulated by his vexations; and the injury done to the Druses, by thus driving them from the Anti-Lebanon to the Hauran, may presently be severely visited upon the Ottoman authorities.

The British protégé is compelled every year in his quality of farmer of revenue to summon the village shaykhs and peasantry, to imprison them, to leave them lying in jail till he can squeeze from them as much as possible, and to injure them by quartering policemen who plunder whatever they can.

For about a year a special commission has been sitting on his case, whose intricacies—complicated by his unwillingness to settle anything—wear out all the members. He is accused of bribing the government secretaries to introduce into documents sentences of doubtful import upon which he can found claims for increased and exorbitant interest, of adding lines to receipts and other instruments after they have been signed, and of using false seals made

at home by his own servants. One of the latter publicly
denounced him but was, as usual, paid to keep silence. He
is reported again and again to have refused, in order that
the peasants might remain upon his books, the ready moneys
offered to him for the final settlement of village liabilities.
His good management has baffled all efforts at detection. He
corrupts, or attempts to corrupt, all those with whom he has
dealings.

The Jews from all times have held a certain position in
Syria, on account of their being the financiers of the country, and even in pre-Saladin days Haim Farhi was able to
degrade and ruin 'Abdullah Pasha of Acre. In the time of
Ibrahim Pasha, when the first consuls came here, a few Jews
were taken under British protection; and this increased their
influence. Then all the richest people of the community tried
to become British-protected subjects, or protégés of some
foreign consulate.

When I arrived in 1869, Shylock No. 1 (Donemberg)
came to me, and patting me patronizingly on the back, told
me he had three hundred cases for me relative to collecting
£60,000 worth of debts. I replied that Her Britannic Majesty's Consul will not assist British protégés to recover debts
from the people of Syria. I then posted a notice to that
effect in front of H.B.M.'s Consulate, Damascus, adding
that British protection extends to life, liberty, and property
in cases where these are threatened by violence or injustice, and protesting strongly against the system adopted by
British-protected subjects who habitually induce the Ottoman authorities to imprison peasants and pauper debtors
either for simple debt or upon charges which have not been
previously produced for examination at this consulate.

Shylock then tried my wife's influence, but she replied
that she was never allowed to interfere in business matters.

This one man alone has ruined and sucked dry forty-one

villages. He goes to a distressed village and offers them
money, keeps all the papers, and allows them nothing to
show, adding interest and compound interest which the poor
wretches cannot understand. Then he gives them no receipts
for money received, so as to be paid over and over again.
The uneducated peasants have nothing to show against the
clever Jew in the courts; and body and soul, wives and children, village, flocks, and land become his property and slaves
for the sake of the small sum originally borrowed.

These men, who a few years ago were not worth much,
are now rolling in wealth. I find villages in ruins and houses
empty because the men were cast into jail, the children
starving and women weeping at my feet, because these
things are done in the name of England—by the powerful
arm of the British consulate.

"No wonder the Arabs hate the Jews!" Isabel said,
handing the report back to her husband. "And all because
of a few infamous Shylocks. Oh well! Darling, it's a good
report. I'm more than certain it'll make Lord Granville sit
up and take careful notice of our case."

"Yaas, well, I'm writing a second one this evening. It
was brought to my attention those two Jewish boys were
at it again, drawing crosses on the walls of mosques."

"Oh, no!"

"Cheeky little buggers, they're pimps and catamites—
the sexual servants of Donemberg and Marco. I promptly
investigated it, took away the official protection of our
two Shylocks, then gave the kids a good bawling out. Poor
little fags, they only acted under orders. How could I
punish 'em? Well, their masters fancied this a fair opportunity to overthrow the 'emperor.' They reported me to
the philanthropic King of the Jews, Sir Moses Montefiore,

telling him I tortured the two boys. Montefiore in turn contacted Sir Francis Goldsmid, Q.C., who got in touch with the Chief Rabbi of London, who passed the word on to Nathan and Lionel Rothschild. And for what? To white-wash a flock of vampires and black-list a 'blatant Jew-baiting beast.'"

"Oh, Dick, don't let it worry you. What can they possibly do? The truth's on our side, and we've enough influential friends to—"

"Yaas, yaas—I know. But it makes my blood boil to think that such men can buy and sell the world and every soul in it. You want to see a sickening sight? Go down and take a long hard look at the *Sijn Shāmī*. I actually found an old man of ninety, half-naked, who endured all the horrors of the Damascus jail during the last bitter-cold winter. Why? Because he owed one of these blood-suckers twenty francs. I set him free. Ever since that day I've been visiting the prison at least once a week to see if any British-protected subject has penned up some poor Muslim on his own responsibility. I'm now a notorious scandal. One of the Shylocks told me to watch my step. Said he knew some royal highness in England. Said he could have any consul recalled at his own pleasure. I laughed and told him he and his clique could know very little of English royalty if they thought it would protect such traffic as theirs. That's when they put their heads together and started sending out a swarm of telegrams and petitions purporting to be from 'all the Jews in Damascus.' The great tragedy is that 'all the Jews in Damascus' know very little or nothing whatsoever about the whole damned dirty affair. These dispatches, backed by letters from the influential Israelites who received 'em, were duly

forwarded to No. 10 Downing Street. Granville has asked
for an explanation, and so he shall get it. *Bang! bang!*—
with both barrels."

"Yes, Dick, and I think you should ask *him* for an explanation—why, after ten years of excellent service, you
can't be transferred to a good post like Tangier or Constantinople or Tehran."

"You know the answer to that as well as I do. I'm
cursed with every pesthole and hotbed for only one reason—they want to get rid of me. The charges against me
are placarded all over Whitehall. *Burton professes atheism and hates the Christian Church. Burton is a Jew-
baiter and violently anti-Judaic. Burton's 'masquerade' to
Mecca has made his name a curse among orthodox Muslims.* They're hardly worth answering. No one knows my
religious views. I've affected the interests of certain mon-
eymongers. I've always been treated with respect by the
Arabs, orthodox as well as unorthodox, and they're always
asking me to come back to Mecca with 'em. That's why
I'm not appointed to a 'good post,' as you call it. Here I
have to put up with all three races and religions. I tell
you, Zoo, they gave me Damascus to devil me to death."

"Oh, Dick, you don't think those awful troublemakers
will stir up any more strife between Christian and Muslim, do you?"

"If I knew the answer to that, I'd damn-soon see they
didn't by catching the whole rotten lot of 'em red-handed.
One thing at least is certain. Jewish usurers have been
accused of inciting racial and religious riots between
Muslim and Christian. Why? Because their lives are perfectly safe, and they profit from the slaughter by grabbing up property at a nominal price. In the massacre of

1860 they enriched themselves greatly, and men possessing three thousand pounds suddenly rose to thirty thousand. Then as now they had at their backs in England such giants as Montefiore, Goldsmid, and the Rothschilds, who don't seem to know the true state of the Jewish moneylenders in this part of the world. The British consulate became a Shylocks' bailiwick, and when I arrived here I found 'em roughriding all over the land."

Several weeks later, Burton came storming into their suburban villa with a newspaper clenched in his fist. "Zoo! Zoo, have you seen this?"

"Seen what, darling?" Isabel came running in from the next room.

"Seen this goddamned—why just look at this! Montefiore delivered a public diatribe against us, Rothschild denounced us in the House of Commons, and Goldsmid and the Chief Rabbi have made a personal protest to the Queen."

"Oh no! How could they?"

"Well they have! And listen to what Goldsmid wrote to Granville: 'I hear that the lady to whom Captain Burton is married is believed to be a bigoted Roman Catholic, and to be likely to influence him against the Jews.' "

Isabel, who had paled in dismay, now reddened with rage as she read the newspaper reports.

"Yaas, a mean and far from lean pack of wolves is howling for my recall—but goddamn 'em for attacking you as well!"

"Oh, Dick, what a vicious and lying charge—'Captain Burton is influenced by his Catholic wife against the Jews.' Thank God I'm proud to say I've never in all my life tried to influence you to do anything wrong, and I'm prouder still to say that if I tried I'd never succeed."

Burton grinned, clasping and kissing her. "Thank God you're right! 'Ask woman's advice, and whatever she advise, do the very reverse and you're sure to be wise!' "

"Oh, Dick, how can you be so facetious at a time like this! Well, I know what I'm going to do—right now! I'm going to write Lord Granville a letter that'll make him wish he never heard of us!"

And so she did:

Salihiyeh
Damascus, Syria
November 29, 1870

My Lord,

I have always understood that it is a rule amongst gentlemen never to drag a lady's name into public affairs, but I accept with pleasure the compliment which Sir Francis Goldsmid pays me in treating me like a man.

Sir Francis Goldsmid has accepted the tissue of untruths forwarded by three persons, the chief moneylenders of Damascus, because they are his coreligionists. He asserts that I am a bigoted Roman Catholic, and must have influenced my husband against them.

I am not so bigoted as Sir Francis Goldsmid; for if three Catholics were to do one-half of what these three Jews have done, I would never rest until I had brought them to justice.

I have not a prejudice in the world except against hypocrisy. Perhaps, as Damascus is divided into three religions, my husband and I are well suited to the place. We never ask anybody's religion, nor make religion our business. My husband would be quite unfitted for public life if he were to allow me to influence him in the manner described, and

I should be unworthy to be any good man's wife if I were to attempt it.

My religion is God's poor. There is no religious war between us and the Jews; but there is a refusal to use the name of England to aid three rich and influential Jews in acts of injustice to and persecution of the poor, to imprison and let them die in jail in order to extort what they have not power to give, and to allow foreign and fraudulent money transactions being carried on in the name of Her Majesty's Government. Also it has been necessary once or twice to prevent the Jews exciting the Muslims to slaughter, by which they have never suffered, but by which they gratify their hatred of the Christians, who are the victims.

I think nobody has more respect for the Jewish religion than my husband and myself, or of the Jews, as the most ancient and once-chosen people of God; but in all races some must be faulty, and these must be punished.

There are three mouths from which issue all these complaints and untruths; and what one Jew will say or sign the whole body will follow without asking a question why or wherefore, nor in Damascus would their consent be asked. It is a common saying here that "everybody says yes to them because they have money." These three men count on the influence of men like Sir Francis Goldsmid, and one or two others, and impose upon their credulity and religious zeal to get their misdeeds backed up and hidden. But will such men as these protect a fraudulent usurer because he is a Jew?

I enclose a true statement of the case and also some private letters, one from our chief and best missionary, which will show you something of the feeling here in our favor.

I have the honor to be, my Lord,

Your most obedient and humble servant,

Isabel Burton

To the Earl of Granville,
Secretary of State for Foreign Affairs
No. 10 Downing Street
London, England

"To this I can only add," she said to her husband, "if the Shylocks of Damascus hate us, so much the more to our credit. I don't think I told you, darling, but the Reverend William Wright of the Irish Presbyterian Mission told me one of the most influential Jews in Damascus was talking with him and the American missionary John Crawford. He said 'Captain Burton is unfit for the British consulate in Damascus,' and the reason he gave was that being an upright and honest man you transact your business by fair means instead of by foul."

"Yaas, I think I know who that one is. He offered me ten thousand to sway a public transaction in his favor. I threw him out."

"Their wives and lady friends keep visiting me with expensive gifts. I was almost tempted to accept them at first, till I realized what they were for. Madam Donemberg insisted I take her pearl necklace, so I did. I dropped it on the floor and stepped on it. That's the last I saw of Madam Donemberg."

"*Ha-ha!* She claims you ripped off her necklace, kicked her, slapped her across the face, and carried on like a banshee."

"Oh, I shouldn't be a bit surprised! I hurt her precious pride. Next thing she'll say I spit on her and called her a damned Jew. Well there's one thing I did say to her and all the rest of them. The effect of their conduct here will fall upon their own heads, and upon their children. They far outstrip us in the race of life, but their sins make them lose in the long run. When the time comes—and it will come—the trampled worm will turn. The Muslim won't rise against the Christian, but against the Jew. *Their* quarter will be the one burnt down, *their* people will be exterminated, and all their innocent tribe will suffer for the few guilty."

The clouds were slowly gathering—thicker, blacker, more vibrant than ever before.

"Rashid Pasha!" Burton roared to his wife. "Where was that yellow lion and his pack of jackals when Damascus was threatened with a second St. Bartholomew's Day? Conveniently *in absentia*, that's where!"

"But why, darling?"

"Because Rashid Pasha's a Machiavellian madman, an arrogating assassin who wants Damascus all to himself. He lives by the law of Sultan Selim: 'Bribe the Jew to bait Christian against Muslim, then bully all three.' He's had the Spanish, Italian, and Russian consuls recalled for refusing his favors; and now he intends to work on me. The Shylocks buy him and he buys them. They all play hand in glove to suck the blood out of the Arabs."

"I met him the other day at 'Abdel-Qadir's. He has such ratty, shifty eyes. He was wearing furs and looked just like a fat lazy tomcat. Why he even purrs and walks like a well-fed cat!"

"Yaas, well he's a cat whose claws need clipping before they rip the city wide open."

"You know what, Dick? He accused you of having made a political meeting with the Druse shaykhs in the

Hauran, thereby doing great harm to the Turkish Government. Knowing you had done nothing of the kind, I told him so; but I saw there was a new intrigue on."

"Yaas, and what a tangled web our Wali is weaving! He bribed some baboon to write a letter signed by me asking the chief Druses if I could pay 'em a private visit. Now he accuses me of meddling in Ottoman affairs, of plotting with the Druses against the Porte. He says I'm inciting 'em to insurrection, offering fraudulent proof I was in the Druse country for that purpose. He's even tried to have me waylaid and butchered in the desert, but I've sent his assassins off on a false scent. Had he succeeded, the verdict would've been: 'Fallen a prey to his wild and wandering habits in the desert.' "

"Oh, Dick, you never told me he tried to—oh, darling, darling—now I'm really scared."

"Don't worry, Puss. He didn't succeed, did he? There isn't *any* Muslim can outwit Haji 'Abdullah! I'm now the only man who stands in his way, and it's killing him. He's afraid of me, Zoo, and that's where I have the upper hand. I let him make his move, then I checkmate. It's all a waiting game for me. One of these days, in a fit of desperation, he's going to make a fatal move. I've never seen it fail. Then we'll say, *Esh-shāh māt*—The king is dead—checkmate Rashid Pasha!"

"Oh, Dick, I love you so madly I couldn't bear to lose you. I'd kill Rashid Pasha, then I'd kill myself."

"You're all the world to me, Puss. I trust you and believe in you with all my heart and soul."

At that moment all their troubles were a tempest in a teapot.

:

A week later, Burton came stalking home with a wild stare.

Isabel gave a frightened look. "Dick, what's wrong?"

"Eldridge, the consul general at Beirut, is in league with Rashid Pasha."

"Oh no!"

"Yaas! The whole damned Foreign Service is a den of thieves. Am I to play 'Ali Baba?"

"Oh but Dick, not the consul general!"

"Why not the consul general! Does that make him God Almighty? Eldridge is a sot and a cad. He drinks beer, thinks beer. I know him and he knows me. That's why we hate each other. He never leaves Beirut for fear of losing his life. If the Bedawin ever catch him they'll cut off his cods. The Druses have a price on his head."

"But how do you know—?"

"'Abdel-Qadir is a second Saladin as far as El-Islam is concerned. He's the Harun er-Reshid of our century. The Arabs worship him as their great patriot and national hero, especially now that he's in exile from Algeria. Consequently he knows everything that's going on in the Arab world. Why even when he was the jihad-preaching emir of Mascara, over twenty years ago, he had the largest spy system in Islam. If the French hadn't captured him he'd have won his holy war."

"Is that all 'Abdel-Qadir told you, that Eldridge is Rashid's flunky?"

"No, that's *not* all! He gave me a detailed history of the sordid relationship between our distinguished bumbailiff-in-chief, the vulture Rashid, and our local Shylocks. And what should await me at the consulate this morning but a communiqué from the F.O. requesting *another* explanation."

"Explanation for what?"

"Well, it seems our friend Eldridge wrote to Granville that I'm pitting the Druses against the Wali, whom they've hated for years without any encouragement from me, and that I'm turning the Syrian countryside into a turmoil of insurrection. And as if that weren't enough, he's sent two religious fanatics up here to rub salt in my wounds."

"Religious fanatics? What religious fanatics?"

"Those two rabid evangelists from Beirut, Mentor and Augusta Mott. Eldridge must be crowing himself sick."

"Oh, Dick, do you think they'll cause trouble?"

"Think? I know they will! In fact, they already have! What the hell d'you think I was doing all day? Chasing after 'em through one end of the city to the next!"

"What were they doing?"

"What they usually do—preaching hate and upheaval, attempting to proselytize by the old bribe-and-threat technique, disseminating their Protestant propaganda, ranting and raving in the streets about Muhammed being a whoremonger and Islam the religion of those who sell themselves to the devil."

"Oh, how awful! Did they—"

"Yaas—nearly caused a riot. I threatened to place both of 'em under arrest if they thought they could come here and make trouble. Mott only laughed in my face. That's when I ordered him and his wife to get the hell out of town before the Arabs nailed 'em to the door of a mosque. Goddamned idiot, he then preached to me the glories of martyrdom. Said I'd aid and abet the Arabs in murdering the two of 'em. Said I was trying to stop the spread of Christianity in the East. Called me an atheist and the devil's disciple. Said he had a host of influential friends in Government—that he'd write to Whitehall and have me removed—*et cetera ad infinitum, ad nauseam.* Well I'm here to keep law and order and protect lives. In 1860 three thousand innocent Christians were slaughtered because of a few leeching Jews and overzealous missionaries. Life is cheap in hot countries, and the brutality of a Muslim mob is phenomenal. It's the instinctive brutality with which wild beasts and birds tear to pieces a wounded companion."

"Did they finally leave?"

"Yaas, *finally.* If I had my way I'd damn-soon show the English-speaking world how they ought to treat that horde of hypocrites, impostors, and moneygrubbers—that Hydra-headed monster that annually devours millions in lip-service extortion loot. As for that lunatic Mott, he should have troubled himself to learn better Arabic before blathering his hocus-pocus."

"Why? What did he say?"

"He kept haranguing the Arabs to lift up their 'dog' unto the Lord—*irfa' kelbek ila Rebbīna*—as if *qalb,* 'heart,' and *kelb,* 'dog,' were perfect rhymes! Mott can lift up his *kelb* unto the Lord that his listeners had a sense of humor!"

On the following evening, Burton stormed in, smashed a vase, and kicked over a coffee table. "Goddamnit!" he shouted. "Here I was running the Motts out of town for indiscreet proselytizing and propaganda, while my own wife was Catholicizing in a quiet way right under my nose! Thanks to you, I'm now the laughingstock of Damascus! The Jews are having a great crow over this in every damned bazaar of the city!"

Petrified for a few seconds, Isabel now attempted to explain in a quavering voice: "But I wasn't trying to convert anyone, Dick. All I did was distribute little medals and crucifixes among the women and children. They use them as charms against the evil eye, and they consider it a part of the cure when they come to me for treatment or advice. Oh, Dick, what harm is there in that?"

"Well, it may please you, but it's certainly not appreciated by the husbands and fathers of these women and children you dose and advise. 'Abdel-Qadir tells me he's heard countless complaints from Muslim leaders about the religious activities of *Es-Sitt* Burton. Why I could hardly believe my ears! He put off telling me long before this, hoping it might stop. But apparently it hasn't. Well goddamnit, it's going to stop—as of now! These people trust me, respect me, and I'll not have it otherwise. How could you be so damned foolish? Didn't it ever occur to you this kind of thing does me a lot of harm?"

"But what did I do, Dick? Why should there be so much hatred of me? If the women and children are curious and want to learn, why should the men be so narrow-minded and bigoted?"

"Because Islam is a man's world, and there's no room in it for feminine sentimentality. Either you reconcile yourself with this or suffer the consequences. I'll be goddamned if I'll have *my* wife baptizing Arab babies, teaching girls the *Ave Maria,* or acting as devil's advocate for Muslim women with a whim to become Catholic."

"Well, what harm is there in that? Why shouldn't they

become Catholics if they really want to? You always say yourself it's not right to interfere between a person and his conscience, so why should Arab women be any different from us? Have they no minds, no hearts, no souls? Are they to be treated like animals fit only for breeding and for man's selfish pleasure? Well I think it's sinful and criminal, and it's about time something was done about it!"

"Yaas, but not by you! You're not going to change overnight what's been the reality for hundreds of years. And if you're fatuous enough to try, you'll try alone—and you know damned-well what I mean by that!"

"Oh, you ungrateful beast! I've done everything for your sake—worked and prayed for you—and I get this thrown up in my face!" She fell upon the couch and burst into tears.

"Yaas, well I heard everything! 'Abdel-Qadir says you walked right into a mosque with some of your philanthropic friends, and when a poor praying Muslim wouldn't get up from a shrine you wanted 'em to examine, you drove him off with that goddamned riding whip of yours. 'Abdel-Qadir was perfectly disgusted to think you couldn't wait. D'you know what harm that does me? What could I say to him? The old man was in tears for my sake. He says they want me to be recalled on account of *your* conduct. You know what that'll mean? Rashid Pasha'll turn Syria into a slave state, that's what! And all because of you and your goddamned Catholicism. Is that what you want? You want to see all these poor people living in death? And to think how long this has been going on behind my back! You and that goddamned whip! You're like Outram in a petticoat! To think I trusted you,

believed in you. Well I'll never forgive you for this—
never—not as long as I live!" He dashed his foot against
a chair, sending it clattering across the floor. "Goddamnit, I feel like killing somebody."

"Then kill *me!*" she sobbed. "I'm not worthy of you
anymore. My usefulness is at an end. I've served my lord
and master, and now I'm no longer needed. But just remember, Richard Burton—Haji 'Abdullah—whoever you
are. Just remember. Who was the only one to send you
news from the outside world when you were in Africa?
Who cheered you on in danger, toil, and heartbreaking
sickness? Who, when you came back from Africa—when
you were cut cold by the Government, bullied by the
India Office, rejected by the Geographical Society, almost
tabooed by the public because of Speke's lies, so you
scarcely had ten friends to say 'good morning' to you—
who sought your side to comfort you? Who for the past
ten years has daily attended to your comforts—had your
slippers, dressing gown, and pipe ready for you every
evening—sat sick at heart if you were an hour late,
watched all night and till morning if you didn't come
back? Who copied and worked for and with you? Who
fought tooth and nail all these years to raise your official
position, and wept bitter tears over your being neglected?
I did! Why I've been wife and mother and comrade and
secretary and aide-de-camp and agent—and God knows
what else to you! But I was proud, happy, and glad to do
it all; and I've never tired day or night working for you.
I've said it before and I'll say it again—I'd rather have a
crust and a tent with you than be a queen elsewhere. So
go ahead and kill me. Isn't that what you Muslims do to

your women when they go astray—just 'cut 'em down,' as you say?"

Burton glared at her for a few seconds, muttered "Go to hell!" into his beard, and walked out of the house.

After getting himself drunk, he staggered home again— back to Isabel's anxiously awaiting arms—back to be forgiven, to be helped, to be loved.

30 : Recalled

In spite of all your dreams of peace, still must the fight unfair be fought Where you may learn the noblest lore, to know that all we know is nought.

In the spring of 1871 the Burtons were joined in their extended journey through the Holy Land by two permanent guests, the young archeologist Charley Drake and the equally young orientalist Edward Palmer. Together they explored almost every known and unknown Biblical site in Syria and Palestine, ending their excursions by spending the Holy Week at Jerusalem.

The gray dawn of Friday, May 5, found them en-
camped outside Nazareth near the road to Damascus. It
was spitting rain.

All of a sudden Richard and Isabel Burton were
aroused by a thundering clamor. Jumping off his cot, Burton ran out of the tent in his stocking feet and long underwear to see a gang of Greeks attacking his Arab servants
and stampeding the horses and pack mules. Darting a
glance to his right, he saw a raging mob of at least a hundred fifty Greeks pouring out of a church nearby. For a
second he was stunned.

Drake and Palmer, also in their underwear, came running out beside him. Just then the three Englishmen were
saluted with a shower of stones and maniacal shouts of
"Kill them! Kill them!"

"Eddy," Burton said to Palmer, "look after Zoo. Charley
and I'll stand 'em off."

The stones were now flying thick and fast, falling with
juicy thuds in the mud at their feet.

Suddenly Isabel rushed out in her nightgown. She was
holding two six-shooters. "Here," she cried. "Take these—
before they kill you!"

Burton waved her back. "You're the one who's going to
get killed, goddamnit, if you don't—Eddy, get her the
hell back in the tent!"

In that instant a rock struck Burton's right arm at the
elbow, paralyzing the ulnar nerve and fracturing the
bone. The stones were hitting like hail. In only a few seconds Drake was badly bruised and cut, the blood trick-
ling down his face and limbs.

Burton immediately recognized the leader of the mob.
It was the Most Reverend Nikolaos Nifon, the influential

Greek bishop of Nazareth. "Kill them!" he screamed. "Kill them all! I'll pay the blood money!"

"Dick! Charley!" Palmer called, tossing a revolver to each.

Burton fired six barrels into the air. A hundred and fifty Greeks turned and ran.

"*Phew!*" said Drake, wiping the blood away from his eyes. "That was a devilish close one!"

Burton said nothing. He just stood there for a moment and stared, scowling at the scattering Greeks. This was an evil omen.

When he was able to write again, Burton jotted in his journal:

I rode down to Tiberias, where the Jews protected by our Government were complaining that the Wali had taken from them and sold to the Greek Bishop Nifon, at Nazareth, a cemetery and synagogue which for the last four hundred years has belonged to their faith. I then proceeded to Nazareth, where I found that the Greek bishop had started a crusade against the local Protestants, preventing them from cultivating their land, which he—backed by the Wali—claims is his by right of inheritance.

I confronted Bishop Nifon and berated him for his scandalous un-Christian behavior, dispatching a full report of his proceedings to the Foreign Office. For these acts I was destined to the same honor as Jesus—namely, being stoned out of Nazareth—and because I did good to the Jews, they betrayed me to the authorities and asked for my recall.

The Greeks charged that I, indecently dressed and armed with a revolver, entered their church to profane it—that I tore down the icons, broke the lamps, and shot at a priest—while Isabel, armed with a saber, followed me in her nightgown, tore everything down, jumped upon the debris, cursed and spat at a priest, and did many other unwomanly things. How can one answer such scandalous nonsense, coming as it does from an influential and highly respected bishop of the Greek Orthodox Church?

On August 16, Burton and Drake were about to go out for an evening ride. The British consul barely got his foot in the stirrup when a mounted kavass drew rein, saluted, and handed him a telegram. Burton knit his brow as he opened it and read:

SIR,

COMPLAINTS RECEIVED FROM THE TURKISH GOVERNMENT IN REGARD TO YOUR RECENT CONDUCT RENDER IT IMPOSSIBLE FOR YOU TO CONTINUE TO PERFORM CONSULAR FUNCTIONS IN SYRIA. YOU ARE THEREFORE INSTRUCTED TO RESIGN THE AUTHORITY OF H.B.M.'S CONSUL AT DAMASCUS TO THE PERSON WHOM MR. CONSUL GENERAL ELDRIDGE HAS APPOINTED TO TAKE YOUR PLACE. YOU ARE FURTHER ADVISED TO MAKE PREPARATIONS FOR AN IMMEDIATE RETURN TO HEADQUARTERS.

GRANVILLE

Burton stood for a second paralyzed.

"What is it, Dick? Bad news?"

"Yaas. I'm superseded." He handed the dispatch to his startled friend. "After all my service, ignominiously dismissed at fifty years of age."

"What are you going to do?"

"Get the hell out of here as fast as I can. What else?" He snatched a pad and pencil out of his jacket pocket and scratched a note. "Here, give this to Zoo. Tell her I'm gone. Tell her I love her."

"But—"

"Never mind, Charley. Just do as I say." Burton climbed on his horse and held out his hand. "*Au 'voir*, Charley," he said thickly, tears in his eyes, then galloped away.

Isabel read the note in a soul-sick daze:

> Don't be frightened. I'm recalled. Pay, pack, and follow at convenience. *Adieu sans adieu.*

"Oh, Rashid Pasha!" she sobbed bitterly. "Oh, Rashid Pasha!"

Burton penciled in his journal:

> *Aug. 18th.*—Leaving Damascus forever. Starting at 3 A.M. in the dark, with a big lantern. All my men crying. Alone in coupé, thanks to the pigs. Have left my wife. Ever again? Feel soft. Dismissal ignominious, at the age of fifty, without a month's notice or wages or character.
>
> 'Abdel-Qadir embraced me as a brother. Wept on my shoulder and said: "You depart, my friend, leaving us the sweet perfume of your charity, your noble conduct in befriending the poor and supporting the weak and oppressed; and your name is great on account of what Allah has put into your nature."
>
> They say three hornets kill a man. Six will kill a horse. I've been stung by seven—Rashid, Donemberg, Rothschild, Mott, Eldridge, Nifon, Granville. Am still living. I must be a mule!

The shattered bowl shall know repair;
    The riven lute shall sound once more.
But who shall mend the clay of man,
    The stolen breath to man restore?

The shiver'd clock again shall strike;
  The broken reed shall pipe again.
But we? We die, and death is one:
  The doom of brutes, the doom of men.

31 : Dark days

Dust and ashes meet my eyes wherever turn their saddened gaze:
The wrecks of joys and hopes and loves, the rubbish of my wasted days.

When he arrived in England, Richard Burton went straight to the home of his sister Maria, Lady Stisted. The shock of his sudden recall told upon him cruelly. Maria had never seen him so depressed. His dejection was abysmal.

Burton never seemed to sleep. For a week he just sat up all night long—sometimes alone, sometimes with his worried brother-in-law Sir Harry Stisted—smoking and drinking incessantly. He ate almost nothing, would see absolutely no one outside the family, and said very little.

Stisted, trying to get Burton to talk about his troubles, once said to him: "Y'know, Dick, the F.O. authorities are now spreading a rumor that the main reason for your recall is that your life was in danger from the bullets of your enemies."

"How kind and considerate of the F.O.!" Burton answered dryly. "Well I've been shot at, at different times, by at least forty men who fortunately couldn't shoot straight. Once more wouldn't have mattered much. The truth is, they can't kill me."

When Isabel reached London, after several days of frantic searching she finally found her husband, stagnating half-drunk, in a filthy little East End hotel.

"The people are shedding bitter tears all over Syria," she said, sitting on the bed next to him. "They kept asking me—the Arabs, I mean—'What have we done that your government has done this thing to us? They sent us a man who made us so happy and prosperous, and protected us, and we were so thankful. Why now have they taken him away from us?' There was no way I could answer them, and it made me feel sick to my soul. All the shaykhs have sent us letters of affection, grief, and praise."

"Yaas, well, I've relearned an old lesson I was foolish enough to forget. The world is a carcass, and they who seek it are dogs."

"No, Dick, you're wrong—about the world, I mean. I don't care what anybody says—the world in general is a good place. Oh, I know, there are always a *few* bad people who make everything and everybody as miserable as they can. But the general rule is good; and whoever is in trouble will always meet with kindness, comfort, and sympathy from some quarter or other."

"*Ha!* Damned little I've ever met with."

"Oh but Dick, you mustn't blame the weaklings. Blame your own discernment. They don't really want to hurt you, but they just can't help themselves. They go to the popular side, the selfish side, whichever way it turns. And why shouldn't they? That's what makes life such a great and glorious challenge for a man like Richard Burton, a man who scorns the dictates of Mrs. Grundy. Believe me, Dick, it's not because they truly dislike or hate you that your pretended friends and open enemies are the way they are. It's because they fear others and themselves more than they could ever love you. Don't you see, darling? That's what life's all about. That's the eternal conflict we must all face. It's a conflict between self-interest and the interests of others. In sensitive youth, this conflict makes almost all our misery. But we should learn to accept it, to suffer it philosophically, in our riper years. England doesn't deserve you—I know that. But why concern yourself with what England thinks of you? What about the Arabs? They know you; they love you; they respect you. When England has forgotten you, will they? You're already a legend in the East. You stood between the poor and the rich, the oppressor and the oppressed. You became one of them, body and spirit. They'll never forget you. Right now they're thanking you in their hearts, singing your praise to their children, weeping and praying for you in the mosques."

Burton broke down and cried. "There's no room for me now, and I don't want anything, but I've worked thirty years for nothing. I'm breaking up, and I want to go free."

"Oh, Dick—Dick! You *shall* be free—you *shall*—but oh God, not that way! Were I struggling only for myself, I should long before have tired. But since it's for your sake, I'll fight on as long as life lasts. Help me, Dick—help me. Oh God, you can't give up now. We have each other. What else do we need? I want nothing but you, your love and trust. Oh Blessed Mother of God, I wonder how old one has to grow before learning the common rules of life instead of allowing every shock to disturb one, as if one were newly born? Disraeli told me that 'no affections and a great brain form the men that command the world,' but a great brain and a great heart he has no description for. Here he stops short, but I can tell him those are the men for whom there's no place. The nineteenth century will have none of them."

"Yaas, well, let's leave it at that. I'm sick and tired of the whole goddamned thing. I don't even want to talk about it."

"All right, our career is broken. But does that mean we give up?"

"Aren't you afraid?"

"Afraid! What, when I have you? You always used to say there's no such thing as fear. Well, if you won't fight, I'll fight for you—fight as I've always done to keep your good name."

"Why beat your head against a brick wall? I've been doing it all my life, and all it ever gave me was one headache after another. All I want is to be left alone."

"All right then, Richard Burton—feel sorry for yourself, if that's what you want to do. But as for me, I'm going straight to the Foreign Office; and they're going to hear me even if I have to break the door down. You've no right to be selfish; and if I know anything of men in general, and you in particular, you'll soon grow dissatisfied with yourself in your present state of inaction. Well, I'm going to see you don't! Why? Because I want to live with you, that's why!"

Isabel Burton confronted the Earl of Granville, George Leveson-Gower, Secretary of the F.O. "It's broken his career, it's shattered his life, it's embittered him towards religion."

"I'm sorry, Mrs. Burton, but—"

"Sorry! Is that all you can say—you're sorry! What are you going to do about it? Don't you—"

"My dear Mrs. Burton, I'm quite familiar with the several employments in Her Majesty's Consular Service which your husband has—er—as you say, 'successfully' held. I don't think it necessary that I should follow you through a recapitulation of these employments, nor for that matter enter into any review of Captain Burton's conduct in the post he last held. With reference to the cessation of his functions as Her Majesty's Consul at Damascus, I think it has been made quite clear to your husband the reason for his recall. Oh yes, madam, I'm willing to give him credit for having endeavored to carry out his duties to the best of his ability and judgment. But having come to the conclusion that it was no longer necessary to maintain a full consul in Damascus at a public cost—including salary and allowances—of a thousand pounds a year, your husband's withdrawal was of course followed by the appointment of an officer of lower rank and at a lower rate of salary. As for Captain Burton's future in Her

Majesty's service, I assure you, Mrs. Burton, I shall do everything in my power to obtain for him a better position as soon as one befitting his rank is available."

In desperation, Isabel wrote to her rich and influential uncle, Lord Gerard. Several days later she received a gracious invitation to visit Garswood Manor in Lancashire, there to remain with her husband as permanent guests of "Uncle Gerry."

Isabel was ecstatic with hope. Burton was cynical, unwilling to accept charity. He said to her: "My purse may be full of cobwebs, but not my brain. We'll get along."

But Isabel was insistent, and he finally relented. "We've nothing left," she said to him. "The sixteen thousand your father left you, the three hundred I took out with me, and our two hundred saved at Damascus—all of it's been spent in this trouble in our defense. We haven't but fifteen pounds to our name."

The Burtons went by train to Lancashire. As they sat alone in a railway compartment, one of the fifteen sovereigns slid out of Isabel's purse and rolled between the boards of the carriage. Unable to find it, she slumped on the floor and burst into tears.

Burton knelt beside her, his arm around her waist, trying to comfort her:

"Oh I could live with thee in the wildwood,
  Where human foot hath ne'er worn a way;
With thee, my city and my solitude,
  Light of my night, rest from cares by day."

"Thank you, sweet love!" she sighed, kissing him and drying her eyes.

:

Through the influence of Lord Gerard, Captain Burton received a new political appointment—the consulship at Trieste. This was to be, as journalist Frank Harris later envisioned it, the desert lion's cage of death.

In the spring of 1872, before Burton was assigned to Trieste, a very special dinner was held in his honor at Garswood. Present were two of the most powerful men in Great Britain, the Prince of Wales and the Duke of Edinburgh.

Prince Edward asked Isabel how the world was faring with her. He got the following reply: "Well, your Royal Highness, my time is now divided between Mother's and Richard's concerns. She's been paralyzed for years now, poor dear, and seems to be growing rapidly worse. I'm working tooth and nail at the Bird's case, and I've got Uncle Gerry to see about a new appointment."

The Prince winked and smiled. "This evening may bring you just what you want, my dear. You know, everyone's talking about the meeting of Livingstone and Stanley and the projected expedition to aid the doctor in Africa. Your husband is just the man to lead that expedition."

"Yes, Mrs. Burton," the Duke of Edinburgh added, "it was thought that Captain Burton's the best man to lead such an expedition, what with all his African experience and knowledge. That's why your uncle has gotten up this banquet, for the express purpose of bringing your husband and us together. You see, we're financing half the enterprise."

Isabel beamed. "Oh, how wonderful! I'm almost certain Dick will accept your generous offer."

At dinner, when the soup was being served, the Prince of Wales turned to Burton and said: "You're the man to go out to Livingstone. Come—consent—and I'll contribute five hundred pounds to the expedition."

Burton spooned his soup. Without looking up, he muttered: "I'll save your Royal Highness that expense."

"But captain," said the Duke of Edinburgh, "you'll get five hundred from me and additional grants from—"

Burton scowled. "I'll save your Grace that expense," he grated.

The Duke responded airily: "I understand you're the famous African explorer."

"I've been to Africa," was Burton's dry reply.

The Prince glared at the hideous scar on his cheek. "Weren't you wounded there?"

Burton glared back at him. "Yaas. In the back. Running away."

"Are we to admire you, Captain Burton?" said the Duke.

"I'll save you that expense," Burton answered, and left the table.

Isabel nearly fainted.

In June, a letter arrived from Lord Granville offering Burton the consulate at Trieste with a salary of £700 a year. He swallowed his pride and accepted it.

"This is a great fall after Damascus," Isabel said to him, "but it's better than nothing."

Burton snorted. "Beggars can't be choosers. We've got to eat! We can't afford to starve."

:

Day after day, Richard Burton grew more and more gruesome-looking. His forked beard and scarred face, fiendish grin and arched brows and sorcerous eyes gave him an unearthly, satanic aspect. And in his new role as Mephistopheles, Burton prided himself in shocking one and all.

At Lord Houghton's home, an Anglican missionary caused the female guests to shudder by alluding to his dreadful experiences of witnessing human sacrifice and attending a cannibal feast.

"Didn't they offer you any?" Burton said.

"They did," the missionary replied, "but of course I refused."

Burton cackled. "What a fool you were to miss such a unique opportunity!"

"Oh, Captain Burton," one of the ladies gasped, "you don't really mean to say you've eaten your fellow man?"

"Madam," he said, stroking his mustachios, "you'd eat your own husband if you were hungry enough! Now in case you're interested, El-Islam's creed of common sense freely allows cannibalism when it serves to save life. Quite a contrast to our mawkish sensibility and Christian sentimentalism, which bring an uncharitable charge of savagery against unfortunate expeditionists."

On another occasion, Burton advised a young doctor: "Now this is one of the things in life worthy of remembrance. Never attack a man. But if he attacks you, kill him."

The doctor's wife said: "Is it true, Captain Burton, that you killed two men at Mecca?"

"Madam," he said, grinning grotesquely, "I'm proud to say I've committed every sin in the Decalogue."

The wife walked away, but the husband remained a moment to ask him: "Tell me, captain—off the record—how many men have you killed in your life?"

Burton glowered at him. "I shot two hundred niggers in Somaliland. But having the fear of the Aborigines' Protection Society before my eyes, I refrained from doing more than hinting at it in my *First Footsteps in East Africa*. Now tell me, doctor—off the record—how many men have *you* killed in your life?"

To members of the Anti-Slavery Society he said: "The slave ships, when chased and hard-driven, simply tossed the poor devil niggers overboard. Many of 'em must've drowned damning the tender mercies of the philanthropes who doomed 'em to untimely deaths instead of a safe passage from blackland to whiteland."

"Old maids—what horrors!" Burton said at almost every social gathering. "I'd be glad to see polygamy allowed in England if only to get rid of all the old maids."

Then Isabel would invariably say: "Now Dick, you mustn't talk like that. They can't help it if no one wanted them."

"Yaas, yaas—no doubt," he replied, fingering his forked beard. "But they shouldn't be old maids. Besides, it's no good telling the truth; for nobody ever believes you. Human society and civilized intercourse are built upon a system of conventional lying."

"Well, captain, what shall we do with our old maids?" someone said with a smile.

"Enlist 'em," was the sharp reply. "With a little training they'd make first-rate soldiers."

"Oh, but Captain Burton," said one horrified widow, "surely they're not as bad as all that!"

Burton leered. "There's one maiden lady I've always admired. A certain Saint Apollonia, who leaped into a fire prepared for her by the heathen Alexandrians. The chief virtue of this admirable martyr wasn't her fidelity to her Christian principles, but the very fact she got rid of herself and so made one less old maid."

"Oh, Dick," Isabel chided, "you mustn't talk that way about a martyred saint."

"Saints! Allah forbid, they're as bad as old maids! Take Joan of Arc, for instance. The *Maid* of Orleans. *Saint* Joan, I should say. I presume she was so called because of the enormity of her crimes."

Burton hated playing the social register except for the cruel delight he took in insulting snobs and sophisticates. Isabel dragged him everywhere, even to one of Gladstone's Liberal soirées. Burton was a Conservative.

"Here's an invitation for us to the Prime Minister's. Now Dick, darling, this time you *must* go. All the important government people will be there, and you know what that could mean for us if we show a good face. Besides, it's a shame you should lose so excellent a chance of going into good society. Other people do it. Why shouldn't we?"

Burton growled: "What won't people do for the sake of a dinner! Well, I'll be goddamned if I will, and the Prime Minister be goddamned! I'm not going, and that's all there is to it."

"But Dick, darling—"

"Gladstone's a beast and a bore, and his wife's an ancient whore. Society courts her, the wicked old sinner; yet what won't men do for the sake of a dinner!"

"But Dick, darling—"

"All right, goddamnit! But don't say I didn't warn you."

"Now darling, mind your manners. You're to be amiable, remember, and not lose your temper. This may be our big chance. Now swear you'll behave yourself, if only for my sake."

"*Ha-ha!* I swear by Allah!"

"All right then, darling. Let's get ready and go."

In the crush of celebrities and status seekers mobbing their way into No. 10 Downing Street, Burton was accidentally pushed into the protuberant posterior of a lady in front. Before he could apologize, she gawked at her husband and gasped: "Oh dear! That horrid man goosed me!"

The husband turned around, took one look, and said: "It's that blackguard of a Burton!"

Burton's eyes blazed and his teeth were bared. "I'll have you out for this, and if you won't fight I'll thrash you like a dog!"

"Oh, Dick, no!" Isabel shrilled, clutching his arm. But it was too late.

The man sneered and smirked, so Burton smashed him in the face. The blow sent the man plowing through the shrieking crowd, knocking him flat on his back.

"Dear God, what's the disturbance out there?" roared the Prime Minister from inside the doorway.

"Only Captain Burton bowling over another Radical!" someone answered, amid howls of laughter.

When the Burtons finally entered, Mrs. Gladstone leered at them through her lorgnette. Then, turning to Lady Granville, she drawled: "Isn't it simply horrid, my dear? Every *Dick*, Tom, and Harry's here tonight!"

Having overheard her, Burton responded loud enough

for the hostess to hear: "Well, Zoo, I don't know about Tom and Harry, but rest assured every dick is welcome here."

Isabel missed the pun and smiled appreciatively.

Burton added: "Another of my pet aversions is any old woman made up to look very young." It was now their turn to shake hands. "Good god, madam!" he greeted Mrs. Gladstone, a painted lady. "You haven't changed since I saw you forty years ago! You're like the British flag that's braved a thousand years the battle and the breeze."

"Oh, Captain Burton," she simpered, "how could you, with that liquid voice of yours, make such very unpleasant remarks?"

"Because, madam," he bowed sardonically, "I'm in a very pleasant mood."

"Oh, look!" said one queen bee to another. "There's that infamous Captain Burton. I'd like to know he's down with some lingering and incurable illness."

Burton turned around, riveted his eyes upon her, and said dryly: "Madam, I've never in all my life done anything half so wicked as a wish like that. Why don't you give me a fighting chance?"

To an old war horse he responded: "Madam, I regret to say I'm no hot amorist. But I require two qualities and two only in a woman—beauty and affection. One night I was walking home alone when a lady past her prime asked whether she might accompany me, as she was rather afraid of the dark. I hate taking care of anyone, so I frowned at her request and shook my head. 'But there can be no scandal, Captain Burton,' she pleaded, grabbing my arm, 'because I'm old.' 'Madam,' I replied, 'while fully appreciating your kindness, I must decline Had you been young and good-looking, I would've considered the matter.'"

Even Isabel revealed herself as somewhat daring: "I'm no admirer of a big cigar in a woman's mouth, or a short pipe, but I know of nothing more graceful or enjoyable than a cigarette."

Lady Granville said: "Why Mrs. Burton, when I met your husband I was inexpressibly shocked by his Chaucerian conversation and Rabelaisian wit."

Isabel answered sweetly: "I can quite believe that on occasions, when no lady was present, Richard's conversation might have been startling."

The Prime Minister, as usual, was a one-man blabfest all during dinner. When dessert was being served, and he finally shut up, Burton blasted: "I can assure you, Mr. Gladstone, that everything you've said is absolutely and entirely opposite to fact. The Chinese are the future race of the East, and the Russians are the future race of Europe. Look at 'Chinese' Gordon. He showed the might that's slumbering in a nation of three hundred millions. China armed and awake would be a colossus. Some day, mark my words, Russia will meet China face to face; and the splendid empire of Central Asia will be the prize."

The guests were aghast. One of them, recovering from the shock, pulled out his pencil and scribbled on a menu card. Burton felt the card tucked into his lap from under the table. He glanced at it with a grin:

Please do not contradict Mr. Gladstone. Nobody ever does. *Granville.*

When they reached their rooms at the St. James Hotel in Piccadilly, Burton roared: "That's what comes of being amiable! Well I'll be goddamned, and may everybody else be goddamned, if I'll ever enter that goddamned house again!"

"So that's how you keep your promise," Isabel said angrily. "You don't even get inside the door before you have a row with someone, and in front of all those people! I was never so embarrassed—"

Burton burst out laughing at Isabel's sad, stricken looks.

Catching the humorous contagion, her scowls turned to a smile. "But you *did* knock him silly, didn't you, darling?" She hugged and kissed him. "Whatever can I do with or without you?"

As they were about to leave for Trieste, Burton said to Isabel: "Contrast the Société Anthropologique, and its palace and professors in Paris, with our 'Institute' on the second floor in a corner of Hanover Square, and its skulls in the cellar! I lent my best help to Dr. Hunt in founding the Royal Anthropological Society of London, whose presidential chair I'm now resigning. My motive was to supply travelers and men of science with an organ which would rescue their observations from the outer darkness of manuscript, and print their curious information on universal social and sexual customs. But we hardly began when 'Respectability,' that whited sepulcher full of all uncleanness, rose up against us. 'Propriety' cried us down with its blatant voice, and the weak-kneed brethren fell away. Well, I refuse to preside over a cowering coterie of castrated Grundyites!"

Burton dashed off a letter and affixed his seal. "I use it

whenever I write to a damned snob," he said, holding up his stamper.

Isabel stared at the letter:

St. James Hotel
Piccadilly
26th October, 1872

Sir,
   Yours of 23rd October received.
   Reply:

I am, Sir, yours most sincerely,
R. F. Burton

Dr. James Hunt, Secretary
Anthropological Institute
Hanover Square

32 : The lion's cage

There is no God, no man-made God—a bigger, stronger, crueler man—
Black phantom of our baby-fears ere Thought, the life of Life, began.

The Burtons rented a ten-room penthouse apartment situated near the railway station in Trieste.

The corridors were adorned with crucifixes, icons of Christ, and statuettes of Mary and Joseph with votive candles burning before them. At one end of the main hallway stood Isabel's shrine, embellished with divers and sundry and ritualistic relics—garlanded altars, fluttering cherubs, hallowed inscriptions, bleeding hearts, Madonnas, monstrances, eucharistials, crosses, holy-water sprinklers, thuribles, cruets, rosaries, sacring bells, candelabra, and a gold pax blessed by Pope Pius IX.

Burton called this area of the apartment "Mrs. Burton's Joss House." Whenever they had an argument, Burton threatened to throw Isabel and her "joss house" out the window. The wild man of Mecca was like a bull in a china shop whenever he saw red. The servants fled, the furniture crashed. Knickknacks flew and images smashed. He ranted and raved; he roared like hell. God and devil toppled and fell.

From Isabel's sanctuary, with its signs of the Christian cross, the corridors led one into rooms enriched with Orientalia. The Muslim crescent and star dangled over Turkish carpets and Persian tapestries, Bedawin prayer rugs, divans, ottomans, Moorish lamps, silver hookahs and chibouks with huge amber mouthpieces, scimitars, Somali spears, fencing swords, Arab matchlocks, Hindu and African idols, necklaces of human bones, Korans, skull goblets, tobacco pouches made of human hide, thousands of books and manuscripts, incense burners, coffee urns, teapoys, and hundreds of other handmade exotic *objets d'art*.

Behind Burton's bed hung a huge map of Africa, and over it a motto in Arabic: *Madz'el-kull*—All things pass.

He told his wife and friends: "This saying has always been a consolation to me."

In one corner of the bedroom stood a cabinet labeled *The Pharmacy.*

"This contains the innocuous medicines for my wife's poor friends," Burton once informed an old acquaintance. "She still continues to manufacture those powders and pills that won her such an unholy albeit undying reputation in the Holy Land. Though nobody was either the better or worse for taking these powders and pills, the rumor circulated that they were invariably fatal. I remember one time a Lebanese peasant woman who was dying sent her son to my wife for help. Isabel, touched and astir, hurried off with him in the middle of the night and satisfied the poor soul by the administration of some use-less but harmless drug. Next morning the woman's son re-turned, thanked my wife warmly for her attentions, and said it was his duty to report that his dear mother was dead. He then begged for a little more of the efficacious white powder, as he had a bedridden grandmother of whom he was also anxious to be relieved."

When asked why they lived so high up, Burton invaria-bly replied: "For two damnably ridiculous reasons. First of all, we're both in good condition and love to run up and down the stairs like squirrels. Second of all, we lead a rather peaceful life—except on Fridays. What a pande-monium! That's when Isabel entertains seventy of her lady friends, all of 'em blathering at the top of their lungs, flitting from one room to the other, my wife the loudest in faulty German, fluent Italian, and slangy English. I call it the Magpie Sanhedrin of Trieste. Every Friday afternoon I have to hide in my sanctum sanctorum and pretend I don't hear it. But far from complaining, I'm rather thankful. If our rooms were lower down, I shouldn't be a bit surprised if a hundred and forty cackling hens instead of a mere seventy old birds came fluttering in to roost!"

In the very midst of one of these raucous "hen parties" there befell a sudden, almost startling silence. Burton stalked into the main drawing room, cast a malignant glance at the assembled members of the "magpie sanhe-drin," laid a thin black book on one of the coffee tables, and stalked out of the room without saying a word. At least a dozen long-nosy dames then proved that "He who pryeth into every cloud may be struck with a thunderbolt." The book was entitled *A History of Farting, by a Professor of Bumbast in the University of Crackow, Revised by a College of Fizzicians.*

On one occasion, a young Italian priest who came to call at the Burton residence was asked by Isabel to conduct a brief service in her "private chapel." But the careless way in which he carried out the sacred ceremonies so upset the Argus-eyed Isabel that she said to him: "Stop! stop! Pardon me, *padre,* but I'm an old English Catholic—and therefore particular. You're not doing it right. Stand aside, please, and let me show you."

The astonished priest stood aside. Isabel approached the shrine and performed all the gesticulations, invocations, and genuflections in the proper style.

Standing behind a door, Burton watched with quiet amusement. When the ritual was over, he stepped into the hall, tapped the perplexed *padre* on the shoulder, pointed to Isabel, and said soberly: "Y'know who that is? It's my wife. And y'know she'll someday die. We all must die. And she'll be judged. We must all be judged. And there's a very long and black list against her. But when the sentence is being pronounced she'll jump up and say: 'Stop! stop! Please pardon my interruption, but I'm an old English Catholic.'"

Captain and Mrs. Burton always dined out together *à la table d'hôte* in the Hotel de la Ville. There they were tolerated as two old English eccentrics.

Dinner was ordered at six every evening. At half past six, when no meal arrived, Burton signaled the waiter. The *garçon* shrugged, made an excuse—the meal wasn't ready.

"*Eh, vilain bougre!*" Burton bellowed, slamming his fist

down on the table. "*Goddam, tu t'es foutue de!*" Then came a volley of Arab vituperation: "*Yā khara! yā men-yūk! yā 'owr!*"

The waiter took French leave, looking back with a "*Mais, mon Dieu, l'Anglais! Oh, les Goddames!*"

"Just look at these prices!" was Burton's usual remark while scrutinizing the menu. "Why goddamnit, we should be gorged to death for 'em!"

When the waiter arrived, Burton roared: "Give me a beefsteak!" When the waiter returned with a little piece of meat on a large plate, Burton stabbed it with his fork, turned it about, eyed it critically, and drawled: "Yaas, yaas. That's it. Bring me some."

When Burton ordered coffee, it came in a cross between a cup and a thimble. "What's this?" he said, scowling.

The *garçon* looked flabbergasted. "Why coffee for one, *monsieur.*"

"Then goddamnit, bring me coffee for twenty!"

From December, 1875, till April, 1876, the Burtons entertained a grand tour of India to relive the sights and sounds and see the stage of Haji 'Abdullah's youth. When they reached home, Richard Burton wrote to his favorite cousin, Dr. Edward Burton, and enlightened him with a piece of good news:

Consulate, Trieste
June 24th, '76

My dear Coz,

We returned here on the 18th instant; and the first thing I heard was the murder of my archenemy, Rashid Pasha. Serves the scoundrel right. He prevented my going to Con-

stantinople and to San'a, in Arabia. I knew the murderous
rascal too well to trust him.

Maria wrote to me about poor Stisted's death. A great
loss for Maria and the chicks. I won't bother you about our
journey, which was very pleasant and successful.

I am, dear Coz, ever
Sincerely yours,
Richard F. Burton

He then wrote in his journal:

Witness that scourge of Syria, Rashid Pasha. Born in 1830
of the Haji Nazir Agha family, Darreh Beys of Macedonian
Draina, he was educated in Paris where he learned the usual
hatred of Europeans. He entered the Egyptian service in
1851 and, presently exchanging it for the Turkish, became
in due time Wali (Governor General) of Syria, which he
plundered most shamelessly. Recalled in 1872, he eventually
entered the Ministry; and on June 15th, 1876, he was shot
down with other villains like himself by gallant Captain
Hasan the Circassian. *Yerhhamhūllāh*—May Allah have
mercy on his soul!

Eight months later, while they were vacationing in
northeast Italy, Isabel induced her husband to sign an informal requisition. He did so capriciously, reminding her
however of a premarital promise that no Roman Catholic
priest was to enter his death chamber. The requisition
read:

Gorizia
February 15th, 1877

Should my husband, Richard Burton, be on his deathbed
unable to speak—I perhaps already dead—and that he may

wish to have the grace to retract and recant his former er-
rors and to join the Catholic Church, and also to receive
the Sacraments of Penance, Extreme Unction, and Holy Eu-
charist, he might perhaps be able to sign this paper or make
the sign of the cross to show his need.

(Signed) *Isabel Burton*
(Signed) *Richard F. Burton*

In August and September of 1881 the Burtons were in
Venice with the celebrated African explorer, Captain Verney Lovett Cameron, who commanded the expedition to
relieve Livingstone—the enterprise Burton declined—
subsequently exploring Lake Tanganyika and all of Central Africa.

Burton said to him: "Y'know, Verney, the thing that's
haunted me these past four years is the fact that Speke
was right after all. Victoria Nyanza is the true source of
the Nile, but it took you and Stanley to prove it."

Cameron nodded, offering his friend a cigar. "Now
what do you think of this, Dick?" he said sarcastically.
"There's a great big geographical conference being held
here today, and representatives from all civilized nations
are duly assembled."

"But naturally," said Isabel, "the first geographer of the
day, Captain Richard Burton, hasn't been invited either to
speak or even to be present."

"Nor has Captain Verney Cameron!" the explorer
added.

"Well!" Burton laughed. "While all the armchair geographers are sweltering in hot air, what d'you say the three
of us treat ourselves by going over to the Lido for bathing
and breakfast."

"Capital idea!"

And so they did—Burton with a gamecock under his arm, and Isabel leading her two bull terriers.

Pitching their umbrella on the beach, the sixty-year-old Burton and the thirty-seven-year-old Cameron rolled up their sleeves, took off their shoes and socks, turned up their trousers, and began building sand castles while Isabel sat on a blanket and watched them in amused wonder.

"Look, nurse!" Burton bawled to Isabel. "See what Cammy and I have done! Look, nurse! We've made such a beautiful pie."

"If you please, nursey," Cameron whined, "Dick's snatched away my spade. Please tell Dicky not to touch my spade."

All of a sudden, along came the high-dried and highly respectable Lord Aberdeen, president of the R.G.S. since Murchison's death. With him was a touring party of starched and stuffy antiquarians and geologists complete with bald domes, pointed beaks, and bespectacled beady eyes. The unforeseen encounter of snob mob and *outré* trio was a sight to behold.

The International Geographical Congress opened in Venice on the fifteenth of September. When Lord Aberdeen entered the assembly hall he found Burton's calling card lying on the lectern, the back embellished with a squib:

To Our Foreign Colleagues:
We're Saville Row's selected few;
   Let all the rest be damned.
The pit is good enough for you;
   We won't have boxes crammed.
               The R.G.S.

A year later, Burton received the following official telegram from London:

27 OCTOBER, 1882
4.40 P.M.

SIR,

H.M.'S GOVERNMENT WISH TO AVAIL THEMSELVES OF YOUR KNOWLEDGE OF BEDOUINS AND THE SINAI COUNTRY TO ASSIST IN SEARCH FOR PROFESSOR PALMER. THERE IS A CHANCE OF HIS BEING STILL ALIVE, THOUGH BODIES OF HIS COMPANIONS CHARRINGTON AND GILL HAVE BEEN FOUND. PROCEED AT ONCE TO GHAZA. PLACE YOURSELF IN COMMUNICATION WITH CONSUL MOORE, WHO HAS GONE FROM JERUSALEM TO INSTITUTE INQUIRY.

GRANVILLE

Burton wired back immediately:

READY TO START BY FIRST STEAMER. WILL DRAW £100. WANT GUNBOAT FROM ALEXANDRIA TO GHAZA OR SINAI. LETTER FOLLOWS.

He then penned excitedly in his journal:

At last!! Once more it is my fate to escape the prison life of civilized Europe, and to refresh body and mind by studying Nature in her noblest and most admirable form—the Nude. Again I'm to enjoy a glimpse of the glorious desert, to inhale the pure sweet breath of translucent skies that show red stars burning upon the very edge of the horizon, and to strengthen myself by a short visit to the wild man and his wilder home.

"Palmer is one of the few orientalists without pride and jealousy," Burton said to his wife as they stood on the dock.

"He's defended me in every way—especially after Damascus—and that's what I call a staunch friend."

Isabel embraced him. "Oh, darling, please remember. If he's really dead, and you're sure of it, don't be put like a ferret in a hole to bring out his body."

"If he's dead, no. But if there's a chance of saving dear old Eddy, I'll go anywhere and do anything."

She kissed him. "It's all so sad in one way, but in another there's the happiness of your returning to the desert—*your* desert, my beloved 'Abdullah."

"Yaas. But what a horrible desert it would be if I didn't have *you* to come back to!"

This was to be the last expedition that Richard Burton undertook in his enterprising lifetime. It was a relative failure. Dr. Palmer's body was never discovered, and his apparent death was declared a mystery.

Burton wrote home to Isabel from Egypt:

Palmer, Charrington, and Gill went into the Sinai Desert to buy camels for Wolseley's expeditionary forces and bribe the Bedawin into revealing information concerning 'Arabi Pasha's base of operations. Eddy's secret mission was to cut the telegraph wire between El-Qantara and El-'Arish, and it was through this wire *not* being cut that foul play was first suspected.

Eddy was a first-rate Arabist, and he was on such friendly terms with the Arabs that there seemed not the slightest danger. Like myself, he had long before established brotherhood with all the Egyptian Bedawin. But the three of them were carrying £3,000 (some say £20,000!) and were marked as infidel spies.

It's reported that two dozen Sa'idi Bedawin led by an old acquaintance of mine, Shaykh Salim bin Selameh, surrounded the three Englishmen and gave them a choice of being shot or jumping over a cliff. It's said that Charrington and Gill elected to be shot, which is why their bodies were later found; but Eddy, covering his eyes, jumped over a cliff and is presumed dead. Not a trace of him has yet been found, which makes me wonder. In fact, to one who knows the Bedawin, this whole ugly affair is a great puzzle. Certainly they were robbed and murdered, but by whom? I can't help feeling there's something about this we shall never know.

By the way, I met Gordon on the road. He offered me the Sudan (Allah forbid!), said we could govern together, but I refused. Told him we were too much alike, which makes for trouble—"I couldn't serve under you, nor you under me"—etc., etc. He left me with our old motto, "Honor, not honors." I don't know why, but I have a strange feeling I'll never see him again.

Burton returned to Trieste in December. There, a year later, he jotted in red ink in his journal:

Thursday, 6th December, 1883.—Today, eleven years ago, I came here. What a shame!!!

33 : The Arabian Nights

When doctors differ, who decides amid the milliard-headed throng?
Who save the madman dares to cry: " 'Tis I am right, you all are
  wrong!"?

Richard Burton read in the *Athenaeum* of November 5,
1881, a notice that the distinguished poet and translator
Mr. John Payne was planning to present to the English-
speaking world a new and complete translation of the ul-
traerotic *El-Kitāb Alf Layleh wa-Layleh* or *Book of the
Thousand Nights and a Night.* Burton wrote at once to the
Athenaeum:

Many years ago, in collaboration with my old and lamented friend Dr. John Steinhaeuser of the Bombay Army,
I began to translate the whole of the *Thousand Nights and
a Night.* The book, mutilated in Europe to a collection of
fairy tales, is unique as a study of anthropology. It is a marvelous picture of Oriental life. Its shiftings are those of the

kaleidoscope. Its alternation of pathos and bathos—of the boldest poetry (the diction of Job) with the baldest prose (the Egyptian of today)—and its contrast of the highest and purest morality with the orgies of Apuleius and Petronius Arbiter, take away the reader's breath. I determined to render every word with the literalism of Urquhart's *Rabelais*, and to save the publisher trouble by printing my translation at Brussels.

Although a host of friends has been eager to subscribe, my work is still unfinished—nor could it be finished without a year's hard labor. I rejoice therefore to see that Mr. John Payne, under the Villon Society, has addressed himself to a realistic translation without "abridgments or suppressions." I have only to wish him success, and to express a hope that he is resolved *verbum reddere verbo* [to call a spade a spade] without deference to any prejudice which would prevent his being perfectly truthful to the original. I want to see that the book has fair play; and if it is not treated as it deserves, I shall still have to print my own version.

On November 28, Payne wrote to Burton at Trieste and suggested collaboration. Thus began one of the most remarkable relationships in literary history.

May, 1882. While on leave in England, Burton visited Payne for the first time at his London address. The two men talked, smoked, and drank for hours. Burton liked the lean, bearded poet. His manner and appearance were dramatically, esthetically Elizabethan. And Payne instantly took to the nineteenth-century reincarnation of Sir Francis Drake and Sir Walter Raleigh.

In the course of their conversation, Burton promised to

assist and advise Payne at any risk—"neck or nothing." And that he did. For three years a steady stream of letters and proof sheets flowed between London and Trieste:

My dear Payne,

Please send me a lot of advertisements. I can place a multitude of copies. Mrs. Grundy is beginning to roar. Already I hear the voice of her. And I know her to be an arrant whore, and tell her so, and don't give a goddamn for her. . . .

The fair sex appears wild to get at the *Nights*. I have received notes from two upon the nice subject—with no end of complaints about stern parents, brothers, and brothers-in-law.

The first volume of Payne's translation appeared in the early fall of 1882. Then came the attack.

In 1840, orientalist Edward William Lane delighted the English-speaking world with his famous but garbled and ungainly translation of the *Arabian Nights*. It immediately cut prestige out of Galland's popular but mutilated monstrosity. After forty successful years, Lane's brutally castrated version stood as standard—a classic like Sale's *Koran* or Burckhardt's *Arabic Proverbs*.

Lane's three most influential nephews and successors, all of them orientalists and historians, wished to keep it that way. They were—in the order of their venom and virulence—Stanley Lane-Poole, Reginald Stuart Poole, and Reginald Lane Poole. They received their greatest support from the bark-bound *Saturday Review* and from William T. Stead, the sensational do-gooder and editor-in-chief of the melodramatic *Pall Mall Gazette*.

My dear Payne,

Some two generations of *poules mouillées* have reprinted and republished Lane's *Arabian "Notes"* without having the simple honesty to correct a single error or to abate one blunder. Perhaps it will be best to let R. S. Poole sing his song. S. Lane-Poole has no end of enemies, and I can stir up a small wasp's nest without once appearing in the matter. Sapient criticaster—when his name was proposed as secretary to the R.A.S., all prophesied the speediest dissolution of that infirm body. The best answer will be showing up a few of Lane's—the Uncle and Master's—mistakes. But this must be done with the greatest care, so that no hole can be picked in the critique. . . .

Glad to hear of a new edition of Lane. It will draw attention to the subject. I must see what can be done with reviewers. *Saturday "Reviler"* and I are at drawn daggers, and W. T. Stead of *Pall Mall (Gutter) Gazette* is such a stiff young she-prig that I hardly know what to do about him. However, I shall begin work at once by writing and collecting the vulnerable points of the clique. Lane-Poole is a very much hated man, and there will be no difficulty. His razor-edged amenity has won for him such dishonor and troops of unfriends. In my own case I should encourage a row with this bête noire, but I can readily understand your having reasons for wishing to keep it quiet.

My dear Captain,

I have no wish to draw the attention of the authorities to the moral question. We would do well to keep this a strictly literary matter. Should they seize the plates and stop the printing, then what would we have gained?

My dear Payne,

I shall write today to Tedder [Henry R. Tedder, secre-

tary and librarian of the Athenaeum Club] to know how
Lane-Poole is best hit. Tedder hates him—so do most people. Meanwhile you must, either yourself or by proxy, get
a list of Lane's laches. I regret to say my copy of his *Modern Egyptians* has been lost or stolen, and with it are gone
the lists of his errata I had drawn up many years ago.

It has been circulated widely enough by the Lane-Poole
clique—*poules mouillées*—that I do not know Arabic. Of
course I don't know Arabic, but who does? One may know
a part of it, a corner of the field, but *all! Bah!!* Let me at
once plead guilty to the charge, adding that I have still to
meet the man who *does* know Arabic. As for that armchair
orientalist, who hasn't even *smelled* Arabia, does he pretend
to know it all? . . .

It will only be prudent to prepare for an attack. I am perfectly ready to justify a complete translation of the book,
and if I'm obliged to say what I think about Lane's edition
there will be hard hitting. Of course I wish to leave his
bones in peace, but Lane-Poole may make that impossible.
Curious to see three editions of the *1,001 Nights* advertised
at the same time, not to speak of the bastard—Galland's. . . .

If anything is in any redaction of the original, in it should
go. Never mind how shocking it may be to modern and
Western minds. If you sin, you sin in good company—in
the company of the authors of the Authorized Version of
the Bible, who did not hesitate to render literatim certain
passages which persons aiming simply at artistic effect would
certainly have omitted.

My dear Captain,

I am inclined to minimize these passages as much as possible. Though determined that my translation shall be a
complete and accurate one, I mean to omit extreme coarse-
ness whenever I find an excuse to do so—when it doesn't

appear in all the Arabic texts. If I find no excuse, I should then clothe the naked idea in esthetic language.

My dear Payne,

You are drawing it very mild. Has there been any unpleasantness about plain speaking? Poor Abu Nowas [an erotic poet of the *Arabian Nights*] is, as it were, castrated. I should say, "Be bold," only you know better than I do how far you can and cannot go. I should simply translate every word. If you would restore Abu Nowas' stolen jewels, I suggest you do so literally—*e.g.*, "And have each other, turn by turn, handling this my tool you see." What an anthropological gem! It refers to what Persian boys call, in half-Turkish phrase, *alish-takish* (give and take). We are overapt to apply our nineteenth century prejudices and prepossessions to the morality of the ancient Greeks, who would have specimen'd such squeamishness in Attic salt. What a national disgrace is this revival of Puritanism with its rampant cant and ignoble hypocrisy!

My dear Captain,

I have pledged myself not to reproduce the work in its completely uncastrated form. It was never my scheme to do so. An unexpurgated translation is in direct opposition to the spirit of my undertaking—to build a monument of prose and verse, to recreate a classic.

My dear Payne,

What I meant by literalism is literally translating each noun in its turn, so that the student of Arabic can use the translation. I hold the *Nights* to be the best of class books, and when a man knows it he can get on with Arabs everywhere. Instead of the extremely archaic *yard, kaze,* and *swive,* I suggest you employ the more modern *prickle, coynte,* and *futter.* After all, a cunt is a cunt in any land or language. Unsexed and unsound versions and perversions like Lane's are survivals of the unfittest. My contention is that every Arab word should have its English equivalent. Sundry students of Orientalism assure me that they are anxious to have the work in its crudest and most realistic form.

The unnatural vice of the *Nights* cannot deprave any mind save that which is perfectly prepared to be depraved. The man must be prurient and lecherous as a dog-faced baboon in rut to have aught of passion excited. Unfortunately it is these offenses—which come so naturally in Greece and Persia, and which belong strictly to their fervid age—that give the book much of its ethnological value. I don't know if I ever mentioned to you a paper (unpublished) of mine showing the geographical limits of the evil. I shall publish it some day and surprise the world. I don't live in England, and I don't give a goddamn for Public Opinion. I would rather tread on Mrs. Grundy's pet corn than not. She may howl on her big fat ass to her heart's content.

My dear Captain,

Absolute literality is impossible to the translator who has any regard for style. My translation is intended as a purely literary work, produced with the sole object of supplying cultivated readers with a fairly representative and characteristic version of the most famous book of narrative fiction now in existence.

All nine volumes of John Payne's unique *Book of the Thousand Nights and One Night* were off the private press in the autumn of 1884. At the end of his "Prefatory Note" he added:

I have to return my cordial thanks to Captain Richard F. Burton, the well-known traveler and author, who has most kindly undertaken to give me the benefit of his great practical knowledge of the language and customs of the Arabs in revising the manuscript of my translation for the press.

Burton and Isabel were then back in London, and their first visit was with Payne.

"Why only five hundred copies?" the anthropologist said to the poet. "Why not a thousand and one? You should bring out a new edition at once. At least fifteen hundred more people are clamoring for it and must endure disappointment."

"Much as I'd like to, captain, I can't—and for two good reasons. We—the Villon Society and I—have pledged ourselves not to reproduce the book but in a limited edition for subscribers only. This means printing, not publication; and as you well enough know, private printing is a costly concern."

"Then let me print a new edition in my own name and account to you for the profits. It seems such a pity to lose these fifteen hundred potential subscribers."

"That's most generous and kindhearted of you, captain, but I must refuse. I couldn't be a party to a breach of faith with my subscribers in any shape or form."

There were a few seconds of reflective silence, then Burton said: "Would you object to my making an entirely new translation?"

Payne smiled, stroking his huge Angora cat. "I'd have no objection whatever. In fact, I encourage you to do it. It's the only reasonable answer to your dilemma."

"*Inshallāh!* Where yours is a literary, mine will be an anthropological work. I have knowledge of certain subjects such as no other man possesses. Why should this knowledge die with me? Facts are facts, whether men are acquainted or reconciled with 'em or not."

As the Burtons were about to leave, the anthropologist grasped the poet's hand and said: "The more I read your translation the more I like it. You've no need to fear the Lane clique, least of all that blatant black beast of the *'Gutter'* Gazette. You can give 'em as good as they can give you. I'm quite ready to justify the moral point. Of course we mustn't attack Lane till he's made the *cheval de bataille* against us. But peace and quiet aren't in my way, and if they want a fight they can have it."

Payne winked and grinned. "To quote the *Nights:*

"For slanderers, myself, and thee,
  An awful day there'll be—
    A time of standing up
    To judgment—wait and see!"

Burton wrote to Payne from Trieste where, cutting his consular duties, he started slaving ten hours a day at his monumental translation:

I'm going in for notes where they did not suit your scheme, and shall make the book a perfect *répertoire* of Eastern knowledge in its most esoteric form. I wish to remove the scales from the eyes of Englishmen who are interested in Oriental literature and ethnology. In the versions and perversions of other translators, the very point which enables you to understand the action is left out because the translator was afraid of Mrs. Grundy. One and all degrade a chef-d'oeuvre of the highest anthropological and ethnographical interest and importance to a mere fairy book, a nice present for little boys.

Arab ideas of morality are different from European. If we are to understand the Arabs, and if the *Nights* are to be of any value from an anthropological point of view, the book can only be written as I am writing it. I intend to show it in decent nudity, not in suggestive fig leaf. I don't give a goddamn about being prosecuted. If the matter comes to a fight I'll walk into court with my Bible, Shakespeare, and Rabelais under my arm and prove that before they condemn me they must cut half of *them* out and not allow them to be circulated to the public. . . .

As you have been chary of notes, my version must by way of *raison d'être* (amongst others) abound in esoteric lore such as female circumcision and excision, etc. I answer all my friends that reading it will be a liberal education, and assure them that with such a repertory of esotericism at their finger tips they will know all the knowable requisite to salvation. My conviction is that all the women in England will read it and half the men will cut me.

It will be a marvelous repertory of Eastern wisdom—how eunuchs are made and are married, what they do in marriage, female circumcision, the Fellahin copulating with crocodiles, etc. Mrs. Grundy will howl till she almost bursts, and will read every word with an intense enjoyment. In order to be quite ready should prosecution ensue, I've compiled what I call *The Black Book,* which consists of specimens of the turpitude of the Bible and Shakespeare.

I want human sexuality to be treated from a materialistic, realistic, and practical point of view. If all science is founded more or less on a stratum of facts, there can be no harm in making known to mankind certain matters intimately connected with their private, domestic, and social life. Alas! complete ignorance of them has unfortunately wrecked many a man and many a woman; while a little knowledge of a subject generally hidden from the masses may enable numbers of people to understand many things which they believed to be quite incomprehensible, or which are not thought worthy of their consideration.

On Saturday, September 12, 1885, the first black-and-gold volume of Burton's avidly anticipated magnum opus rolled off the private press into the public arms:

A Plain and Literal Translation
of the Arabian Nights' Entertainments,
Now Entitled
THE BOOK OF THE THOUSAND NIGHTS AND A NIGHT
With Introduction, Explanatory Notes
on the Manners and Customs of Moslem Men,
and a Terminal Essay Upon the History of *The Nights*
by Richard F. Burton
El-Hhājj 'Abdullāh
Benares: MDCCCLXXXV
Printed by the Kamashastra Society
for Private Subscribers Only
Limited to One Thousand Numbered Copies

Burton told the world in his "Translator's Foreword":

This work, laborious as it may appear, has been to me a labor of love, an unfailing source of solace and satisfaction during my long years of official banishment. . . . This translation is a natural outcome of my Pilgrimage to El-Medina and Mecca. . . . Professional ambition suggested that literary labors are not likely to help a man up the ladder of promotion. But common sense suggested to me that, professionally speaking, I was not a success; and, at the same time, that I had no cause to be ashamed of my failure. In our day, when we live under a despotism of the Philister, the prizes of competitive services are monopolized by certain pets and prime favorites of that jealous and potent majority—the Mediocrities. It is hard to realize how perfect is the monopoly of commonplace, and to comprehend how fatal a stumbling stone that man sets in the way of his own advancement who dares to think for himself, or who knows more and who does more than the mob of gentlemen-employees who know very little and who do even less.

Burton penned in his journal:

No. 1 volume is accompanied by a circular earnestly requesting that the book might not be exposed for sale in public places or permitted to fall into the hands of any save curious students of Muslim manners. Yet the birth of the first-born is accompanied with no small trouble and qualms to the parent and to all who assisted at the parturition. Will the "little stranger" robed in black and gold, the colors of the Abbaside Caliphs, be kindly welcomed or will it be regarded as an abortion, a monster?

Between September, 1885, and September, 1888, ten lavish tomes and six supplementary volumes shook the literary world and set the critics into two warring camps.

Such great guns as Alfred Austin, A. C. Swinburne, John Addington Symonds, and Henry Irving were profuse in their praise.

A "respectable" Methodist devoted to "Christian chivalry," William T. Stead, labeled Burton's labor of love "the garbage of the brothel." In gruesome detail he denounced London as "the world's center of sodomy and child prostitution," then landed three months in jail for "abduction and indecent assault" in his attempt to prove it.

Stanley Lane-Poole led the assault with Stead:

It is bad enough in the text of the tales to find that Captain Burton is not content with plainly calling a spade a spade, but will have it styled a dirty shovel; but in his notes he goes far beyond this, and the varied collection of abominations which he brings forward with such gusto is a disgrace and a shame to printed literature. . . . Probably no European has ever gathered such an appalling collection of degrading customs and statistics of vice as is contained in Captain Burton's translation of the *Arabian Nights*. . . . Captain Burton's experience in the East seems to have obliterated any sentiments of chivalry; for he is never weary of recording disparaging estimates of women, and apparently delights in discovering evidence of "feminine devilry." . . . The different versions, however, have each its proper destination—Galland for the nursery, Lane for the library, Payne for the study, and Burton for the sewers.

"I have scant reason to expect mercy from the clique," Burton said to Isabel, "and I want none. Payne was assaulted by Mr. Reginald Stuart Poole, the front of the monopolists; and now I'm being assailed by little Stanley, the apprentice orientalist."

"But why, Dick?" said the bewildered Isabel. "I don't understand. Why should these men be so mean? I should think they'd welcome your work."

"*Ha!* The *poules mouillées* of the clique think they hold a monopoly to the *Nights* as popularized by the Uncle and Master, E. W. Lane, eponymous hero of the house. Suffice it to say the nephews want to keep their private gold mine, whatever the cost."

"Well, they're mean and malicious men, that's all I can say, and one of these days they'll be sorry for it."

Burton didn't waste any words defending his super-sexed translation, his eroto-anthropological footnotes, and his terminal essay on "Pederasty" against the onslaughts of what Swinburne called "a rancorous and reptile crew." He shut up the carping criticasters in short order:

I have no apology to make for the details offered to students of Muslim life. Nor am I ashamed of lecturing upon these esoteric matters, the most important to humanity. Nay, I take pride in so doing in the face of silly prejudice and miserable hypocrisy; and I venture to hold myself in the light of a public benefactor. While Pharisee and Philister may be or may pretend to be "shocked" and "horrified" by my pages, the sound common sense of a public which is slowly but surely emancipating itself from the prudish and prurient reticences of the early nineteenth century will in good time do me, I am convinced, full and ample justice. Amongst the civilized this fruit of the knowledge tree must be bought at the price of the bitterest experience, and the consequences of ignorance are peculiarly cruel. Where then is the shame of teaching what it is shameful not to have learned? But we are compelled to keep silence concerning the one side of human nature which is the most interesting to mankind, the sexual, and the consequences of that imbecility are afflicting. Shall we ever understand that ignorance is not innocence?

In an age saturated with cant and hypocrisy, here and there a venal pen will mourn over the "pornography" of the *Nights,* dwell upon the "garbage of the brothel," and lament the "wanton dissemination of ancient and filthy fiction." This self-constituted *censor morum* reads Aristophanes and Horace, perhaps even Martial and Petronius, because "veiled in the decent obscurity of a learned language." He allows men to write Latin, but he is scandalized at plain English.

To be consistent he must begin by bowdlerizing not only the classics, but also the Bible. Why doesn't this inconsistent puritan purge the Old Testament of its allusions to human ordure and the pudenda, to carnal copulation and impudent whoredom, to adultery and fornication, to onanism, sodomy, and bestiality? But this he will not do, the whited sepulcher!

What hypocrisy to blaterate about the *Nights* in presence of such triumphs of the natural! How absurd to swallow such camels and to strain at my gnat! It appears to me that when I show to such men, so "respectable" and so impure, a landscape of magnificent prospects whose vistas are adorned with every charm of nature and art, they point their unclean noses at a little heap of muck lying in a field corner. To those critics I can reply only by quoting the words said by Dr. Johnson to the lady who complained of the naughty words in his dictionary: "You must have been looking for them, madam!"

To the interested critic of the Lane-Poole clique I return my warmest thanks for direct and deliberate falsehoods. Lies are one-legged and short-lived, and venom evaporates. A virulently and unjustly abusive critique never yet injured its object. In fact, it's generally the greatest favor an author's unfriends can bestow upon him. And a paper like the *Pall Mall Gazette,* which deliberately pimps and panders to aphrodisiac excitement, is much more infamous than a loose book as hypocrisy is more hateful than vice. And when such vile system is professionally practiced under the disguise and in the holy names of Religion and Morality, the effect is loathsome as that spectacle sometimes seen in the East of a wrinkled old eunuch garbed in woman's nautch dress ogling with painted eyes and waving and wriggling like a young bayadere.

The sensational success of Burton's *Arabian Nights* allowed him to live in comfort and kudos for the rest of his life.

"I've struggled for forty-seven years," he said to his wife. "I've distinguished myself honorably in every way possible. I never got a compliment, a thank you, or a single farthing. I translate an erotic book in my old age and immediately make over sixteen thousand pounds. Now that I know the tastes of England, we need never be without money."

Many years later, Stanley Lane-Poole wrote for the *Encyclopaedia Britannica:*

> As a monument of his Arabic learning and his encyclopedic knowledge of Eastern life, the translation of the *Thousand and One Nights* was Burton's greatest achievement. It is open to criticism in many ways; but when all is said, it is a remarkable performance. . . . As a witness to his profound acquaintance with the vocabulary and customs of the Muslims, the translation is unimpeachable. . . . With grave defects, but sometimes brilliant merits, the translation holds a mirror to its author.

34 : Of Heaven and Hell

What know you, Man, of Life? and yet, forever 'twixt the womb, the grave,
You prattle of the Coming Life—of Heaven and Hell you fain must rave.

On Friday the thirteenth of February, 1885, the Burtons were shocked when news reached them concerning the assassination of Gordon Pasha at Khartoum. Isabel showed her husband an editorial cartoon depicting General Gordon lying alone in the Sudanese desert, his Bible in one hand and a revolver in the other, with a cluster of vultures sitting around waiting for him to die.

"Take it away!" he said. "I can't bear to look at it. I've had to feel that myself. I know what it is." A moment later Burton added bitterly: "They left him there to die. Now the vultures can feast at their success."

On Friday the fifth of February, 1886, a telegram addressed to "Sir Richard Burton" arrived at Trieste. Burton tossed it over to Isabel, saying: "Either some bastard's playing a practical joke or else it isn't for me. I shan't open it, so you may as well send it back to the telegraph office."

"Oh no!" Isabel said impulsively. She then smiled. "I'll open it if you don't."

Burton made no reply, but went on with his writing.

Isabel opened the telegram in tremulous excitement. "Oh, Dick, look! It's from Lord Salisbury." She read:

SIR RICHARD,

I AM PLEASED TO ANNOUNCE THAT HER MAJESTY THE QUEEN, AT MY PERSONAL RECOMMENDATION, HAS CONFERRED UPON YOU THE HONORARY DISTINCTION OF KNIGHT COMMANDER OF THE MOST DISTINGUISHED ORDER OF ST. MICHAEL AND ST. GEORGE IN RECOGNITION OF AND REWARD FOR YOUR SERVICES IN H.B.M.'S GOVERNMENT. "AUSPICIUM MELIORIS AEVI."

SALISBURY,

PRIME MINISTER AND FOREIGN SECRETARY

TO THE CROWN

"Oh, darling, how fabulously wonderful! *Captain Sir Richard Francis Burton, K.C.M.G.* I'm so awfully proud of you."

Burton scowled, shifting uncomfortably in his seat. "You had something to do with this, didn't you? *Auspicium melioris aevi*—An omen of a better age. *Ha!*" He flicked his hand disdainfully. "I shan't accept it."

"Oh yes, you shall! It *is* a good omen. Lord Salisbury is an old-school Conservative like yourself; and he told me how disgusting and disgraceful it is that our national heroes should be spurned and destroyed by mean, envious, illiberal Liberals. Did you read what he said in the House of Commons? 'Before middle age Burton had already crowded into his life more of study, more of hardship, and more of successful enterprise and adventure than would have sufficed to fill up the existences of half a dozen ordinary men. Such a career does as much as a successful campaign to keep up in the minds of the English people that spirit of adventure and of enterprise, that looking to reputation rather than to money, to love of effort rather than to ease—the old native English feeling which has made this country what it has become, and without which our wealth and our material prosperity would not be worth one year's purchase.' "

Burton threw down his pen. "There's no rise for me now, and I don't want anything! I've worked forty-four years for *nothing*. Zoo, I tell you I'm breaking up. I want to go free."

"Then you'd better accept it, Dick, because it's a certain sign they're going to give you Tangier."

Burton growled. "All right, all right—I'll take it as a handsel."

Isabel smiled, reaching over to clasp his hand. "And as Her Majesty's gift for our silver wedding anniversary."

Lady Burton honored her knighted husband with a soirée attended by all the elite of Trieste.

In the course of the evening, Burton was approached by a dark handsome man who muttered while lighting a cigarette: "Beg pardon, but—ah—are you one of the waiters?"

Burton cocked an eye, pulled his mustachios, then drawled: "No—are you? For you look a damned-sight more like a waiter than I do. And I was in hopes you were, because I might've got something to drink!"

The two men laughed and shook hands heartily.

"How are you, Frank?"

"Just fine, Sir Richard. How are you?" It was Frank Harris of the *London Evening News*.

"Still kicking. Have to hop around with a bloody stick, y'know. Got a touch of the gout, goddamnit."

"Sorry to hear that. It's one hell of an ailment for a man who's been active all his life."

"Yaas, well—" Burton lit a long black cigar. "Marvelous weather here, what? I'm suffering from only one other thing, a want to be in Upper Egypt. But of course they won't employ me. Not after that fiasco in the Sudan! I have the notorious reputation of 'independent' in the official catalogue. The one unpardonable sin. 'Chinese' Gordon was sacked for being 'eccentric,' which society abominates. Now he's dead, poor devil, and I'm the only dangerous man left in the Government. England's now ruled by irresponsible clerks, mostly snobs. My misfortunes in life began with not being born a Frenchman."

"How do you like it here?"

"Hate it. It's as bad as London. Perhaps even worse. Y'know, Frank, the dreadful dull life of England accounts for many British madnesses. The consulate at Trieste is like a cage at the zoo—a cage in which a man can't lie down or stand up. He must get free or pine away in captivity."

"Do you ever think of breaking loose?"

"Yaas, yaas. That and a thousand other things. Needless to say, the press is calling me 'the neglected Englishman.' But I still believe in 'Honor, not honors.' Besides, what can any of us hope for? Man is suspended by a thin rope in a bottomless well we call the world; and a rodent, which I call Fate but others God, is continually gnawing at that rope, amusing itself now and anon by licking a honeycomb lying on the ledge."

"Grim reality, eh? And behold the grim realist! Did anybody ever tell you, Sir Richard, you look intriguingly like the prince of the bottomless pit?"

"Yaas, yaas. And I can't quite decide which I'd rather be called, the '*Encyclopaedia Britannica*' or the 'devil's disciple.'"

"Yes, but that forked beard, those fiery eyes, that satanic look—"

"*Ha-ha!* I pride myself on looking like Mephistopheles. He's my alter ego. I've changed my identity, you might say. Years ago, when I wandered around London in a shabby black slouch hat, people used to remark: 'Why, Captain Burton looks like an old gypsy!' Today I roam the streets of Trieste in a tasseled tarboosh, adding a forked beard to my monstrous mustachios. People are curious and ask questions. I tell 'em I don't want to be mistaken for anyone else. They stop and stare. Now Captain Burton looks like the devil!"

"Your satanic majesty, I salute you! 'The prince of darkness is a gentleman.'"

"*Inshallāh,* would that he were! I once began to write a biography of the devil, but I found that European folklore had made such an unmitigated fool of the grand old archfiend as to take away from him all human interest. Still and all, Satan is the true hero of *Paradise Lost*. By his side

God and Man aren't worth the powder and shot to blow 'em to hell. Yaas, Mephistopheles is much better society than Faust and Margaret."

"They say the devil always dances. What fiendish fun he must have!"

"I never dance. After all, not every devil has a cloven foot! The last time I danced it was with the King of Dahomey, to the tune of chopping off heads. The best of it was, the authorities at home were in a towering rage with me—Her Majesty's Commissioner—for dancing with him. But I'd like to have seen *them* refuse his nigrescent highness and be instantly impaled with a dozen spears!"

"You and Lady Burton seem to jog along pretty well together."

"Yaas. I'm a spoiled twin and she's the missing link. Y'see, my wife and I are like an elder and younger brother. We divide the work. I take the hard and scientific part and make her do all the rest. We get out of bed at five or six in the morning. I grab my iron stick and fez and head out for the consulate or parts unknown, while my wife busies herself with charitable work and other philanthropic fatuity. We always dine together—and dine well, mind you. I show those rascals a thing or two about feeding a human being! My wife makes me wear these wretched dress clothes. I hate 'em! A livery of shame—shame of being yourself. Convict stripes would improve 'em. In the East, common sense—not fashion—rules dress. Men, who have a protuberance to be concealed, wear petticoats and women wear pants."

"Symbolically as well?"

"Well, the Turks always say: 'Of ten men nine are women!' Many readers of the *Nights* remark to me with much astonishment that they find the female characters more remarkable for decision, action, and manliness than the male. They seem wonderstruck by the Muslimeh's masterful attitude, by the supreme influence she exercises upon public and private life. But they fail to realize that women, all the world over, are what men make 'em. The main charm of Amazoniana is to see how they live and move and have their being without any masculine guidance. In the highly emotional Arab world, they're creatures of impulse blown about by every gust of passion—stable only in instability, constant only in inconstancy. The sexual powers of Muslim females greatly exceed those of the males, hence the prevalence of a crude form of polyandry popularly termed whoredom. Coleridge was right when he said the man's desire is for the woman but the woman's desire is for the desire of the man. Still and all, I never pretend to understand Woman. As Balzac says, no wonder man fails when He who created her was by no means successful!"

"What do you think of your wife's Catholicism?"

"I like to think of her as a figure strayed somehow from the Middle Ages. If the medieval Mrs. Burton likes to illuminate the day with sacrificial lamps and camphorated tapers, that's her business. The light of the sun is good enough for me. I used to object to her going to confession, but now I never mention it. I contemplate her religion with amused complacency. Once—in a moment of weakness—I gave her five pounds to have Masses said for her dead brother, just as one might give a child a penny to buy a top. Muslims pray for the dead, y'know. But since they don't pay a priest to do it for 'em, all their prayers are in vain."

"How do you manage to reconcile yourself with such superstitious nonsense?"

"I try to do what I think is right, fair, and honorable—not for the sake of reward, but simply because it's right, fair, and honorable. So I sometimes go with her to Mass, much as I would visit a mosque. It satisfies her that I have such 'good principles.' She's always saying to our friends, 'If I could only save Dick's soul!' But what a sweet devotee she is! Only yesterday she burst into my sanctum sanctorum in tearful distraction: 'Oh, Dick, have you seen that little crucifix blessed by the Pope? Oh God, I must have mislaid it!' When we were at Rio in '66, my wife got a touch of the cholera. I was away at the time, looking for diamonds. Thinking she was dying, she got up at three in the morning, went to her desk and settled all her worldly affairs, put on her clothes, carried her last instructions to the maid—who was of course sound asleep in bed—and then, by Allah, went out to confession and communion! I think it cured her."

"And I used to read 'All hope abandon, ye who enter here' on the front of every Catholic Church!"

"Roman Catholicism is a terrible religion for a man of the world to live in, but a good one to die in. Think of it! A century ago my wife should've been burned at the stake for the heinous sin of marrying a heretic, an act which in this century Cardinal Wiseman sanctioned with the blessings of Pope Pius IX. How quickly civilization, progress, and education are marching!"

Frank Harris later wrote:

In Trieste I found the desert lion dying of the cage, dying of disappointment and neglect, dying because there is no field for the exercise of his superlative abilities. . . . Burton is a man of action, a great leader, a still greater governor of men.

On January 13, 1887, the Burtons arrived in Paris for business, then left for a brief vacation at Cannes. Isabel now noticed her husband dipping his pen anywhere but in the ink, and when he wanted to say something he couldn't find words to express himself.

Burton suffered ineffable agony, but he never mentioned it. His extreme agitation and savage expression told her of the torture. Half-sick with anxiety, she sat up all night with him. While Burton thrashed and growled in epileptoid convulsions, the effect of gout, Isabel murmured prayers at his bedside till she slumped asleep on the floor.

Three German specialists concluded that Sir Richard Burton could never recover. After advising Isabel of their diagnosis, they then informed her that she had cancer.

"So I'm a hopeless case too," Lady Burton sighed, holding back the tears. "Oh well. God's will be done. But please don't tell my husband. It might make him worse if he knew I was no better off than he is."

The physicians thought it better that their opinion be conveyed to Burton by a perfect stranger. They therefore deputed Dr. F. Grenfell Baker, a young English practitioner vacationing at Cannes, to perform the painful duty.

Baker entered Burton's hospital room, stood by the bed, and broke the news as best he could.

"Then you s'pose I'm going to die of this goddamned gout?"

"The specialists have held a consultation. That's their opinion, I fear."

"Ah well!" Burton shrugged. "Sit down. Let me tell you my favorite tale out of the *Thousand Nights and a Night*—'How Abu Hasan Broke Wind.'"

From that day on, Dr. Grenfell Baker became Sir Richard Burton's personal physician and permanent guest.

When the British consul returned to Trieste, he learned by letter from Lord Salisbury that the anti-Conservative agitator Wilfrid Scawen Blunt had written to the Foreign Office:

> As Sir Richard Burton is nearly always away from his post and the vice-consul has to do the greater portion of the work, why on earth don't you get rid of Sir Richard Burton and let the vice-consul take his place? I wonder the Foreign Office can put up with him at all.

Salisbury sent Blunt the following reply:

> We look upon the consulship of Trieste as a gift to Sir Richard Burton for his services to the nation, and we must decline to interfere with him in any way.

"How could Blunt write such a mean letter?" Isabel said.

"Because," her husband replied, "I called him a Radical and a traitor for singing with joy at the news of the fall of Khartoum and Gordon's ignominious death. And just to be damnably nasty, I suggested to Salisbury that he send Blunt to the Sudan, where his beloved niggers—Arabs he calls 'em!—would castrate him and make him the Khalifa's chief eunuch."

"I'm an atheist," Burton said one evening to Dr. Baker and Vice-Consul Cautley. "But I was brought up in the Church of England, and that's officially my church."

The Burtons had bought a large house with a garden in the suburbs of Trieste; and the three men were seated on the terrace discussing religion, medicine, and politics. Isabel listened in despair as her husband raked Christianity over the coals, taking heart when he roasted other religions as well:

"Y'know, the more I study religions the more I'm convinced that man never worshiped anything but himself. Man depicts himself in his god. God is the racial expression.

"Man worships self; his God is Man:
   The struggling of the mortal mind
  To form its model as 'twould be,
   The perfect of itself to find. . . .

"Christianity and Islam have been on trial for the last eighteen and twelve centuries. They've been ardent in proselytizing, yet they embrace only one-tenth and one-twentieth of the human race. I'd account for the tardy and unsatisfactory progress of what their votaries call 'pure truths' by the innate imperfections of these so-called revelations. Both faiths propose a reward for mere belief and a penalty for simple unbelief, rewards and punishments being very disproportionate. Thus they reduce everything to the scale of a somewhat unrefined egotism, and their demoralizing effects become clearer to every progressive age.

"The so-called Books of Moses deliberately and ostentatiously ignored the future state of rewards and punishments, the other world which ruled the life of the Egyptian in this world. But when the Jews were removed to Mesopotamia, the second cradle of the creeds, they soon caught the infection of its Asiatic media. Superadding Babylonian legend to Egyptian myth, they stultified The Law by supplementing it with the absurdities of foreign fable and ended—as the Talmud proves—with becoming the most wildly superstitious and otherworldly of mankind. The same tragic change befell El-Islam. . . .

"All forms of 'faith'—belief in things unseen, not subject to the senses, and therefore unknown and in our present stage of development unknowable—are temporary and transitory. No religion hitherto promulgated among men shows any prospect of being final or otherwise than finite.

"Religious ideas, which are necessarily limited, may all be traced home to the old seat of science and art, creeds and polity in the Nile Valley. To this day they retain the clearest signs of their origin.

"All so-called revealed religions consist mainly of three portions—a cosmogony more or less mythical, a history more or less falsified, and a moral code more or less pure. . . .

"Christ gave an impetus to the progress of mankind by systematizing a philosophy of the highest moral loveliness, showing what an imperfect race can and may become. But after the death of St. Paul, Christianity sank into a species of idolatry. When things were at their worst, Muhammed first appeared upon the stage of life.

"El-Islam systematically exalts human nature, which Christianity takes infinite trouble to degrade and debase.

"Travel and conversation with Christians and Jews must've convinced Muhammed that Christianity was calling as loudly for reform as Judaism had done. An exaggerated Trinitarianism or rather Tritheism, a 'fourth person' and saint worship, had virtually dethroned the Deity. Mariolatry had made Christianity a woman's religion, and superstition had drawn from its fetid fecundity an incredible number of heresies and monstrous absurdities. The Kingdom of Heaven had become a hell.

"Muhammed found two vital defects equally fatal to its energy and longevity. These were and still are its egotism and its degradation of humanity. It needs a 'higher law.' Its cosmogony is a myth read literally. Its history is, for the most part, a highly immoral distortion. And its ethics are those of the Talmudic Hebrews. Christianity has done good work in its time, but now it shows only decay and decrepitude in place of vigor and progress. It's dying hard, but it's dying of the slow poison of science. . . .

"As Judaism promised the good Jew all manner of temporal blessings—issue, riches, wealth, honor, power, length of days—so Christianity offered the good Christian, as a bribe to lead a godly life, personal salvation and a future state of happiness—in fact, the Kingdom of Heaven with an alternate threat of Hell. It never rose to the height of the Hindus and Chinese, of Gautama Buddha and Lao-tze, who believed and taught that virtue is its own reward. It never dared to say, 'Do good for Good's sake.' Even now it doesn't declare with Cicero: 'What is right should be sought for its own sake, because it is right and not because it's enacted.' It doesn't even now venture to say with Philo Judaeus: 'The good man seeks the day for the sake of the day and the light for the light's sake, and he labors to acquire what is good for the sake of the good itself and not of anything else.' What a far cry from the naive and unconscious egotism of Christianity, whose burden is 'Do good to escape Hell and gain Heaven!'

"What can sensible people say to these papal propositions? 'Good works are an obstacle to salvation. God does by no means will the salvation of all men. He does will sin, and He destines men to sin.' What can we think of a deity —the author of man's existence, temptation, and fall—who deliberately preordains sin and ruin? And year after year, volumes of divine scandal are written by those who know little for those who know less! Some lies are very long-lived, especially those begotten by self-interest.

"Christianity is still infected with the 'bribe-and-threat doctrine.' I once immensely scandalized a consular chaplain by quoting the noble belief of the ancients, and it was some days before he could recover mental equanimity. The degradation is now inbred.

"A no less defect in the School of Galilee is its low view of human nature. The Fathers of the Church adopted as sober and authentic history an Osirian-Hebrew myth which Philo and a host of rabbis explain away, each after his own fashion. Christianity dwells lovingly upon the 'fall' of man and seems to revel in the contemptible condition to which 'original sin' condemned him, thus groveling before God *ad majorem Dei gloriam*—for the greater glory of God.

"What are we to think of that hateful and immoral doctrine theologically called 'original sin'? What can be said about the innate depravity of human nature? This so-called sin was either caused by God or arose without leave of God, in either case degrading God to man. I once asked my old friend Cardinal Newman why the Omnipotent and Omniscient didn't prevent, or rather why He created, sin. His answer was: 'He kindly permitted, created, and sanctioned it that man might repent.' If anyone thus reasoned of mundane matters he'd be looked upon as the merest fool! Of the doctrine of the 'fall' the heretic Marcion wrote: 'The Deity must either be deficient in goodness if He willed, in prescience if He did not foresee, or in power if He did not prevent it.' . . .

"The sublime doctrine which commands us to love our enemies and tolerate those who despitefully entreat us is in perilous proximity to the ridiculous. At any rate it's a vain and futile rule of life which few people ever think of obeying

unless they be lunatics and martyrs. It contrasts poorly with
the common sense of the so-called pagan, *Fiat justitia, ruat
caelum*—Let justice be done, though the heavens fall. . . .

"The cloven foot shows itself everywhere, teaching us that
the only solid stratum underlying priestcraft is one composed of pounds, shillings, and pence. I often wonder, can
infatuation or hypocrisy—it must be one or the other—go
on forever? Christianity, like Judaism, utterly ignores the
progress of humanity—perhaps the only belief in which the
wise man can take unmingled satisfaction. Both have proposed an originally perfect being with hyacinthine locks,
from whose type all subsequent humans are physical and
moral degradations. I on the other hand hold, from the evidence of my senses, that early man was a savage very little
superior to the brute beast; that during man's millions of
years on earth there has been a gradual advance towards
perfection, at times irregular and even retrograde, but in
the main progressive; and that a comparison of man in the
nineteenth century with the cave man affords us the means
of measuring past progress and calculating the future of
humanity. This is also my answer to those who contend with
much truth that we moderns are by no means superior to
the ancients. They look at the results of only three thousand
years instead of thirty or even three hundred thousand. . . .

"I laugh to think how the canting hypocrites have attacked
the *Nights*, when there's no more immoral work than the
Old Testament. Its deity is an ancient Hebrew of the worst
type who condones, permits, or commands every sin in the
Decalogue to a Jewish patriarch. He orders Abraham to
murder his son and allows Jacob to swindle his brother,
Moses to slaughter an Egyptian and the Jews to plunder
and spoil a whole people after inflicting upon 'em a series
of plagues which would be the height of atrocity if the tale
were true. The nations of Canaan are then extirpated. Ehud,

for treacherously disemboweling King Eglon, is made judge over Israel. Jael is blessed above women for vilely murdering a sleeping guest. The horrid deeds of Esther are made examples to mankind. And David, after an adultery and a homicide which deserved ignominious death, is suffered to massacre a host of his enemies, cutting some in two with saws and axes and putting others into brickkilns. For obscenity and impurity we have the tales of Onan and Tamar, Lot and his daughters, Amnon and his fair sister, Absalom and his father's concubines, Aholah and Aholibah, and the Song of Solomon. For all the horrors forbidden to the Jews, who therefore must've practiced 'em, read your Old Testament.

"Then turn to the Babylonian Talmud and peruse the rabbinical and cabalistic commentary. Learn how Adam copulated with all the beasts of the field and how Eve was created from his foreskin—not 'rib,' a mistranslation—which was removed by Yahveh during a wet dream. Read how Yahveh created the universe by forty-two acts of cosmic masturbation. How jealous Cain killed his rival Abel for sexual possession of one of their sisters. How the Flood was caused by Yahveh's continuous masturbation. How Ham, seeing his drunken father with an erection, abused Noah sexually and was transmogrified into a Negro slave. How envious Sarah cut out Hagar's clitoris. How Lot's wife was buggered by all the Sodomites, then metamorphosed into a phallus of salt. How Leah, Jacob's barren wife, was futtered by his jackass and made fertile. How Dinah enjoyed being raped by Shechem and couldn't bear to leave him after continuous copulation, but had to be dragged from his house by her father and brothers, because he had a big uncircumcised penis. How Joseph was used and abused as a catamite by the eunuch Potiphar, and how he became Pharaoh by selling his body for sodomy. How Er was slain

for practicing anal intercourse with Tamar, and how Onan
and Tamar were equally perverse for onanizing each other.
How Balaam achieved the power of prediction by sodomizing she-asses. How Zimri copulated with Cozbi four hundred and twenty-four times in one day, and how Phinehas
speared them through the genitals while *in flagrante delicto*.
How Jael had coition seven times with Sisera before driving
a tent peg through his head. How Samson was compelled
to swive all the Philistine women in order to propagate a
race of superhumans, and how he was then forced to abuse
himself in front of all the people in the palace. How David
mounted Bathsheba thirteen times in succession, shooting
his semen all over the sheets. How Amnon's testicles were
entangled in Tamar's pubic hair, thus strangling him for his
incestuous crime. How Esther allowed Haman to jump her
while Ahasuerus was out of the room, after which she
accused him of rape. How Mary played fast and loose with
all the carpenters' sons, and how Jesus was born a sorcerer
by Joseph's swiving of Mary during her menstrual period.
And so on and so forth, *ad infinitum* and *ad nauseam*. . . .

"My creed is quite simple. I make self-cultivation, with
due regard to others, the sole and sufficient object of human
life. I worship with single-minded devotion the holy cause
of Truth—of truth for its own sake, not for the goods it may
bring. Like Confucius, I cultivate common sense. In the
presence of endless contradictions which spring from the
idea of a personal deity, I take refuge in the sentiment of
an unknown and an unknowable. I neither personify nor
debase the Higher Law by calling it a 'He,' a masculinized
noumenon, or by dragging it down to earth till the very
name 'God' has no meaning whatsover. When I repeat the
Greek's 'Remember not to believe,' I mean strive to learn—
to know, to understand—for right ideas lead to right actions.
That's the religion of humanity—a passion for life and light,

for culture and intelligence, for art, poetry, and science.

"When the praiser of the past contends that modern civilization has improved in relatively nothing upon the ancients, who were also plagued by the *laudator temporis acti*, he is apt to overlook the fact that every schoolboy is a miracle of learning compared with the cave man and the paleolithic race. And as the past has been, so shall the future be."

35 : Death rides a camel

And now the last have slipped away, yon drear death-desert to explore;
And now one Pilgrim, worn and lorn, still lingers on the lonely shore.

"I'm getting tired of everything—even living." Burton dropped his pen and flipped shut his journal. "We're always wandering, and the places that delight you I say to myself, *Dry rot!* And the next place I say, *Dry rotter!* And the third place I say, *Dry rottest!*"

Isabel, who was sitting across from him at the table,

smiled and said: "In one more year, darling, we'll be free
—free to go home for good."

"What a blessing it'll be! I can hardly wait for the moment when we're settled quietly in England together, independent of the Government and of all the world besides."

"I'm counting the days. It shan't be long. Thirty years'
service is enough for any man, not to mention your previous twenty years in the Indian Army."

"Fifty years of sweat and blood. It hardly seems a reality. I believe by the time we get back to London nearly all
our old friends will be dead."

"We'll still have many new ones. You know, Dick, we
mustn't let the world pass us old fossils by."

"Yaas, but there's nothing like an old friend. You can be
and feel like yourself when you're with an old chum. Ah
well! I wonder whether you or I will be the first to go?"

"Why Dick, whatever should make you ask that?"

"Because. When we're both dead I'd like us to lie in a
tent side by side."

"We shall, darling—we shall."

"Yaas, the world will be very much surprised when I
come to die."

"How do you mean?"

"Y'know, I'm in a very bad way. I've got to hate everybody except you and myself. And it frightens me because I know perfectly well that next year I'll get to hate
you, and the year after that I'll get to hate myself, and
then I don't know what will become of me."

"Oh, Dick, how can you say such awful things?"

He reached over and clasped her hand. "Do I hurt you
when I talk like that?"

She smiled sadly, laying her other hand over his. "Well, yes—a little."

"Well then I promise you, after I'm free from the Government and our present surroundings, I won't talk like that anymore."

"How I long for that time to come!"

"So do I." There was a warm, happy moment of silence. Then Burton said: "Y'know, Puss, no one has helped me but you these past thirty—I should say thirty-five—years. I know you'll do everything for me, body and soul, that you'd wish done for yourself."

"I love you, darling. You know that. I'd die for you."

"Did you like Damascus?"

"Like it! Oh, Dick, my eyes fill and my heart throbs even at the thought of it. When I look back on those dear days and friends in Damascus, I can't help crying."

"Yaas, I know. I sometimes feel it myself. It's a haunting depression, an incubus of the past."

"Oh, Dick, when I think of all those memories, none is dearer to me than the evenings we four—Jane Digby, 'Abdel-Qadir, you, and I—used to spend together on the top of our house. Often after the reception was over and the sun was setting—remember, darling?—we used to ask those two to stay behind the others and have a little supper with us. And we'd go up to the roof, where the cushions of the divans were spread about, and have our evening meal. And after that we'd smoke our narghilehs, and talk and talk and talk far into the night. I'll never forget the scene on the housetop, backed as it was by that sublime mountain, a strip of sand between it and us; and on the other three sides was the view over Damascus, and beyond it the desert. It was all so wild, so romantic and solemn. And sometimes we'd pause in our conversation, and listen to the weird and wonderful sounds around us— the last call to prayer on the minaret top, the soughing of the wind through the mountain gorges, the creaking and groaning of the water wheel in the neighboring orchard. Oh, Dick, it's like a fairyland dream. It haunts me day and night."

"Yaas. It's a part of us, a fragment of our identity. That's why I want us to lie in a tent together, side by side, like Arab lovers at rest and final peace in the desert."

Sunday, October 19, 1890.

Returning from Mass at eight in the morning, Isabel found her husband slaving away at a new translation, *El-Kitāb Rōdzet el-'Ātir fī Nuzhet el-Khātir—Book of the Scented Garden Site for Heart Delight*—an Arab classic of erotology. She kissed him. "How's it coming?"

Burton sighed. "Tomorrow I'll have finished this, and then we'll begin our biography."

"What a happiness that will be!"

"Yaas. I promise you I'll never write another book on this subject again."

"Good. Darling, have you eaten yet?"

Dr. Baker, who just entered the room, chortled: "Indeed not! What are we to do with him, Lady Burton? He's up at five, slaving incessantly till dusk. Begrudges himself a mere hour for food and exercise. Wolfs down what little he *does* eat. Can't wait to get back to his work. This book has become an obsession with him. Why Sir Richard, you haven't even drunk your whiskey!"

Burton growled. "All you goddamned leeches are alike! If you don't kill a man with drugs, you kill him with advice. Well, I'm trying to get this goddamned thing done before I die. I've put my whole life and all my lifeblood into this *Scented Garden,* and it's my great hope that I shall live by it. It's everything I know about the sexual anthropology of the Arabs. It's my legacy to the twentieth century, to the coming great renaissance of science and art. It's the crown of my life!"

"But darling," Isabel said, frowning, "what about your *Arabian Nights?* You worked so long and hard—"

"*Bah!* The *Nights* was a baby tale in comparison to this. Besides, I didn't dare tell everything I know in that first attempt to breach the bastions of Mrs. Grundy's maidenhead." Burton grinned wickedly. "I'm afraid it'll make a great row in England—stir up a horde of holier-than-thou hornet's nests. But now that I know the tastes of civilized society, we need never be without money." Suddenly he scowled, staring at one of the windows.

"What's wrong?" Isabel said.

"That window we never open. It was a bad omen. I heard a bird peck three times early this morning."

"Funny I didn't hear it. Oh, darling, it must have been your imagination."

"Imagination hell! I tell you a bird has been tapping on my window for the past three days. That's an evil omen, y'know."

"Oh, Dick, you mustn't think such things. No; you feed them every morning. Poor thing, perhaps he's one you missed."

"Say what you will. This is a sign of death."

The Burtons retired to their bedroom, as usual, at nine-thirty. While Isabel was saying the customary night prayers to her husband, a dog suddenly let out a long dreadful howl in the garden. She stopped for a second and looked up.

"How ominous!" Burton said, touching her arm. "A harbinger of death."

Isabel frowned, then continued praying. Again the dog howled, and again. "Oh my God," she said, getting up from the bedside and going over to the window, "what's the matter with that dog?"

Burton cackled faintly. "The Arabs say a dog can distinguish the awful form of Azrael, angel of death, hovering over a doomed abode; whereas man's spiritual sight is dim and dull by reason of his sins." Isabel didn't seem to hear him, so he said aloud: "When a dog howls without apparent cause it forebodes death."

"Oh, Dick, how can you be so morbid? I'll send someone out to see what's wrong."

"Why bother? Dogs are fine-nosed animals, and every human being has his or her peculiar scent which varies according to age and health. That's how animals often detect the approach of death."

"Oh, Richard Burton, you're absolutely impossible!"

Isabel left the room, went downstairs, and asked the porter to go out and quiet the dog. When she returned, Isabel knelt by the bed and finished her prayers. She then kissed her husband and handed him a soft-bound copy of Robert Buchanan's *Martyrdom of Madeline*. Burton lay in bed reading it for about an hour. His wife, in her own bed next to him, was "attacking" Annie Besant's *My Path to Atheism*.

At midnight, still awake, Burton seemed unusually restless.

"What's the matter?" Isabel said.

"I've got a gouty pain in my foot. When did I have my last attack?"

"Just a minute. I'll look and see." She fetched his journal and skimmed backwards through the pages. "It was three months ago you had a real gout. You know, darling, the doctor considers it a safety valve that you should have a 'healthy' gout every three months. He says it's good for your general condition. Your last attack was at Zurich in July, and your next will be due in January. How is it now, Dick?"

"No better."

"Let me call Dr. Baker."

"No, don't disturb him. Poor fellow, he's been in frightful pain with his head. Great sufferer from neuralgic headaches, y'know. I think he's at last got a little sleep."

"All right, darling, but if it gets any worse I'll call him in."

Burton dozed off for a short while. When he awoke, Isabel, who had been watching him anxiously, said: "How do you feel? You seemed to twitch a lot, as if there was much pain."

"It was some relief. I dreamt I saw our little flat in London, and it had quite a nice large room in it."

"Try to get some more sleep, darling. It'll help soothe the pain if I massage your foot."

"No, go back to bed. Don't bother about me."

Isabel sat by him on the bed, kneading his foot to ease the agony. Burton laughed, joked, and talked about the future for a few moments, then drifted off again. He moaned and stirred in his troubled slumber. When he awoke, the pain was even worse than before.

"Offer it up, offer it up—" Isabel murmured, still massaging his foot. "Pray, my beloved, pray. Only prayer will bring relief."

Burton couldn't stop shifting and groaning. The sharp, tearing ache was becoming almost unbearable.

Isabel, kneeling by the bedside, began to pray. "Oh, offer it up, dear—offer it up!" she kept repeating.

Burton grumbled and swore, his face twisted in a hideous expression of torture. "I dreamt of a camel," he said. "In Arabia, death rides a camel. To dream of a camel is an omen of death."

At 4 A.M. Isabel stood up and said: "I'm going for Dr. Baker."

Burton scowled fiercely, waving his arm. "No—no, goddamnit! Don't disturb him, I tell you. He can't do anything."

"Well, what's the use of keeping a doctor if he's not to be called when you're suffering?"

Burton growled and looked away.

Dr. Baker came in his nightshirt, took Burton's temperature, applied the stethoscope, then said to Lady Burton: "I see no cause for alarm. He's in perfect order. The gout's 'healthy.' But I'll give him a sedative to relieve the pain and help him get some rest."

Baker then returned to bed.

A half hour later Burton lifted his arm and gasped: "Zoo, open the windows. There isn't any air!"

"But they *are* open, darling," she said, getting out of bed. "What's the matter? You can't breathe, can you? Oh my God, I'm going for Dr. Baker."

"Poor chap," he sighed. "Don't disturb him."

Isabel ran out screaming for Baker, who came rushing in to find Burton fighting for air.

"Oh, doctor, what is it?" she said, touching Baker's shoulder. "Is he in any danger?"

Baker nodded. "I'm afraid he may be dying."

"Oh, God in Heaven, I knew it!" Isabel ran out into the hall and roused all the servants. "For God's sake, find a priest," she cried. "My husband's dying! Do you understand? *A priest*. Get a priest!"

Hurrying back into the room, she heard her husband rambling: "Jack, where are you? Jack! I hear the camel bells. Get away from me, goddamnit! *Yallah—yallah—*"

"We must do something, doctor," Isabel uttered. "Try everything—"

Baker shook his head. "I'm afraid there's nothing I can do."

"Oh Blessed Mother of God, you've got to save him! Do anything—give him chloroform!"

"No, it would kill him."

Burton suddenly reached out, gazing at Isabel. "Puss, quick!" he gasped. "Chloroform—ether—or I'm a dead man!"

An anguished and tearful woman dropped to her knees at the bedside. "My darling," she said, "the doctor says it will kill you. He's doing all he knows." Isabel glared at Baker. "My God, I'll give him the blood out of my own veins if it'll save him!"

Burton's breathing became even more labored, and after a brief struggle for air he cried: "I'm dying." A second later a sigh left his lips: "I'm dead."

Isabel held him in her arms, and she felt him grow heavier.

"He's quite insensible now," Baker said. "A clot of blood to the heart. God help him, he won't suffer anymore."

"Is he dead?" Isabel murmured.

"I'm not sure. I'm going to apply the battery. Perhaps we'll get a response. Then I'll know for certain."

The doctor routinely applied an electric battery to Burton's heart. Isabel knelt next to the bed, clasped her husband's hand, and prayed: "Oh please, dear God, keep his soul here till a priest comes!"

A Slavonian priest, Pietro Martelani, entered the death chamber at approximately six-thirty in the morning of October 20. He stared for a moment at Burton's body, then he said to Baker: "Is there still any life?"

Before the doctor could answer, Isabel cried: "He's alive! But I beg of you, *padre,* don't waste a moment. The soul is passing away!"

Father Martelani frowned. He touched the body. It was warm. He suspected that Lady Burton was in shock —knowing her husband was dead, yet not wanting to believe it. Dr. Baker absolved himself by looking the other way.

Martelani then said: "If he's a Protestant, *signora,* he cannot receive the Holy Sacrament in this way."

Isabel answered angrily: "My husband has abjured the Protestant heresy and belongs to the Catholic Church. Quick! His brain still lives! Please administer the last comforts."

Father Martelani crossed himself and did as she asked.

"Quick, *padre,* quick—before it's too late!" Isabel said, as the young priest slipped a holy wafer into Burton's mouth.

While Pietro Martelani administered Extreme Unction, Isabel Burton held her husband's left hand in her own, two fingers pressed on his lifeless pulse. She knelt thus by the bed, gazing intently at him and praying, till seven o'clock. The electric battery buzzed on Burton's chest all that time.

Dr. Baker then said to her: "Sir Richard's dead, Lady Burton. Come away now."

"No—no, he isn't," she said, staring at Burton with a slight smile on her lips. "I shan't leave him till I'm absolutely certain. Look, doctor! Look, his mouth and left eye moved!"

"No, Lady Burton, it's only your imagination. Your husband is dead."

"Yes—perhaps. But what's no imagination is that the brain lives after the heart and pulse are gone. Richard always said that. He believed it, and I believe it too. Look —" She gently lifted his eyelids. "Look, doctor, his eyes are as bright and intelligent as in life—the brilliancy of a man who sees something unexpected and wonderful and happy. Yes, Dr. Baker, the brain lives. Thank God all is over for him now. Thank God for him! He's happy at last, in peaceful sleep. Let the world rain fire and brimstone on me now! I've lost everything in him. The world is a dead letter to me now. It can no longer touch me."

Later that morning, Vice-Consul Cautley was called in by Dr. Baker. The German undertaker, who was already there, said to Lady Burton: "As a matter of procedure, *mein Frau*—to what religion did Sir Richard belong?"

Turning to Cautley, a confused Isabel said: "What religion shall I say?"

Cautley looked her straight in the eye. "Tell him Sir Richard's true religion."

She glanced at the undertaker and snapped: "Catholic."

"But—!" Cautley blurted.

"*Yes*," Isabel said, staring at her husband's body with a faraway look. "He was a Catholic."

Captain Sir Richard Francis Burton was embalmed and buried according to the rites of the Roman Catholic Church. His body was laid to rest in an Arab tent of stone and marble embellished with camel bells, crucifixes, and the crescent and star.

The wild man of Mecca—agnostic, orientalist, and adventurer—still lies entombed outside London, the center of a civilization he could not endure, in Mortlake Catholic Cemetery, the resting place of a religion he could not tolerate.

With him into eternity went all his private journals, his personal papers, and his *Scented Garden*. Isabel Arundell Burton burned Haji 'Abdullah at the stake. Committed to the flames with the heretic was every secret record of his Arab identity. She then wrote:

> At the moment of his death I had done all I could for the body, and then I tried to follow his soul. I *am* following the soul, and I *shall* reach it before long. There we shall nevermore part.
>
> Agnostics! "Burnt manuscript" readers! Do any of you pretend or wish to take him away from me in death? Oh, for shame! for shame! Let him rest where he wanted to rest, and be silent, or do not boast of your "free country" where a man may not even be buried where he will—where he may not speak his mind, and tell the truth. Be ashamed that History may have to say that the only honor that England accorded to Richard Burton, having failed to do him justice

in this life, was to bespatter his wife with mud after he was dead and could not defend her.

He said always: "I am gone—pay, pack, and follow."

I have paid, I have packed, I have suffered. I am waiting to join his caravan. I am waiting for a welcome sound— the tinkling of his camel bell.

She now lies side by side with her lover, under the Arab tent, in the Catholic cemetery.

Do what your manhood bids you do; from none but self expect applause.
He noblest lives and noblest dies who makes and keeps his self-made laws.

All other life is living death, a world where none but phantoms dwell:
A breath, a wind, a sound, a voice, a tinkling of the camel bell.

R.F.B.